CELSUS

II

# CELSUS

## DE MEDICINA

WITH AN ENGLISH TRANSLATION BY
### W. G. SPENCER
MS. LOND., F.R.C.S. ENG.

IN THREE VOLUMES

II

CAMBRIDGE, MASSACHUSETTS
HARVARD   UNIVERSITY   PRESS
LONDON
WILLIAM  HEINEMANN  LTD
MCMLXI

*First printed 1938*
*Reprinted 1953, 1961*

*Printed in Great Britain*

# CONTENTS

v

# INTRODUCTION

Book V, Chapters 1–25, contains a list of drugs and prescriptions.[a] Celsus does not classify the ingredients as organic or inorganic, but he first gives a list of substances classified according to their effect on the body (styptics, agglutinants for wounds, substances to repress or mature suppuration, to cleanse wounds, induce healing, relieve irritation and encourage the growth of new flesh, caustics of varying strengths, and emollients), and then passes on to give the prescriptions for poultices, plasters, pastils, pessaries, dusting powders, ointments, gargles, antidotes, anodynes, liniments, draughts and pills.

In his prescriptions Celsus gives quantities, which have been reduced to modern measures,[b] but as we have no means of ascertaining the standard strength of the preparations which he used, it is impossible to dispense his prescriptions or compare them with those in use to-day.

The internal remedies prescribed by Celsus were chiefly foods or drink (*alimenta*), and he gives details of their use and effect on the body in Book II,

---

[a] A few additional prescriptions occur in the description of treatment in Books VI and VII; in Books I–IV, although many foodstuffs or drugs are recommended for use in various diseases, no instructions for compounding are given.

[b] See below, pp. lxv–lxvii.

# INTRODUCTION

chapter 18 ff.,[a] but when the *medicamenta* proper are described in Book V it is noteworthy that very few are for internal use, and that nearly all are for external application. In the same way in the treatments described in Books I and II, much more attention is given to massage, rocking and remedial exercise [b] than to internal treatment by the purge and vomit, as to the value of which Celsus was very doubtful.[c]

The preference for external remedies was perhaps due to the limited use of dissection, which resulted in a very imperfect knowledge of anatomy and internal conditions, so that Celsus and his contemporaries inclined to prescribe remedies, the results of which could be seen. While in Egypt the practice of embalming had early made men familiar with internal anatomy and the Alexandrian surgeons used dissection of dead bodies and vivisection for purposes of study and investigation,[d] both methods were strongly condemned by the Empiric school, to whose views Celsus attaches great weight,[e] and evidently became gradually discredited, for when Galen studied at Alexandria in A.D. 152–157, he had no opportunity of studying human anatomy or morbid conditions by means of dissection. The prejudice against this con-

[a] See also vol. I, p. 483 ff. for a list of *alimenta*. *Alimenta* and *medicamenta* overlapped to some extent and several of the former (*e.g.* honey, mustard) were ingredients or prescriptions for external use.

[b] These formed a very important part of medicine from the earliest times; the use of remedial exercises as a treatment is said to have been introduced by Herodicus, the teacher of Hippocrates.

[c] Vol. I, Pro. 28 ff.

[d] Celsus relates that the Ptolemies gave Herophilus and Erasistratus the bodies of criminals to vivisect (Pro. 23, 24).

[e] Pro. 27 ff. The school was founded by Philinus.

tinued during the succeeding centuries and contributed to keep these methods of study in abeyance, and it was not until the renaissance, when they were revived by painters and sculptors eager to regain the standard of Art which had been reached in ancient Greece, that they again became the basis of medical training. The conclusion reached by Celsus himself is that dissection is necessary for the instruction of students [a] and in his treatise he directs attention to what, in his opinion, the Art of medicine could then accomplish. He writes without any real knowledge of internal conditions, he treats the symptoms and not the disease.

In the introduction to his whole work, Celsus had already noted with approval the views of the Empirics that physicians should not be bound by hard and fast rules, and that treatment must vary according to climate and other conditions; though treatment must be based on experience, difference of conditions caused the experience of individual practitioners to vary [b]; he had also noted the division of remedies into *secunda* and *contraria* [c]; when the ordinary remedies fail, contrary ones may be employed. An instance was the treatment given to Augustus by the physician Antonius Musa. [d] When the regular treatment with hot poultices failed to relieve a pain in the liver, he applied cold ones. It has been suggested that Augustus was suffering, not from a liver abscess, such as Celsus has described (vol. I, p. 415), for which such hot applications were given, but from typhoid

[a] Pro. 74.
[b] Pro. 30 ff.
[c] Pro. 71; see also VI. **6**. 8 E and note *b*.
[d] Suetonius, *Augustus*, 81.

fever, and that Antonius Musa applied a cold pack,[a] a treatment still used, a well known instance is that of King Edward VII, who, when Prince of Wales, was in danger from typhoid fever in 1871. The bold originality of the remedies applied by Petron [b] were still remembered by Galen writing a century later.[c] A similar type of " shock " remedy was the treatment of epilepsy by a draught of gladiator's blood [d] and of hydrophobia by throwing the patient into a pond,[e] though the latter may have been more of a homeopathic nature, and would certainly cause the death of a genuine case, though it might be effective in the cases of hysterical symptoms simulating hydrophobia which, as Pasteur observed in his native district, often accompany an outbreak of the disease. But such methods were not always safe, and though they sometimes resulted in spectacular cures, they sometimes killed the patient. [f]

Turning to the actual ingredients of the prescriptions, the greater part were derived from herbs and vegetables, which, as Celsus himself points out [g] have been used medicinally from the earliest times and by the rudest tribes, but, in addition, many animal organic and inorganic substances were employed. If the herbs used by Celsus are compared with those in a modern materia medica, it will be seen that though many are the same, he often mentions plants which are no longer used, as the drug which they contain can be obtained in a stronger form, or one more satisfactory for use, from some other

[a] Cf. Buchan, *Augustus*, pp. 161, 162.
[b] III. 9. 2–4.    [c] Galen, I. 144, XV. 436.
[d] III. 23. 7.    [e] V. 27. 2 C.
[f] III. 9. 4.    [g] I. Pro. I.

source; [a] in other cases the preparation which he used was evidently much weaker or applied for some other purpose than to-day,[b] and some of the most important drugs are missing from his list.[c]

In the same way among the inorganic substances, arsenic, iron and mercury [d] are only used externally.

## INTERNAL REMEDIES

Purgatives are comparatively few and treatment by clystering the bowel was preferred by Asclepiades, whom Celsus is inclined to follow, but he mentions several substances as useful for the purpose, aloes, hellebore, sea-spurge, and others.[e]  Castor oil is not included.  For inducing a vomit he recommends only

[a] The squill provided a substance akin to digitalis (which Celsus does not know) but less satisfactory in use.

[b] Opium and castor oil (see list below), *papaver* and *cicinum* (sc. *oleum*).

[c] For instance strychnine (prepared from strychnos, nux vomica, a plant from the E. Indies) which was first used in comparatively modern times and aconite (aconitum napellus), still a frequent ingredient of liniments, though seldom prescribed now for internal use.  Aconite had been known as a poison from the time of Hippocrates and the *staphis agria*, identified by Celsus with *uva taminia* (I.316 and list below) is said by Pliny (*N.H.* XXIII, 17) to be a kind of larkspur (delphinium staphisagria).  He used it as a vermicide and under the name " stavesacre " it is still so used in the United States.

[d] There is no mention of calomel, bismuth, iron or magnesia as internal medicines.  The only trace of iron used internally is in the popular remedy for enlarged spleen—water in which a smith's red hot tools have been dipped (I. 416); mercury Celsus only mentions in the form of cinnabar, used externally, see list s.v. *minium*.

[e] I. 3. 25; II. 12;  copper chips were also used, see list *aes*.

# INTRODUCTION

the simplest means, tepid water with salt, mustard, honey or hyssop, or a radish;[a] pills, pastils and draughts were prescribed for the relief of pain, cough and bladder trouble, and to induce sleep.[b] The " antidotes " were a class of remedy held in high esteem; Celsus said they were not often used, but were important because of the help they gave in the gravest cases. He gave the prescriptions for three; they are mildly stimulant mixtures chiefly characterised by the very large number of their ingredients; it is difficult to see what value they can have had beyond a slightly tonic effect.[c]

## External Remedies

It is noteworthy what great importance Celsus attached to tannin in local applications. This substance, now generally recognised as a useful immediate application for burns and scalds, was the chief effective constituent in many of the substances included in his prescriptions.

In addition to the plasters, poultices and other applications whose use is sufficiently explained in the text itself, one large class of remedies may be grouped under the modern term antiseptics, though no general name is applied to them by Celsus.[d] These substances have the general characteristics of opposing the growth of micro-organisms in wounds and of promoting a free discharge, they include the essential oils, especially rose oil (obtained by steeping the petals in cold water, and keeping them in the cold air till the oil rose to the top and was skimmed off).

[a] 1. 3. 22.     [b] V. 24, 25.     [c] V. 23.
[d] There were many others, see Galen on *Antidotes*, a work devoted to such medicines (vol. XIV, of Kühn's edition).

thyme oil, pitch and turpentine. The phenol or carbolic acid derived from gas tar and used by Lister as an antiseptic was akin to the thymol derived from thyme flowers, though the latter was weaker in its action. The antiseptic which largely replaced phenol in surgical practice was mercuric chloride. Celsus frequently recommends orpiment and sandarach, the arsenic sulphides, for cleaning wounds and ulcerations, but as antiseptics these are much weaker than the mercury chloride. Salt solution, so largely used in the great war in the treatment of wounds, was used in ancient medicine for the same purpose, that of prompting a thin discharge, and is often mentioned by Celsus.[a]

### Homoeopathic and Rustic or Popular Remedies

Throughout history a knowledge of herbs and drugs and their medicinal uses has been connected with the early systems of philosophy and occult lore. The " doctrine of signatures " expressed the popular belief that certain plants and minerals bore symbolical marks which indicated the diseases which nature intended them to cure, or that their outward appearance corresponded with the bodily condition of the patient.[b] Traces of this theory and of a belief in sympathetic magic are to be found in many of the remedies, especially the rustic or popular remedies, mentioned by Celsus. A sympathy or " homoeopathy "

[a] See list *s.v. sat.* A split fig, which he mentions as a common application on wounds (vol. II., pp. 159, 161, 289) was used for the same reason, as the sugar in the pulp would promote a thin discharge.

[b] For an account of the " doctrine of signatures " cf. T. J. Pettigrew, *Superstitions connected with Medicine or Surgery,* 1844.

was believed to exist between the remedy and the disease, and they are "homoeopathic" in a much more fundamental sense than that in which the term is used by those who claim to practise homoeopathy to-day. Instances of such remedies are the black hellebore (a powerful aperient) supposed to be especially effective in the black bile disease (melancholia),[a] or the white hellebore given to reduce swollen glands in the neck because it tended to produce expectoration of white phlegm.[b] Ox spleen was given as a remedy for enlarged spleen,[c] a poultice of pole reed was applied to a gathering on the hand caused by a splinter, because the commonest source of such splinters was the pole reed;[d] a decoction of worms boiled in oil was poured into suppurating ears where there were maggots.[e] Other well known examples, not mentioned by Celsus, are the application of the roots of the lesser celandine (pilewort) as a remedy for piles, because small excrescences which grew on them resembled the disease, and the use of red light and red cloth in treating smallpox with the idea of bringing out the rash and so evacuating the disease, though here again the treatment has been thought to have a real value as excluding harmful rays from the skin.[f]

[a] II. 12. 1 B.

[b] V. 28. 7 B (vol. II., p. 140 note).

[c] IV. 16. 3. This no doubt originated in the idea that the remedy should resemble the disease; on the other hand the modern treatment of thyroid disease by thyroid extract or liver disease by liver, is at once brought to mind.

[d] V. 26. 35 C.

[e] VI. 7. 1 D.

[f] For many other instances see Sir J. G. Frazer, *The Golden Bough, The Magic Art*, vol. I, p. 78.

# LIST OF MEDICAMENTA

*(References are to volumes and pages of text)*

## I. LIST OF REMEDIES USED AND THE DRUGS, HERBS AND OTHER INGREDIENTS OF PRESCRIPTIONS

Abrotonum (Habrotonum); Artemisia abrotonum; southernwood.

This yields a bitter oil resembling that of hops and was used internally as a carminative, I. 316, 386, and topically to clean wounds, II. 6, 10, and to relieve gout, II. 30.

Absinthium; Artemisia absinthium.

The twigs supply wormwood; the dried flowers wormseed, from which the bitter oil, absinth, was distilled; this was taken with honey as a carminative and diuretic, I. 204, 210, 316, 340, 382, 398, 400, 414, 416, 422, II. 64. It was a remedy against worms, I. 438; santonin, made from certain species of artemisia is still used for this purpose. It was also used topically, I. 412. Wines were flavoured with it to make them keep, I. 498. The harmfulness of the modern absinth liqueurs is due to the deleterious alcohol used in their manufacture.

Acacia; Acacia Arabica.

The gum mucilage from this, which included astringent tannin, was used to arrest bleeding and agglutinate wounds, II. 4, as an exedent,

II. 8, and generally as an astringent gum in eye salves and lozenges. The juice was also used, II. 190 note, 196.

Acetum ; vinegar.

As a drink, I. 196 ff. ; used constantly both externally and internally, I. 212, 258, 270, 286, 292, 308, 310, 338, 346, 366, 388, 390, 394, 398, 406, 416, 438, 458 ; mentioned, II. 4, 8, as a styptic and exedent.

Achariston ; name of a salve, II. 194 and note *b*.

Acopa ; Anodynes, substances to deaden pain, II. 56 note *b*. *See* Anodyna.

Acorus ; Acorus calamus ; sweet flag.

The rhizome was dried and eaten, or the oil pressed out of it ; it is included among diuretics, III. 316, as an ingredient in an antidote, II. 56, and perhaps (under the name of *calamus Alexandrinus*) in an anodyne salve, II. 56.

Adurentia (*medicamenta quae adurunt*, caustics); a list of these is given, II. 8, *see also* 130 ff.

Aes Cyprium or Cuprum ; copper.

Many forms of this were used in prescriptions ;

(1) Aerugo ; basic subacetate and carbonate of copper or verdigris. This was scraped off sheets of copper which had been steeped in vinegar and used as an astringent, repressive or caustic, II. 4, 6. 8.

(2) Chalcitis ; basic carbonate and sulphate of copper, copperas or green vitriol. This was mixed with oak bark or galls to make *atramentum sutorium*, blacking, and used as a caustic and exedent, to arrest haemorrhage, to clean wounds and form a scar, II. 4, 6, 8, 10.

(3) Aes combustum ; calcined copper ore.

# LIST OF MEDICAMENTA

This was used as an erodent, II. 8; or was fused with salt, sulphur or alum into a sulphate chloride and oxide of copper and used to make emollients and eye salves, II. 10, 194, 204, 210–14.

(4) Flos aeris or Chalcanthus; red oxide of copper.

This substance was like millet seeds and was produced by pouring cold water on molten copper and used as an exedent, II. 8, or as an agglutinant for wounds, II. 8, 10, 44.

(5) Squama aeris; black oxide of copper, copper scales.

These were chipped off molten copper, and when washed, pounded and dried acted as a mechanical aperient, I. 168.

(6) Chrysocolla; borate, carbonate and silicate of copper, gold solder.

This was used as an erodent and caustic, II. 8.

(7) Diphryges; sulphide and oxide of copper, mixed with iron and zinc ores.

This was used as an exedent and caustic and for cleaning ulcerations, II. 8, 50.

(8) Stomoma; red oxide of copper, copper scales hardened in the fire.

These were used to arrest haemorrhage and in making an eye salve, II. 4, 194.

(9) Psoricum; itch salve, consisted of chalcitis and cadmia (*see below* Cadmia) boiled together in vinegar to form hydrated oxides of copper and zinc, and then buried underground till used, II. 218, 220; the preparation was also applied to the eyelids, II. 220.

LIST OF MEDICAMENTA

Alcyonium; II. 8, 28, 174; probably a species of coral, perhaps leather coral. It was incinerated to produce quick lime and used as an exedent and for skin diseases.

Alipe; plasters without grease, II. 32.

Allium; Allium nigrum, garlic.

As a food, I. 192 ff., 490; a febrifuge, I. 276; *see also* I. 208, 330, 370, 390, 424, 436, 438, 448; used topically as an erodent, II. 8.

Aloe;

(1) Aquilaria agallocha, lign-aloe.

The perfumed wood of this yields an oil and decays into a resin used in making incense and also (as it was rich in tannin) applied as a topical astringent; to suppress haemorrhage, II. 6, to agglutinate wounds, II. 44, and as an ingredient in eye salves, II. 194, 196, 212, and ear lotion, II. 232.

(2) Aloe Socotrina; aloen.

This was (and still is) used as an aperient, I. 62.

Alumen; Aluminium sulphate and silicate; alum. The following varieties were used:

(1) Alumen liquidum; alum brine, a styptic, II. 4.

(2) Alumen scissile (schiston); split or feathery alum, a repressive, II. 4, 44.

(3) Alumen rotundum; round alum; an epispastic and erodent, II. 6 and 10.

(4) Pumex; silicate and carbonate of aluminium (and other alkalies), pumice. This had been formed by volcanic action and was used for cleaning wounds or as an epispastic, II. 6, 24, 28.

(5) Lapis Phrygius; rock alum from Phrygia and Cappadocia coloured by iron and copper sulphates; an exedent, II. 8; in an eye salve, 218.

(6) Alum earths; terra Eretria, II. 10, 180; terra Cimolia, glutinous hydrated silicate of aluminium coloured by iron and copper, I. 212, 304; II. 4, 102, 124, 184, 534; terra Melia, silicate of aluminium (*alumen Melinum*), II. 2, 288; cf. Pliny, *N.H.*, xxxv. 188. 87, also Hippocrates, *Ulcers*, 11, 12 (Littré VI. 412, 414); terra Lemnia, silicates and sulphates of aluminium, magnesia and iron; the well known *rubrica Lemnica*, red ochre, was exported in packets stamped with the figure of a goat, as the colour due to oxide of iron was ascribed to an admixture of goat's blood; similarly terra Samia, alum earth from Samos, was exported with a star stamped on it, II. 204 note.

Alvum ducunt, medicamenta quae; purgatives and enemas, I. 62, 168, 172, 208; II. 10; *see below* Purgatio and General Index Clyster, Enema.

Amaracus; Origanum majorana, sweet marjoram. Used as a discutient, II. 10.

Ambrosia; name of an antidote (so called from its success in preserving life), II. 54.

Ammoniacum (Hammoniacum) thymiatum; Dorema ammoniacum or Ferula Tingitana, silphium.

The milky juice of this plant (specially cultivated around the temple of Jupiter Ammon) was used for incense; it formed a resin containing salicylic acid and a volatile oil which was much used by Celsus, as a cleanser of wounds, II. 6, and a discutient and emollient, II. 16–30, and in poultices and plasters, II. 36, 38, and eye salves, II. 210, 214, 216.

Ammoniacum sal ; *see* Sal.

Amomum ; *see* Cardamomum.

Anastomotica; openers of pores, II. 6 note, 26.

Anesum ; Pimpinella anisum, anise.

Aniseed (still a common flavouring) is indigestible as a food, I. 200 ff., 490; used against flatulence and as a diuretic, I. 206, 210, 340, 418.

Anethum; Anethum graveolens, dill.

Among foods, I. 200 ff., 208, 448, 490, 491 ; as a diuretic, I. 210, 488; as a snuff, I. 272.

Anodyna; Anodynes (*see* Acopa, *also* Hyoscyamus, Mandragora, Papaver, Solanum).

(1) Prescriptions given as pills, II. 58 ; *see also* I. 211.

(2) Used topically, I. 458, *also* II. 56 note, 191.

Antherae; preparations from flower blossoms, II. 254 note, 258, 260, 264, 272.

Antidota; antidotes, II. 54, note, 56.

The word is not used when remedies against individual poisons are described, II. 122.

Antiseptics; essential oils from aromatic plants and trees; especially cedar, cinnamon, juniper, pine, thyme, used for their antiseptic qualities, II, xii.

Apium ; Apium graveolens, celery or Petroselinum sativum, parsley.

As a diuretic, I. 210; *see also* I. 416, 418, 450, 491.

Apyron ; *see* Sulphur.

Argemonia ; Papaver argemone, prickly poppy.

The soothing mucilage of this contains a small

Argenti spuma ; *see* Plumbum.

amount of opium and was applied to poisonous stings, II. 120.

Arida Medicamenta; dry drugs pounded, used as dusting powders, II. 48; and blown through a quill, II. 156, III. 448; or formed into pastiles by means of a little fluid, II. 14.

Aristolochia; A. longa and A. rotunda, birthwort.

The root yields an irritant glucoside, which was used in poultices and plasters, II. 20, 30, 34, 38, 46, 50, 52, 62.

Aromata; Dried aromatic flowers imported from abroad, I. 316; II. 14, 212.

Armoracia; Cochlearia armoracia, horse radish.

This was prescribed as a remedy for spleen affections, I. 416; II. 106.

Arsenicon; *see* Auripigmentum.

Arteriace; a medicine for the windpipe, II. 64, note *b*.

Arundo (Harundo); Arundo donax, polereed.

The juice of the root was used for earache, II. 228; its splinters were dangerous, II. 106–8.

Asafoetida; *see* Laser.

Asclepion; name of a salve, II. 214.

Aspalathus; Calcycotoma villosa.

A decoction from the rose scented wood of this (*lignum rhodium*) was applied to painful sinews, II. 58.

Atramentum; blacking;

(1) A. scriptorium, ink made from the soot of torches, used as an application for baldness. II. 182.

(2) A. sepiarum, cuttle-fish ink, used as an aperient, I. 208.

(3) A. sutorium, *see* Aes, 2.

Auripigmentum; $AS_2S_3$, the yellow trisulphide of

arsenic, orpiment; sandaraca, $As_2S_2$, the golden disulphide of arsenic, sandarach (modern realgar), which becomes orpiment when heated.

The two forms were used alternatively in prescriptions (in some both were included) for cleaning wounds, and as erodents, caustics and counter irritants, II. 6, 10, 28, 50, 52; they were used in the treatment of all sorts of ulcerations, II. 154, 162, 208, 246, 264, 286, 290.

Celsus does not mention them in his chapter on poisons, II. 110 ff.; nor does he refer to the poisonous arsenious oxide, white arsenic, produced by the oxidation of orpiment and sandarach which was known to Geber in A.D. 750, but was perhaps not in use earlier.

Balanos myrepsica (βάλανος μυρεψική), or Myrobalanos; Hyperanthera decandra, bennut.

The rind was used for spleen disease, I. 416; II. 18, an ointment was also made from it, II. 110 note.

Balsamum; Balsamodendron opobalsamum, balsam of Mecca; B. myrrha, myrrh.

The resin of these trees was known as opobalsam and an almost equally valuable essence was obtained by boiling the wood, leaves and seeds (xylobalsam).

It was used internally as a diuretic, I. 316, and the seeds in an antidote, II. 54, 56; externally as an erodent, suppurative, wound cleaner and emollient, II. 6, 8, 12, also in poultices, II. 16, 20, and as a remedy for neuralgia, II. 58, and in an eye salve, II. 220.

Basilicon; a name given to a plaster, II. 32, and to an eye salve, II. 218, 220.

Bdella or Bdellium; Borassus flabelliformis, the Palmyra palm.

This tree yields a resin like ammoniacum which was used for incense. Celsus used it externally as a pore-opener, epispastic and emollient, II. 6, 10, 18.

Bitumen; found in the Dead Sea and Euphrates valley.

This was used on plasters as a mild counter irritant, I. 348; II. 6, 10, 32, 34, 40, 44, 250.

Cachry; perhaps the fruit of the herb Libanotis, (Lecokia Cretica), the medicinal uses of which are given by Theophrastus, *Enq. into Plants*, IX. II. 10.

Used by Celsus in a prescription for abscesses, II. 18.

Cadmia (terra);

Zinc ores from Cyprus, which when heated in water produced carbonates and hydrosilicates of zinc; these stuck to the reed (*calamus*) with which the mixture was stirred, and so the name "calamine" is still applied to zinc lotions. Cadmia, when heated, gave off zinc oxide vapour which was sublimated and adhered to the wall of the furnace in clusters; these consisted of oxide of zinc and were scraped off and known as *spodium* (ash).

Cadmia was used as an exedent, desiccant and extractive, II. 6, 50, 344, and in the treatment of malignant ulceration, II. 154; the clusters (*botruites Cadmiae, spodium*) to relieve irritation, II. 10, 166, and also for eye salves, II. 194, 204; III. 344, and for earache, II. 234.

Calamus;

  (1) C. Alexandrinus, *see* Acorus.

  (2) C. scriptorius, a reed or quill pen, *see* list II.

Calefacientia; heating foods, medicines or applications; I. 62, 206, 214; II. 16.

Calx; limestone;

  (1) *Calx viva*; calcium oxide, quick lime; an exedent and caustic, II. 8.

  (2) *Cinis*, ash, produced by burning various substances containing lime; *e.g.*, stag's horn (*cornu cervinum*), used as an exedent, erodent and caustic, II. 6, 8, *see also* Alcyonium, Corallium, Salamandra.

  (3) Limestone from Assus, used as a preservative, *see* index of proper names, Assus.

  (4) Saxum calcis; silicates of lime, and magnesia, asbestos; used as an application for a hardened fistula, II. 154.

  (5) Lapis molaris; millstone, used as a discutient, II. 10.

  (6) Lapis pyrites; limestone mixed with sulphides, used as a discutient, emollient, and to relieve irritation, II. 10, 22, 166.

  (7) Gypsum; the sulphate mixed with the carbonate of lime, plaster of Paris, used as an external refrigerant and repressive, II. 212; III. 304.

Campana sertula; *see* Sertula.

Canina lingua; Cynoglossum officinale, hounds-tongue.

  The leaves yield a bitter astringent juice, which was applied to burns, II. 124.

Canopus; name of a salve, II. 214.

# LIST OF MEDICAMENTA

Cantabrica herba ; *see* Scammonea.

Cantharides ; Cantharis or Lytta vesicatoria, Spanish fly.

> Used externally as a caustic and cleanser for wounds and papules, II. 8, 50, 172. If taken internally it was poisonous, and remedies are prescribed for it, II. 122.

Carbo hirundinis ; *see* Hirundo.

Cardamomum ;

> (1) Amomum cardamomum subulatum ; Nepaul pepper, I, 296 ; II. 20, 22.
>
> (2) Elateria cardamomum, cardamon.
>
> The seeds (brought from Malabar and Ceylon) produce an aromatic oil, used internally as a diuretic, I. 316, and externally as a counter-irritant, agglutinant, erodent and emollient, II. 4, 8, 12.

Casia, Cassia ; *see* cinnamon.

Castoreum ;

> A material derived from the genitals of the Castor fiber, beaver. It had a pungent taste, suggesting musk, was used internally as a stimulant, I. 286, 310, 338, 376, 448, externally in eye and ear salves, II. 196, 240.

Cataplasma ; poultice, I. 214. *See also* Malagma.

Catapotium ; pill, I. 316 ; II. 58–64. Eight of the prescriptions are to procure sleep or relieve pain, four for cough.

Cedrus ; Juniper communis.

> The oil from the berries was used externally as a discutient, II. 10, and in poultices for gout, II. 30.

Centaurios ; Centaurea salonitana, centaury.

> The bitter juice from the roots was used in-

# LIST OF MEDICAMENTA

ternally against snake bite, II. 120, and externally for ear discharge, II. 230.

Cera; wax, used as a discutient, emollient and to form flesh, II. 10. *See also* I. 272, 368, 378, 384, 410, 442, 446, 448, 458, 460; *ceratum*, cerate, an ointment made with wax.

Cerussa; *see* Plumbum.

Chamaeleon; Atractylis gummifera, a thistle, whose gum (similar to mastic and birdlime) was used in a poultice for gout, II. 30.

Chamaepitys; Ajuga chamaepitys.

This yields a bitter astringent juice, like pine resin, used as a pore opener, II. 6.

Charta combusta; *see* Papyrus.

Chelidonium maius or Herba hirundinis; the greater celandine, *see* II. 226 note.

The juice was applied to an inflamed uvula, II. 262.

Cicinum oleum; an oil produced from the seeds of the Ricinus communis, castor oil.

It was used as an emollient, II. 42, 58; Celsus does not mention its use as an aperient, but this is referred to by Dioscorides and Galen.

Cicuta; Conium maculatum, hemlock.

Used internally as an anodyne, 11. 62; externally as an emollient, 11. 12, and in a poultice for gout, II. 16, and in an eye salve, II. 190. Remedies for those poisoned by it, II. 122.

Cinis; wood-ash (especially from vine twigs).

Used as a refrigerant and repressive, II. 212; III. 298; cinis Cyprius (from Lawsonia inermis used as an erodent, II. 8.

Cinnamomum; Cinnamomum cassia from China

C. zeylanicum from Ceylon, cinnamon or casia. In two prescriptions (I. 450; II. 30), both names occur. They were perhaps preparations from different parts of the plant.

The unripe fruit or the rolled bark were used internally as a diuretic and remedy for cystalgia or snake bite, I. 316, 414, 450 or externally as a pore opener, erodent and discutient, II. 6, 8, 10, and for podagras, II. 30.

Coccum (or granum) Cnidium (Gnidium); Daphne Gnidium, spurge laurel (from Cnidus).

Used by Celsus externally as a wound cleanser and caustic, and in a poultice to ease pain in side, II. 6, 8, 20; he does not mention the use of the berries as a drastic purge (Galen, *Nat. Fac.*, p. 67, L.C.L. trans.).

Colicos; a medicine against colic, invented by Cassius, I. 430; II. 64 note.

Collyria; salves, II. 154 note, and list II.

Comprimentia; astringents, I. 36, 64, 208, 432, 444, 452; II. 280.

Concoctio; assimilation of food stuffs, digestion, I. 74, 326, *see* General Index, Digestion. *Medicamenta quae concoquunt*, drugs to mature abscesses, II. 6.

Corallium; coral. C. rubrum, red coral; *see also* Alcyonium cortonium, leather coral. Both substances were incinerated for the quick lime in the ash and they are included among erodents, exedents and caustics, II. 6, 8.

Coriander; Coriandrum sativum, coriander.

As a diuretic, I. 210; *see also* I. 206, 212, 316, 491; used externally, II. 16, 166 note.

Cornu cervinum; stag's horn.

When incinerated used as a wound cleanser,

# LIST OF MEDICAMENTA

II. 6, as the ash contained quick-lime (calcium oxide) with some phosphate and carbonate, *see* Calx; the vapour of it while burning was a stimulus in cases of lethargy, as it included a little ammonium carbonate, and when cooled in vinegar it was a remedy for toothache, I. 308; II. 248; it was boiled to a glutinous mucus for use in an eye salve named after it, *see* II. 208, note *a*.

Costus; costmary.

The roots of Saussurea Lappa, a plant of Kashmir, the oil from which was used internally in an antidote and as a stimulant in cases of snake bite, II. 54, 120, and externally as a suppurative and wound cleanser, II. 6.

Creta; Calcium carbonate, chalk.

(1) Creta Cimolia, chalk from Cimolus mixed with alum, *see* Alum (6); used externally as a repressant, I. 212, 304; II. 102, 124, 184; III. 534; also as a styptic, II. 4.

(2) Creta figularis, potter's clay, a styptic, II. 4; cf. Pliny, *N.H.*, xxxi. 3, 28.

Crocus; Crocus sativus, the autumn flowering crocus.

From the styles and stigmas saffron, a condiment with a slightly bitter taste, was obtained, and from this an orange-coloured oil was expressed which left a residue known as crocomagma, saffron dregs. The best variety came from Cilicia. Saffron was used internally as a diuretic, I. 316, and in an antidote, II. 54, externally in an ointment for headache, I. 296, as a wound cleanser and discutient, II. 6, 10, as a remedy against scabies, II. 168, and especially as an ingredient of eye salves, II. 194–220, one of which was named the dia crocu, II. 220. Crocomagma was also used in an eye salve, II. 214, and in the poultice of Nileus, II. 20, 22.

Cuminum; Cuminum cyminum, cummin.

Among foods, I. 200 ff., 416, 491; *see* Git.

Cummis; a gum mucilage, source not specified; often used with acacia gum and juice, I. 448; II. 4, 10, 190, note *a*, 196.

Cupressus; C. sempervirens, the pyramidal ever-green cyprus.

Wood, leaves and seed yield *oleum cupressum* containing an aromatic and astringent tannin; the crushed leaves were used internally as a repressive and refrigerant, I. 312, and the seeds as a diuretic, I. 316; externally the leaves were used in a poultice for spleen disease and the oil as a discutient and for erysipelas, eye salves, and gum boils, I. 416; II. 10, 102, 208, 258, and a decoction of the leaves was put in a bath for use after lithotomy, III. 448.

Cycnon ; name of an eye salve, II. 196 note *a*.

Cyperus quadratus and C. rotundus ; *see* Iuncus.

Cyperus papyrus ; *see* Papyrus.

Cyprus ; Lawsonia alba.

From the leaves with their lilac-like perfume *oleum cyprinum*, cyprus oil, was distilled and used as a calefacient, I. 214, and for tetanus, dyspnoea, enlarged spleen, hysteria, and podagra, I. 378, 384, 446, 460; the oil was an emollient and an ingredient in eye and ear salves, II. 58, 220, 228; cyprus ash (*Cyprius cinis*) contained caustic soda and is included among exedents, II. 8.

# LIST OF MEDICAMENTA

Cytisus; C. scoparius, broom.

> The broom tops contain the alkaloid spartein, and a decoction was used for splenitis, III. 416, and for toothache, II. 248, 250.

Daphne; Dia-daphnidon.

> A plaster containing laurel leaves, II. 10, 36; *see* Laurus.

Daucus Creticus; Athaminta Cretensis, Cretan or Candy carrot.

> An ingredient of an antidote, II. 56.

Diaceratos, Diacodion, Diadaphnidon, Diacrocu, Dialibanu; *see* Cornu cervinum, Papaver, Daphne, Crocus and Libanotos.

Diachylon; Emplastrum plumbi, lead plaster, *see* Plumbum.

Diaphoretics; see Sudorem evocare.

Dictamnus Creticus; Origanum dictamnum, Cretan dittany (called after Mount Dicte, in Crete, where it grew in abundance) was a famous remedy for wounds, cf. Virgil *Aeneid*, XII. 411.

> The volatile oil from this is prescribed for expelling a dead foetus, II. 64.

Diphryges; *see* Aes (7).

Discutientia (*Medicamenta quae discutiunt*); dispersives of diseased material, I. 36, 178, 276, 394; II. 10.

Ebenus or Hebenus; Diospyrus ebenum or melanoxylon, ebony.

> The sawdust from this containing humic acid and black pigment (a remedy used in ancient Egypt) was prescribed by Celsus internally as

a diuretic, I. 316; externally as an exedent,
epispastic and relief for irritation, II. 8, 10.

Ebur, ivory; the raspings were used as a wound
cleanser, II. 6.

Elaterium; Ecbalium or Mormodica elaterium, juice
of the wild cucumber, Cucumis agrestis.

Used as an epispastic, II. 10; the root in a
poultice for pain in the side, II. 20; the root
and juice for pain in the uterus, II. 48; the root
to heal wounds, II. 108; the juice for sycosis
and toothache, II. 180, 250.

Elephantinum; name of a plaster containing white
lead, so called from its likeness to ivory, II. 42.

Emollientia; emollients, I. 212, 214; II. 10; *see also*
Malagma.

Emplastra; plasters, List of, II. 32–44, *also* 14, 24,
46; distinguished from pastils, II. 44, by the
method used in compounding, and from emollients by the materials; they were divided into
classes, *alipe*, without grease, *lenia*, soothing,
*lipara*, greasy, *septa*, exedent, II. 32, 42; many
had names, *barbarum, Coacon, Alexandrinum,
smaragdinum, rhypodes, raptousa, diadaphnidon,
enhaema*, which referred to the place whence
they came, their colour, material or effect, II.
32, 36, 38, 42. Others were called after their
inventors, Philotas, Attalus, etc., II. 32 ff.; two
in common use were the tetrapharmacum and
enneapharmacum with 4 and 9 ingredients, II.
34. There were also *emplastra reprimentia* or
*epispastica*, II. 32, 36 ff. Pitch plasters, I. 326,
346, 366, and mustard plasters, I. 346, 434,
were among those commonly used.

Enchrista; liniments and liquid ointments, II. 58,

note; only two prescriptions are given under this heading (for ulcers and erysipelas).

Epispastica; Epispastics, substances that extract diseased matter, II. 10, 16, 36, 38.

Eruca; Brassica eruca, rocket.

The plant yields an oil like mustard with an acrid flavour and was indigestible when eaten, I. 200, 202; it increased the secretion of urine, I. 210, 452, and reduced an enlarged spleen, I. 416; applied externally the oil acted as an erodent, I. 212, and caustic, II. 8.

Ervum; Ervum ervilia, bitter vetch.

In a poultice, I. 214; II. 156.

Erysimum; Sisymbrium polyceratium, hedge-mustard.

The oil was used in a poultice to open pores, II. 26, and was administered internally in cases of difficult labour, II. 64.

Exedentia; substances that eat away diseased flesh, II. 6 note *b*, 8.

Feniculum; F. vulgare, Anethum foeniculum, fennel.

This was indigestible when eaten, I. 200, but relieved flatulence, 206; was used as a diuretic, I. 210, and the seeds (externally), as a repressant and refrigerant, I. 212.

Ferrum; oxides, silicates and sulphates of iron:

(1) Lapis haematites, haematite, ferric oxide ($Fe_2O_3$) mixed with silicates and sulphates of aluminium; the name came from the colour which resembles dried blood.

(2) Bolus rubra or rubrica, ruddle or red ochre; sulphates and sulphides of iron, especially from Sinope, *see* Index of Proper Names, s.v.

(3) Sil or yellow ochre, oxide and sulphate of iron.

(4) Sory or inkstone, sulphates of iron with copper and lead.

(5) Scoria ferri, iron slag composed of oxides and silicates of iron.

(6) Ferrugo or Robigo, iron rust.

(7) Squama ferri, scales chipped of from red hot iron bars, ferrous oxide (FeO).

These substances are only used externally, to arrest haemorrhage, clean wounds, as exedents and erodents, II. 4, 6, 8; the yellow ochre from Attica and Scyros made flesh grow (*see* Index of Proper Names, s.v.); sory was used in a prescription for loosening a carious tooth, II. 248. Celsus only mentioned the internal use of iron once as a "rustic remedy" for enlarged spleen—"water in which a blacksmith has dipped his red-hot irons," I. 416, but treatment by *ferrugo*, iron rust, was mentioned by Pliny, *N.H.* xxxiv. 43, and fully described by Dioscorides v. 93.

Ficus; (1) F. Carica contains the digestive ferment papain and externally was used on wounds, II. xiii; *see* General Index, s.v. Fig.

(2) F. Aegyptiaca; *see* Sycaminus.

Filicula; Polypodium vulgare, the polypody fern.

This contains a saccharine material resembling liquorice and was used as an aperient, I. 168. This fern was also a frequent source of splinters in the hand, II. 108.

Foenum Graecum; Trigonella foenum-graecum, fenugreek.

The plant itself was eaten as a vegetable, I. 491; its oil was used in enemas, I. 172, and

xxxiii

LIST OF MEDICAMENTA

heating poultices, I. 214; also in a bath to
relieve spasm, I. 378.

Furfur; bran (for poultices), I. 214, 218; in a gargle,
I. 382; for snake bite, II. 17, 118.

Galbanum; Ferulago galbanifera, galbanum, *see*
Panaces.

This yields an aromatic resin (used for incense,
Exodus xxx. 34) and was prescribed internally
as a diuretic, I. 316, and for dyspnoea, I. 386,
and externally as a suppurative, pore-opener,
erodent and emollient, II. 6, 8, 12, as an ingredient in a poultice for contracted joints, II.
28, and as an antidote for cantharides poisoning,
II. 122; the fumes were inhaled as a stimulant,
I. 308.

Galla; Oak gall (chief constituent gallic acid).

Used externally as an astringent, erodent and
exedent and to relieve inflammation, II. 6, 8, 46;
especially for inflamed gums, II. 370.

Gargarizationes; gargles, II. 52–54.

Gentiana; Erythraea centaurium, gentian, fever-wort.

The bitter juice of the roots has been in use
from the earliest times as a stomachic remedy and
febrifuge, but Celsus only once mentions it, in
the prescription for an antidote, II. 56.

Git; Nigella sativa, melanthium, melanospernum or
black cumin.

The seeds, like carraway, but hotter, and more
like nutmeg, were used as a spice, I. 200, also
internally as a diuretic, I. 416; for worms, 438;
and uterine trouble, 448; externally in heating
poultices, I. 214; II. 16, and as an application
for papules, II. 172.

# LIST OF MEDICAMENTA

Gluten;

Glue made from hides and horns was used as an agglutinant and cleanser of wounds, II. 4, 6, or to keep eyelashes in position, III. 338. Joiners' glue is referred to, III. 518.

Glutinantia (*Medicamenta quae glutinant*); agglutinants (of wounds), II. 4, 44, 82.

Habrotonum; *see* Abrotonum.

Halicacabus; *see* Solanum.

Hammoniacum; *see* Ammoniacum.

Hedera; Hedera Helix, ivy.

Decoctions of the leaves and berries yield helicin and tannin and were used externally as repressants and refrigerants, I. 212, for the relief of lethargy, I. 310, and erysipelas, II. 138; berries were used in dental treatment, II. 250, and to promote the healing of wounds, III. 554.

Helenium; Inula helenium, elecampayne (*see* Panaces).

The root yields a bitter (helenin) and a glucoside (inulin). It was used externally for the relief of coxalgia, I. 452, and as a dispersive, II. 10.

Heliotropion; Herba solaris, sunflower or turnsole.

The seeds and leaves, which yield an oil with a nutty flavour, are prescribed once by Celsus in a decoction against scorpion bite, II. 118.

Hellebore; *see* Veratrum.

Herba Cantabrica, hirundinis, muralis, salivaris, sanguinalis, solaris, Vettonica, *see* Scammonea, Chelidonium, Parthenium, Pyrethrum, Polygonum, Heliotropium, Vettonica, respectively.

Hibiscus; *see* Ibiscus.

Hirundinis carbo; swallow's ash, a popular remedy
for angina, III. 382.

Hirundinis herba; *see* Chelidonium.

Hyoscyamus; H. niger, swinebean or henbane.
This yields the alkaloids hyoscyamine and
hyoscine, isomeric, but not identical with
atropine; they are hypnotics and anodynes.

Used by Celsus as a hypnotic, I. 296, and the
seeds as a local anodyne, I. 348; the bark was
used in a poultice for the joints, II. 28, and the
seeds to promote sleep (*see above*); the leaves
in an eye salve, II. 202, the juice for earache,
II. 234, and the root for toothache, II. 246.
Remedies against poisoning by it are prescribed,
II. 122.

Hypericum; H. perforatum crispum, St. Johns' wort.
The juice was used to make a pastil to expel
stone from the bladder; and in an antidote,
II. 46, 56.

Hypocistis; Cytinus hypocistis.
A scarlet parasite found on the hips of the
dog-rose and the roots of the rock-rose.

The astringent juice (chief content gallic acid)
was used in an antidote, II. 54, and externally
as an exedent, II. 8.

Hysopum; hyssop.
This has not been identified, I. 491; Celsus
employed it as a food, I. 200 ff.; as an emetic,
stimulant, carminative, expectorant and diuretic,
I. 60, 210, 370, 382, 384, 388, 410, 416, 428, 436.

Ibiscus (Hibiscus); Althaea officinalis, marsh mallow.
The root yields a mucilage like linseed, which
was cooked in wine to make a heating plaster for

inflamed joints, I. 456; Pliny, *N.H.* XX. 4 (14),
copies the prescription from Celsus.

Iris; Iris pallida, Florentina or Illyrica, iris.

The root yields orris camphor (commonly
known as essence of violets) which was used by
Celsus, in the form of hot iris ointment and oil,
externally as a calefacient and cleanser, discutient, repressive and anodyne, II. 6, 10, 12;
as a calefacient it was particularly general, I.
214, 270, 296, 378, 384, 412, 448. He also used
it in poultices for gland enlargements, II. 18,
abscesses, II. 20, 56, painful joints and feet,
II. 28, and for neuralgia, II. 124. It was
commonly used for burns, II. 198, 220, 224, and
the hot ointment for eyes, headache, deafness,
II. 228, 236, 240, and for dressing wounds of the
cerebral membrane, III. 514. Internally it was
used as a diuretic and in an antidote, I. 316;
II. 54.

Iuncus quadratus; Cyperus longus, schoenon. Iuncus
rotundus; Cyperus rotundus, sweet flag, rush,
sedge, galingale.

The rhizomes, flowers and seeds of these marsh
plants have a scent resembling bay and orris.
The seeds of both varieties were used as a diuretic,
I. 316, and the flowers of C. rotundus in antidotes, II. 54, 56. Externally the rhizomes of
Iuncus quadratus were used as a pore opener
and discutient, II. 6, 10, and in a preparation to
cure uterine ulceration, I. 448.

Lactuca marina; Euphorbia paralias, sea-spurge,
wolf's milk (also referred to by its Greek name
Tithymalus).

This was used internally as a drastic purge, I. 168, 320 note, externally as an exedent and caustic, II. 8.

Ladanum; Cistus villosus Creticus, rock-rose.

The resin of this (combed off sheep's fleeces with a *ladanisterium*), with its musk-like perfume, is still used in pastilles for fumigation. Celsus prescribed it internally as a diuretic, I. 316, and externally as an epispastic, II. 10, and an ingredient of the eroding plasters called *septa*, II. 40. It was also used to encourage the growth of hair, II. 178, 180.

Lana; wool.

(1) L. succida or oesypum; unscoured (and therefore greasy) wool. The grease, when purified is now called lanolin; it consists largely of cholesterin. It was often used, II. 36 note, 280, 282, etc., in topical applications. *See also* I. 308, 366, 402, 406; II. 192; III. 312, 442.

(2) L. mollis, soft scoured wool, II. 250; III. 446; lanula, a flake of wool, II. 250; III. 446.

(3) L. sulphurata, wool impregnated with sulphur, I. 398, 406. The word *absus* for a sheet of sulphurated wool is only found in Celsus, I. 406; III. 442, and later in a passage of Scribonius Largus copied from Celsus (Comp. XLIII). For *lemniscus*, a strip of wool, *see* III. 454 note.

Lapatium; Rumex acetosella, sorrel.

As a food, I. 200 ff.; also as an aperient, 208, and febrifuge, 260.

Lapsanum; Raphanus raphanistrum, white charlock.

As a food, I. 204 ff.; as a diuretic, I. 210.

Laser, Laserpitium; Ferula silphium, a mild form of asafoetida.

This was used with grated cheese as a condiment and as a mild stimulant, I. 286, 370, 376, 390, 426.

Laurus; Laurus nobilis, the cultivated bay tree.

The crushed berry (lauri bacca or daphnis) yielded laurel oil, used as an epispastic and in a plaster called after it diadaphnidon, I. 310, 366 ; II. 10, 36 and note ; and internally it was used for liver disease, I. 414.

Lavandula Stoechas; Lavender from the isles of Hyères (Stoechades) used to relieve cough, III. 532.

Lentiscus; Pistacia lentiscus, mastich.

This came from Scio (Chios) and yields a turpentine-like gum now used as a chewing gum, for flavouring wine and for fumigation.

Celsus used it internally as a repressive, I. 212, 450, externally as an erodent, II. 6, and for aural ulceration, II. 232. Mastich leaves formed part of an application for ulceration of the genitals, II. 272.

Libanotis; *see* Cachry.

Libanotos or Tus; Boswellia Carteri, and other species of frankincense trees ; the gum was used for incense ; and in an application to a paralysed limb, I. 346 ; dialibanu, II. 204 note, 206, was a plaster made from it ; the soot (*fuligo*) was used as a styptic and caustic, II. 2, 4, 6, 8, 24. The gum was sipped in a draught to stop haemorrhage from the mouth and throat, I. 394.

Ligustrum; L. sempivirens, privet.

This yields ligustrin and tannin ; it was used externally as a repressive and refrigerant, I. 212 and chewed for ulceration of the gums, II. 260.

# LIST OF MEDICAMENTA

Lilium ; L. candidum, the white lily.

> The roots yield an oil and glucoside used as a discutient, II. 10; unguent made from lilies grown at Susa formed an ingredient in a pessary, II. 48.

Linum ; L. usitatissimum, flax.

> (1) Dressed flax, lint, II. 84, 88, 102, 148, 208 ; III. 304, 336, 378, 406 ff., 464, 536 ; penicillus, a pad of lint, I. 164, 272 ; II. 196, 200 ; III. 334.

> (2) Lini semen, linseed, yields mucilage, glucoside and an ethereal oil, which includes a little hydrocyanic acid. It was used externally as a discutient and epispastic, to agglutinate wounds, and in a heating poultice, I. 214, 388, 432 ; II. 4, 10.

Lipara ; plasters with grease, II. 42 note.

Litharge ; *see* Plumbum.

Lolium ; L. temulentum, Italian ryegrass.

> The seeds of this when ergotized yielded *farina lolii*, darnel meal, which when eaten produced headache and symptoms of intoxication. Lolium was used internally in an antidote, II. 56, and topically as a calefacient, anodyne and epispastic, and as an application to ulcerations, poisonous stings and papules, I. 214, 452 ; II. 10, 50, 120, 172.

Lupinum ; Lupinus alba, lupin.

> A decoction of the seeds was given as a remedy for worms in the intestine, I. 436, 438, and externally in a heating poultice, I. 214.

Lycium ; Rhamnus infectorius, boxthorn or lycium.

> This was exported from Lycia and largely used in dyeing; medically, owing to the tannin it contains, it was an astringent and Celsus

prescribed it as an application to relieve haemorrhage and ulceration of the throat, I. 388, also
generally to arrest bleeding and induce wounds to
heal, II. 2, 98.     It relieved ulcerations of the
genitals, fingers and nostrils, also those due to
scabies, II. 168, 270, 288; III. 366, as well as
ear ulceration following an injury, III. 522; it
was a frequent ingredient in eye salves, II. 196–
212, and checked discharge from the ears and
nose, II. 230, 232, 244.


Magma; dregs, *see* Crocus (crocomagma).

Malabathrum; Folia Malabathri Indica, leaves of
Malabar or Indian cinnamon.

The oil of this was used in two of the antidotes
(II. 54, 56).

Malagma; poultice; list of, II. 14–30; distinguished
from emplastra and pastilli, II. 14.   Generally
heating, I. 214, but cooling poultices applied to
podagra, I. 458; II. 16.

They were usually applied to disperse diseased
matter, or draw it out (*digerere*, *extrahere*) the
latter were known as *epispastica*, II. 16, but
were used also to relieve pain, II. 18.   They were
often called after their inventor (Lysias, Andreas,
etc., II. 18 ff.),

Malva; Malva rotundifolia, mallow.

Mallows were included in a frugal diet, and
were a bland and aperient food, I. 208, 260, 390;
the mucilage formed a soothing enema, I. 172,
and was used externally as an emollient, I. 456.

Mandragora; Mandragora officinarum, mandrake.

Both the root and the fruit yield the allied
alkaloids scopolamine, hyoscine and atropine.

The plant was used internally as a soporific and anodyne, I. 296; II. 60; externally it was used in an eye salve, 190, and for the relief of tooth-ache, 246.

Probably Celsus refers to the plant mandrake, but he may have meant Atropa belladonna, the deadly nightshade which was perhaps known as mandragora, though the identification is not certain. Cf. Theophrastus, Plants, 6. 2. 9.

Marrubium; M. vulgare, horehound.

The ethereal and bitter oil from this, cooked in honey, was, till recent times, in use as a remedy for coughs, as it was employed by Celsus, I. 332; 350, 388, 390; externally he used it as an exedent and cleanser, II. 8, 10, and for foul ulcerations, II. 50, 124, 134, maggots in the ear, II. 236, and nasal and genital ulcerations, II. 244, 268; III. 448.

Mastich; *see* Lentiscus.

Memigmenon; name of a salve, II. 210.

Mentastrum; *see* Mentha.

Mentha; Mint and catmint, I. 492; *see also* Nepeta.

(1) Mentha piperita, peppermint.

(2) Mentha viridis, green mint; as a food, I. 200, 204; a diuretic, 210, 414; in a draught for cough, I. 390, 404; as a stimulant snuff, I. 422; in a decoction for worms, I. 438.

(3) Mentha pulegium, pennyroyal; as a stimulant, I. 210, 212, 422; externally as a pore opener, II. 6.

(4) Mentastrum, used against snake bite, II. 120, 250. The calamint of Dioscorides, which is similarly used, is probably the same plant; others think mentastrum = wild mint.

LIST OF MEDICAMENTA

Minium; HgS, red sulphide of mercury, cinnabar.
    This was largely obtained from Sinope, it was
mixed with red oxides of copper, iron and lead.
It was used as an antiseptic, I. 434; II. 6, 8, 40,
210, 216; also applied to nasal polypus and foul
genital ulcerations, II. 272.
Misy; *see* Stibium.
Morum; mulberry; *see* Sycaminus.
Muralis herba; *see* Parthenium.
Muscus; moss.
    Used as a repressive and refrigerant, I. 212.
Myrrh; Balsamodendron myrrha, myrrh; but the
name was probably applied generally to various
species of shrubs in Arabia and Africa with a
sweet scented gum.
    The gum resin, with its volatile oil, exuded
from the trees in drops (*stacte*, II. 56) and had a
powerful and lasting odour. It was used internally as a stimulant and diuretic, I. 286, 316, and
in an antidote, II. 56, and externally for otorrhea,
II. 230.
Myrtus; Myrtus communis, myrtle.
    Included among vervains, I. 493; The berries
were added to wine, I. 444, though the taste is
now esteemed very disagreeable; myrtle oil
(olive oil infused with myrtle berries) was used as
a repressive and refrigerant, I. 210 ff., 260, 304,
496; II. 42, and in soothing plasters for eczema
of the scalp, II. 180.

Narcissus; N. serotinus, narcissus.
    The juice of the root was an emollient which
reduced the pain of erodents and discutients and
was therefore mixed with them, II. 8, 10.

Nardum; Nardostachys Jatamansi, spikenard or nard. The name was also applied to the resin of Valeriana Celtica, nardum Gallicum.

The resin was used internally as a diuretic, I. 316, 450, and in an antidote, II. 54, 56, and externally in a plaster for the liver, II. 62.

Nasturtium; Lepidium sativum, cress.

As a food, I. 200 ff.; as a diuretic, I. 210; *see also* I. 208, 212, 338, 386, 416, 438, 492; II. 6.

Nepeta; N. cataria, catnip or catmint, mint.

As a food, I. 200, 204; as a diuretic, I. 210; against snake bite, II. 120; *see also* I. 370, 382, 416, 458.

Nitrum; *see* Sal.

Nuces; Nuts; for almonds, hazel nuts, walnuts, and nuts of all kinds as food stuff *see* index s.v. and vol. I. appendix, p. 495.

Bitter almonds (*nuces amarae*) were used medicinally as a diuretic, I. 316, for jaundice, 340, cough, 388; externally in an emulsion and aperient for headache and podagra, I. 270, 458, for thrush, II. 256. The sweet almonds (*nuces Graecae*) were also used, I. 418, in a draught given for renal pain; *see also* II. 8, 10, 12, 50, 166, 184, 228, 232, 240.


Ocimum; Ocimum basilicum, basil.

Among foods, I. 200 ff., 330, 492; as a diuretic, I. 208, 210, 212.

Oenanthe; *see* Vitis alba.

Oesypum; *see* Lana.

Olibanum; *see* Libanotos.

xliv

# LIST OF MEDICAMENTA

Omphacium.
> Juice of unripe olives and grapes. Cleans ulcers and wounds, II. 6; erodent 8, epispastic, 12, for tonsilitis, 252, 262, 272.

Opopanax; *see* Panaces, all-heal.

Origanum; There were several varieties of this shrub:
> (1) O. Dictamnus; *see* Dictamnus.
> (2) O. majorana, Amaracus, sweet marjoram, used as a discutient, II. 10.
> (3) O. vulgare, Tragoriganum, goats' marjoram, used as a diuretic and discutient, I. 316; II. 10.

Panaces, Panax (πανάκεια); "All-heal"; an emollient mucilage, without further activity, from several distinct plants, so called because of its healing properties.
> (1) Ferulago galbanifera, galbanum, q.v.
> (2) Panaces Cheironium = Inula helenium, elecampayne; *see* Helenium.
> (3) Panaces Asclepieium = Ferula nodosa.
> (4) Opopanax hispidus or Panaces Heracleium.

> Celsus refers several times to "all-heal" (panaces), as a remedy against snake bite, II. 120, as a pore-opener, II. 6, and to opopanax as a diuretic, I. 316, and in a poultice for suppuration, II. 18, in an eye and ear salve, II. 214, 230.

Papaver; Papaver rhoeas, the wild poppy. (For the Papaver argemone, prickly poppy, *see* Argemone.)
> The juice contained a small quantity of opium and was recognised as a mild narcotic

and anodyne. It was probably the source of the pills made from " poppy tears," II. 60; the juice (*lacrimae*) expressed from slits below the capsules of the poppy was the strongest. The dried capsules were also used, II. 60, for the pills known as *diacodion* (διὰ κωδείων). Cf. Pliny, *N.H.* 18. 76 ; 19. 79.

Celsus never alludes to the cultivated poppy (papaver somniferum) from which opium is obtained and this name was first used by Dioscorides, IV. 647. As Celsus does not include poppy juice in his list of poisons, II. 122, he probably only knew a mild variety of the juice. He used it internally to produce sleep and relieve pain, I. 210 ; II. 54, 60 ; and externally in decoctions to any painful part, I. 272, 296, 418, 448, 458.

Papyrus ;

(1) Rolled papyrus (*papyrus intortus*) was used to apply remedies for fistula, II. 156.

(2) Charta combusta, papyrus ash.

This yielded caustic potash and soda and was used as a caustic and application to ulcers and putrid wounds and also to bald patches on the scalp, II. 8, 50, 182, 264, 288.

Parthenium or Herba muralis ; Parietaria officinalis, pellitory.

This was used externally as a repressive and refrigerant, I. 212, or the juice was applied to the head in fever, or to painful joints or papules, I. 294, 458 ; II. 170.

Pastillum ; pastil, Greek τροχίσκος.

Pastils were in tabloid form and could be used internally or externally ; a list is given, II. 44–46, and they are distinguished from plasters, II. 14. A celebrated pastil of Polyides was called " the seal," II. 44.

**Personina planta**; Arctium lappa, burdock.

Used as an application for snake bite, II. 120.

**Pessoi**; pessaries for diseases of women, II. 46, 48.

**Peucedanum**; P. officinale, sulphurwort.

The root yields a bitter foetid resin peuce-danine, which was used as an application to painful joints, II. 28.

**Pinus**; Pinus pinea, the stone pine.

The pine kernels (*nuclei pinei*) were eaten, I. 200, 202, 210, and were given in honey for cough, and to relieve inflammation of the kidney, I. 410, 418, 452; as was the *flos pini* in liver disease, I. 414; externally the resin was given as a suppurative, pore-opener, erodent and epispastic, II. 8, 10, 12, and pitch was also used in the same way and as an emollient, II. 8, 12, 38; pitch plasters were also commonly used, I. 326 note. 346, 366.

Pitch resin was closely akin to turpentine (*see* Terebinthus).

For other refs. to pine products, *see* I. 308, 410, 414, 418, 452, 458.

**Piper**; Piper nigrum, pepper. Two varieties are referred to, long and round, I. 210, 492; among foods, I, 206, 210; as a diuretic, I. 210; in fever, I. 286; to promote sneezing, 308; *see also* I. 376, 378, 382, 418, 436, 452; used in local applications, I. 214; II. 6, 8, 18–30, 56, 58–64, 250.

**Plantago**; P. major, plantain.

Plantain and especially the seeds yield a very glutinous mucilage; it was used as a food, I.

208 ff., and in a draught for phthisis, haemorrhage, and dysentery, I. 332, 394, 436; it was also applied externally for elephantiasis, I. 344.

Psylleum; Plantago psyllium, fleawort.

An agglutinant for wounds, II. 4.

Plumbum; lead.

(1) Galena (μολύβδαινα) sulphide of lead; when fused this was known as *plumbum combustum*, and after washing as *plumbum elotum*; it was used to arrest haemorrhage, II. 4.

(2) Plumbi stercus or recrementum plumbi (σκωρία μολύβδου), lead slag. This was applied externally as an emollient, for burns and ulcerations, II. 12, 42, 124, 242.

(3) Spuma argenti (λιθάργυρος), litharge; oxide of lead separated after heating lead and silver ores; litharge was heated with oil to make lead plaster (*emplastrum plumbi*), diachylon. It was used to check bleeding, II. 32; and sweating in cardiac disease, I. 304; to clean wounds, II. 6, 8; and was applied to putrid flesh, 50; to pustules, 166; and to nasal ulcerations, 242.

(4) Cerussa (ψιμύθιον), white lead (basic lead acetate) formed by pouring vinegar over lead shavings; when heated cerussa produced the yellow and red oxides of lead, I. 272, 458. It was used as an application for recent wounds and ulcerations, II. 42, 166, also for headache and joint pain, I. 272, 458. Remedies against poisoning by it are given, II. 122.

(5) Plumbum album, perhaps tinstone, *see* II. 108 note.

Polium; Teucrium polium, polygermander, the grey evergreen germander, hulwort.

xlviii

The popular name for this was trixago, because its leaves resembled the castor oil plant, trixis.

A decoction of the leaves was used for the relief of pain in the side and cough, I. 406; III. 532, and also for snake bite, II. 120.

Polygonum; P. aviculare, knotgrass.

The juice of this was very rich in tannin and gallic acid, and so was a powerful astringent, much used to arrest haemorrhage; hence it was known as *herba sanguinalis*, I. 212, 332, 414; II. 4, 166, 236.

Populus; P. alba, the white poplar.

An application was made from the bark of the roots for toothache, II. 246.

Portulaca; Portulaca oleracea, purslane.

As a food, I. 200 ff., 212, 492; also used as an aperient, I. 208; to promote urination, I. 416; and chewed to check bleeding from the gums, I. 394.

Potio; a draught, I. 64, 496–499.

Psoricum; *see* Aes (9).

Psylleum, fleawort; *see* Plantago.

Puleium, pennyroyal; *see* Mentha.

Pulvis (ex via); road dust.

In an application for inflammation of the stomach, I. 398.

Punicum malum; Pomum or Malum granatum, pomegranate.

The fruit was regarded as specially digestible, I. 204. All parts of the plant contained tannin, and so were used as astringents, I. 212; the flowers (which yielded the scarlet dye *balaustrium*) were used as a mild corrosive, II. 50; the fruit

and its juice were used in several prescriptions,
II. 230, 232, 234, 252, 256 ; as were the *capituli*, the
red fleshy calixes, II. 38, 44, 46 ; and the bark,
*cortex mali punici* or *malicorium*, which was dried,
I. 442 ; II. 232, 248. *See also* I. 210, 404, 432,
444, 492.

Purgantia ; drugs to cleanse wounds, II. 6, 12.

Purgatio, purging ; value of, I. 58 ; purgatives, I. 168,
208.

Pyrethrum or Herba salivaris ; Anthemis pyrethrum,
chamomile.

   The plant yields a brown acrid resin with a
volatile oil and much tannin ; it served as a pore-
opener, caustic and epispastic, II. 6, 8, 40 ; and
in applications for pain in the side, scrofulous
tumour, and toothache, II. 20, 22, 50.

Pyrron ; name of a salve, II. 210 note *c*.

Pyxinum ; name of a salve, II. 214.


Quinquefolium ; Potentilla reptans, cinquefoil.

   The juice contains a great deal of tannic acid
and was used internally for dysentery, I. 432, and
externally, with hyoscyamus, for toothache, II.
246, and in heating poultices, I. 214.


Radix, Radicula ; Raphanus sativus, radish.

   Mentioned as a bland food stuff, I. 192, 202,
286 and a diuretic, I. 210, but of bad juice,
I. 200. It was commonly used for morning
emesis, I. 60, and was probably coarser than the
modern variety.

Radix dulcis ; Glycorrhiza glabra, liquorice.

   This root yields a peculiar sugar, valuable as
an adjunct to honey before the introduction of

l

# LIST OF MEDICAMENTA

cane sugar, I. 492; medicinally it was used internally in an antidote and to expel stone from the bladder, II. 46, 54, and externally in a gargle for the throat, II. 252.

Radix Pontica; probably Rheum Ponticum, rhubarb. Used in an antidote, II. 56.

Refrigerantia; cooling foods, drugs or application. refrigerants, I. 206, 212, 214; II. 10.

Reprimentia (*Medicamenta quae reprimunt*); repressives (to check inflammation), I. 154, 212; II. 4.

Resina; *see* Pinus and Terebinthus.

Rhus Syriacum; R. coriacius Syriacus, the currier's or tanner's tree.

The astringent sumach obtained from this was applied to ulceration of the mouth following thrush, II. 256.

Ricinus; castor oil plant; *see* Cicinum.

Rodentia (*medicamenta quae rodunt*); substances that bite or blister the flesh, II. 6 note *b*.

Rosa; Rosa Gallica, rose.

Rose oil (*oleum ex rosa*) was made from the fresh petals, and the dried petals were used especially as discutients and emollients, I. 212, 260, 270, 272, 292, 304, 306, 316, 366, 398, 400. 432, 448; II. 10, 12.

Ruta; R. graveolens, garden rue or Peganium harmala, wild rue. This plant with its foetid odour and acrid taste was used for food, I. 200 ff. and also medicinally as a local irritant I, 210, 310, 446, 452; II. 6.

Sagapenum; Ferula Persica, sagapenum. This yields a gum resin akin to asafoetida; used in an antidote, II. 56.

Sal; sodium chloride, salt.

It was constantly included in prescriptions, without any qualification, I. 168, 172, 188, 212, 260, 318, 366, 368.

Rock salt (sal fossile) is specified as an ingredient in an eye salve, II. 214; salted water is constantly used, I. 212, 172, 270, and strong brine, *salsuga muria dura*, I. 416.

Salt (sodium chloride) has no aperient action, II. 6, but was used in an enema, I. 172; the aperient compounds, sulphates of sodium and magnesium were not distinguished.

Several compounds of sodium chloride were used by Celsus.

(1) Nitrum, soda. Hydrated carbonate of sodium mixed with chlorides and calcium carbonate. This was especially obtained from pools north west of Cairo and received its name from the Arabic natrum, I. 172, 214, 260, 338, 346; II. 238.

(2) Spuma nitri, soda-scum, aphronitrum. Carbonates and nitrates of soda and potash coloured by copper and iron oxides. This was used as an erodent and on a poultice for abscesses and inflamed joints, II. 8, 20; *see also* II. 30.

(3) Sal ammoniacum (ammoniac salt); sodium chloride rendered hygroscopic by the inclusion of calcium and magnesium chloride; this substance, which was also mixed with gypsum (calcium sulphate) was so called because it was found in the sand near the temple of Jupiter Ammon in Libya.

It was used in preparations to draw out inflammation and mature abscesses, II. 16, 20,

22, 24, 38; for a black eye, II. 226, and in a draught to expel a dead foetus, II. 64.

Salamandra; Lacertus Salamandra, the salamander.

The ash (cinis) produced by burning this was rich in lime and used as an erodent, exedent and caustic, II. 6, 8.

Salivaris herba; *see* Pyrethrum.

Salix; Salix alba, white willow.

The leaves boiled in vinegar yielded salicin and astringent tannin; applied to ulcerations of the anus, II. 286.

Sampsychus Cyprius; *see* Origanum.

Sandaraca; *see* Auripigmentum. (Celsus does not mention the bee bread and gum resin, also known as *sandaraca*, Aristotle, *H.A.* IX. 40; Pliny, *N.H.* XXXIV. 18. 55, 56.)

Sanguinalis herba; *see* Polygonum.

Sanguinem supprimentia; styptics, haemostatics, II. 6.

Satureia; Satureia thymbra, savoury.

Used with other herbs as a food stuff and diuretic, I. 200, 210; *see also* I. 416, 493.

Saxum Calcis; *see* Calx.

Scammonea; Convolvulus scammonia, scammony (Herba Cantabrica).

This was a drastic purge, I. 310 note, 340; used as a vermifuge, I. 436, and for snake-bite, II. 120; topically it was used as an exedent, II. 8.

Schiston; *see* Alumen.

Schoinon; *see* Iuncus.

Scilla; Scilla urginea maritima, squill.

The bulbs yield scillin, which resembles digitalin, but is much less certain in its action as a cardiac stimulant and often produces vomiting;

the bulb, its bitter taste disguised by vinegar or
honey was sucked or taken internally for dropsy
as a diuretic, I. 318, 320, 390, 416; externally it
was applied as a counter irritant in paralysis,
I. 346, as an emollient or exedent or mouth
wash, II. 46, 156, 244, 264.

Serpyllum; Thymum serpyllum, creeping thyme.

The serpollet from this resembled oil of thyme,
and acted as an antiseptic and discutient,
I. 212, 272, 282, 292, 416; II. 10.

Sertula Campana; several plants were included under
this name, especially Melilotus officinalis, a
species of lotus (melilot).

The plants had a sweet smell like new hay and
were applied to foul ulcerations, II. 10, 12, 50,
184, 282.

Sesamum; Sesamum Indicum, sesame.

The oil from this, which was an inferior sub-
stitute for olive oil is included among emollients,
I. 196; II. 10.

Sinapis alba, nigra; Brassica alba, nigra mustard.

As a food, I. 493; indigestible, 200; acrid,
202; heating, 286, 416; in local applications and
plasters, erodent and extractive, I. 212, 318,
346, 368, 370, 434, 446; inhaled as a stimulant,
310.

Siser; Sium sisarum, skirret.

One of the medicinal herbs mentioned as a
repressive, I. 212; also as a food, I. 200 ff.,
493.

Solanum or Strychnos; bitter-sweet or night shade.

There were several species, one specially
mentioned by Celsus was the winter cherry or
Halicaccabus (Physalis Alkengi).

All the varieties yielded scopolamine, which is allied to atropine and hyoscine, and so acted as local anodynes while the tannin which they contained made them astringents as well; they were used to soothe the insane (in a local application to the scalp) and the hysterical, I. 212, 294, 448; the bark of halicaccabus was used as an application to foul ulcers, solanum leaves for erysipelas, and solanum juice for prominent navels, II. 46, 102, 266.

Solaris herba; *see* Heliotropion.

Sordes; used as a local suppurative, II. 10 note *a*, 12, 60 note *a*; *see also* II. 38, 52, 86.

Spartes; *see* Cytisus.

Sphaerion; name of a salve, II. 212.

Spodium; *see* Cadmia.

Spongia; sponge, mentioned as a repressive, I. 212; in fomenting, I. 382; II. 154, 156.

Staphis agria; I. 316, *see* Tamus (Uva Taminia); for another identification, *see* p. xi, note *c*.

Stibium; Antimonium sulphide, antimony sulphide or misy, Arabic kohl.

This was much adulterated with oxide of lead and charcoal and was used as a slight irritant and caustic in plasters and pastils for ulcers, II. 19–56 and 268–286, and especially in eye salves, II. 194 ff., of which it has been an ingredient from very early times.

Stoechas; *see* Lavandula.

Stomoma; *see* Aes.

Storax; *see* Styrax.

Strychnos; *see* Solanum.

Sudorem evocare; methods of eliciting a sweat, diaphoretics, I. 184, 314, 316.

Styrax; Storax officinalis, storax.

The resin of this shrub (Liquidambar orientalis) includes styrax and benzoin resins, and the perfume of the balsam resembles jasmin. It was used internally as a diuretic and in antidotes, I. 316; II. 54, 56, and externally for maturing abscessions and promoting suppuration and for cleansing wounds, and as a discutient, emollient and epispastic, II. 6, 10, 12, 18; also for contusions and painful joints, II. 26, 28.

Sulphur; sulphur.

This was chiefly used in external applications; *apyron,* unheated sulphur, was used in its natural state, II. 22; *s. praeparatum,* sublimed sulphur, was used to impregnate wool (*lana sulphurata,* q.v.).

It was used as a suppurative, pore opener and cleanser, II. 6, an exedent, II. 8, and a discutient, II. 10; and in a fomentation to relieve pain in the limbs, I. 348; internally it is once prescribed to relieve cough, I. 390.

Sycaminus; this name was applied to two distinct species.

(1) Morus nigra, mulberry tree, I. 296.

The mulberry (morum) is used as a food, I. 204 ff.; as a soporific, I. 210; for thrush, I. 256; as a purgative, I. 208. *See also* p. 495. There was a medicine of mulberries, I. 382; II. 256; a decoction of the leaves was used, I. 436.

(2) Sycamorus Aegyptiaca, Egyptian fig; this was called *Sycamorus* or *Sycaminus,* the former name being derived from the likeness of its leaves to those of the white mulberry, *see* 1. 296;

II. 20. *Lacrima sycamini* (the gum) was used in an application for headache, I. 296, and for pain in the side, II. 20; the figs grow on the stem (not like ficus carica on the twigs). *See* S<sup>t</sup>. Luke. xvii. 6.

Tamarix; T. tetrandra, tamarisk.

This tree exudes a manna containing various sugars and much tannin. It was used as a repressive and refrigerant, I. 212.

Tamus; Tamus communis, black bryony, lady's seal.

The berries (*uvae taminiae*) hang in bunches, like grapes; hence their name. They were much used by Celsus as diuretics, I. 316, and in local applications, II. 6–12, 30, 48, 50, 208. 250, 280.

Terebinthus; Pistacia terebinthus, turpentine tree.

The resin (*terebinthina resina*) was constantly used, with pitch resin, as an erodent, II. 6, and internally to relieve dyspnoea, I. 386.

Thapsia; Thapsia garganica, scorching fennel.

The very powerful juice of this was used as a counter irritant, especially for contusions of the face, II. 26 (Pliny, *N.H.* XIII. 22. (43), also mentions this use), and for baldness, II. 182.

Thlaspis; Capsella bursa pastoris, shepherds' purse.

The seeds had a flavour like mustard; used in an antidote, II. 56.

Thymum; Thymbra capitata, Cretan thyme.

The flowers yield the antiseptic thymol; they were an indigestible food, I. 200, 204; a decoction served as a diuretic, I. 210, 416; also in a gargle for paralysis of the tongue, 370; and for angina, 382.

# LIST OF MEDICAMENTA

Tithymalus, II. 8; *see* Lactuca marina.

Tragacantha; Astragalus Creticus, tragacanth.

> The pith is a mass of mucilage from which gum exudes, it was used especially as an excipient, I. 388, also as an agglutinant, to relieve irritation and in eye salves, II. 4, 10, 196, 204.

Tragoriganum; *see* Origanum.

Trixago; *see* Polium.

Trixis (castor oil plant); *see* Cicinum.

Trifolium; Trifolium fragiferum, trefoil.

> This herb, which yields a mucilage with a fragrance like honey, was used in a poultice for enlarged spleen, I. 416, and also against snake bite, II. 118.

Trygodes; a salve invented by Euelpides, II. 196.

Tus (Thus) or Olibanum (Greek, λιβανωτός), frankincense, *see* Libanotos.

Unguenta; ointments, II. 10, 48, 58 note.

Urinam moventia; diuretics, I. 52, 210, 316, 340, 418; II. 10.

Urtica; Urtica urens, nettle.

> Used internally as a food-purgative, I. 208, 390, and part of a light diet for fever, I. 260; for intestinal worms, I. 438; externally in paralysis to irritate the skin, I. 346.

Uva; Grape. *See* General Index, grapes; *also see below*, Vitis; for *uva taminia*, *see above* Tamus.

Veratrum nigrum or album; Veratrum album, Hellebore (the two varieties are not now distinguished).

> Celsus, like Hippocrates, used the rhizomes and rootlets as a drastic purge, and as an emetic; it

was especially employed for cases of mental excitement and as a treatment for the insane, I. 110, 152, 168, 174, 298, 300, 308, 334, 336, 342, 368, 412, 436.    Externally it was used as an erodent and caustic, II. 8, 10, to excite sneezing, II. 52.    It was also used as an emetic for cases of struma, II. 140.

Vervains; aromatic shrubs, I. 212, 292, 434, 452, 458; *see further*, vol. I. Appendix, p. 493.

Vettonica herba; Betonica officinalis, betony.

This herb was introduced at Rome by Antonius Musa, physician to Augustus.    He found it used medicinally by the Vettones, a tribe of North west Spain.    The dried leaves were used as snuff, the juice of the root as a purge.    Celsus mentions it only once as a cure for snake bite, II. 120.

Viola; Viola odorata, violet.

The flowers and seeds yield an expectorant and emetic, violin, which resembles ipecacuanha. It was used by Celsus externally as a pore opener and discutient, II. 6, 10.

Viscum; Viscum album, the berry of Loranthus Europaeum, mistletoe.

The unripe berries resemble gutta percha, and were used in the poultices of Apollophanes and Andreas, II. 18, 20.

Vitis; Vitis alba silvestris, wild vine.

The juice of the flowers (oenanthe) was a diuretic, I. 316, and used locally as a caustic, II. 8.

The cultivated vine (V. vinifera), besides producing grapes, had tendrils, *caprioli*, which yielded tannin and were included under repressives and refrigerants, I. 212.

Vomitum inducere; methods of inducing a vomit, I. 58, *see* General Index, Emetics.

Zingiber; ginger.
    This is only once mentioned as an ingredient in an antidote, II. 56.
Zmaragdinum (emerald-like); name of a plaster, II. 32.
Zmilion (razor-like); name of a salve, II. 214.


## II. LIST OF SURGICAL INSTRUMENTS AND APPLIANCES USED IN TREATMENT

Absus, a woollen bandage, I. 406; III. 442 note.
Acia, a suture of twisted wool, *see* suture (Genera index).
Acus, needle (surgical), III. 344, 364, 378, 386; for cataract, 350; cautery needle, III. 336, 338, 344, 360.
Ancter, *see* Fibula.
Calamus, a reed or quill pen, used to blow powders into a fistula or gangrene, II. 156, III. 448; in the treatment of ear or nose tronble, to keep the passage open, III. 360, 366; in extracting missiles from a wound, III. 318.
Canalis, gutter splint, III. 528, note *c*, 550, 584; fitted with straps (*lora*), III. 546, 568.
Cluster; (1) Clyster oricularis, ear syringe, II. 268; III. 444, 450, 468.
    (2) For clystering the bowels, *see* General index, Clyster.

# LIST OF MEDICAMENTA

Collyrium, II. 154 note
> (1) A salve, especially an eye salve, II. 192–196, 200, 216.
> (2) A medicated bougie, tent, used to probe a fistula, II. 154 note, III. 306.

Corvus, a surgical knife, III. 404.

Cyathiscus (of Diocles), a surgical instrument used for extracting missiles, III. 318.

Fascea, bandage, I. 164; II. 88, 192, III. 320, 408; for fractures and dislocations, III. 524 ff.

Ferrum, Ferramentum, a surgeon's knife, I. 2; a lithotomy knife, III. 426; that invented by Meges, 436; a knife used to cut away a polypus, 364, and in a case of dropsy, 382; an instrument to extract missiles, III. 316; *Ferrum candens*, cautery, I. 330, 356; II. 134; III. 300, 374; *Ferrum* was also used of a smith's tools, I. 416; II. 130.

Ferula, a cane splint, made from the stem of the Narthex communis, was used in fractures of the clavicle, humerus, etc., III. 528 and note, 540 ff.

Fibula, Greek ἀγκτήρ, originally a brooch, safety pin, was used by Celsus of pins passed through the margin of wounds and fixed by a thread twisted round them in a figure of 8, similar to the " hare-lip pin " still in use, though now largely super-seded by clips, II. 82; III. 308, 324, 416; *infibulare adulescentulos*, III. 422, 424.

Fistula, a straw, or pipe of reed, used to drink through, I. 74; a pipe of brass or lead, used as a catheter, III. 424; for drainage, 382, 454.
> For an anatomical or pathological fistula, *see* General index, Fistula, Urethra.

Forfex, a forceps, III. 318, 320; a dental forceps,

# LIST OF MEDICAMENTA

# LIST OF MEDICAMENTA

Uncus, a hook, used in embryotomy, III. 456, 458, for
    lithotomy, III. 426, 434.
Volsella, a small forceps or tweezers, II. 274, 372;
    also a smith's instrument, small tongs or pinchers,
    III. 552.

# WEIGHTS, MEASURES, SYMBOLS

*(Weights and measures are converted to the metric system)*

*Dry measures.*

LIBRA or PONDUS, pound, about 336 grammes.
Bes librae, two thirds, 224 grammes.
Selibra, one half, 168 grammes.
Triens librae, one third, 112 grammes.
Quadrans librae, one quarter, 84 grammes.
Sextans librae, one sixth, 56 grammes.
Sesquiuncia (sescuncia) librae, one eighth, 42 grammes.
Uncia librae, one twelfth, 28 grammes.

DENARIUS, DRACHMA, one seventh [a] of an uncia librae, about 4 grammes.
Bes denarii, two thirds, 2·66 grammes.
Semi denarius, one half, 2 grammes.
Quicunx denarii, five twelfths, 1·66 gramme.
Triens denarii, one third, 1·33 gramme.
Quadrans denarii, one quarter, 1 gramme.
Sextans denarii, one sixth, 0·66 gramme.
Uncia denarii, one twelfth, 0·33 gramme.

SCRIPULUM, one twenty-fourth of an uncia librae, 1·16 gramme.

OBOLUS, one sixth of a denarius, 0·66 gramme.
Hemiobolium, half an obolus, 0·33 gramme.

---

[a] This measure was not universal ; in V. 17. 1 C Celsus explains the system that he follows.

*Liquid measures.*

AMPHORA, about 30 litres.

SEXTARIUS, about $\frac{1}{2}$ litre, 500 c.cm.
Hemina sextarii, about $\frac{1}{4}$ litre, 250 c.cm.
Quadrans sextarii, about $\frac{1}{8}$ litre, 125 c.cm.

ACETABULUM, $\frac{1}{8}$ sextarius, 63 c.cm.

CYATHUS, $\frac{1}{12}$ sextarius, 42 c.cm.

*Fractions.*

— $\frac{1}{12}$.

= $\frac{1}{6}$.

= — $\frac{1}{4}$.

= = $\frac{1}{3}$.

= = — $\frac{5}{12}$.

= = = $\frac{2}{3}$.

*Symbols.*

P followed by a numeral. one pondus (libra) or more.
P with no numeral following, *pondo*, by weight.
PS, selibra, $\frac{1}{2}$.
P —, uncia librae, $\frac{1}{12}$ of a pondus (libra).
P bes, bes librae, $\frac{2}{3}$.
P = = or P ZZ, triens librae, $\frac{1}{3}$.
P = —, quadrans librae, $\frac{1}{4}$.
P = or P Z, sextans librae, $\frac{1}{6}$.

✳ followed by a numeral, one denarius or more (also represented by H or X followed by a numeral).

P ✳ — or P ✳ ~ , uncia denarii, $\frac{1}{12}$ of a denarius.

P ✳ S, semi-denarius, $\frac{1}{2}$.

P ✳ = = or P ✳ ZZ, triens denarii, $\frac{1}{3}$.

P|✳ = — or P. ✳ ꛍ, quadrans denarii, $\frac{1}{4}$.

P ✳ = or P ✳ Z, sextans denarii, $\frac{1}{6}$ (one obolus).

P ✳ = = —, quicunx denarii, $\frac{5}{12}$.

P ✳ $\begin{matrix} = = \\ = = \end{matrix}$, bes denarii, $\frac{2}{3}$.

Pᴄ, dextans denarii, $\frac{10}{12}$ (this sign only occurs **V. 18.** 17).

Э, followed by a numeral, one scripulum or more.

S, followed by a numeral, one sextarius or more.

S, with no numeral following, *semi*, one half.

# CELSUS

## DE MEDICINA

# A. CORNELII CELSI

## DE MEDICINA

### LIBER V

Dixi de iis malis corporis, quibus victus ratio
maxime subvenit: nunc transeundum est ad eam
medicinae partem, quae magis medicamentis pugnat. His multum antiqui auctores tribuerunt, et
Erasistratus et ii, qui se empiricos nominarunt,
praecipue tamen Herophilus deductique ab illo viro,
adeo ut nullum morbi genus sine his curarent.
Multaque etiam de facultatibus medicamentorum
memoriae prodiderunt, qualia sunt vel Zenonis
vel Andriae vel Apolloni, qui Mys cognominatus est.
2 Horum autem usum ex magna parte Asclepiades
non sine causa sustulit; et cum omnia fere medicamenta stomachum laedant malique suci sint, ad
ipsius victus rationem potius omnem curam suam
transtulit. Verum ut illud in plerisque morbis
utilius est, sic multa admodum corporibus nostris
incidere consuerunt, quae sine medicamentis ad
sanitatem pervenire non possunt. Illud ante omnia
scire convenit, quod omnes medicinae partes ita
innexae sunt, ut ex toto separari non possint sed ab

---

<sup>a</sup> The word *victus* like the δίαιτα (regimen) of Hippocrates
includes not only dieting, but rubbing, rocking, rules for
exercise, etc.

# CELSUS

## ON MEDICINE

### BOOK V

I HAVE spoken of those maladies of the body in
which the regulation of the diet<sup>a</sup> is most helpful:
now I pass on to that part of medicine which
combats them rather by medicaments. These were
held of high value by ancient writers, both by Erasistratus and those who styled themselves Empirics,
especially however by Herophilus and his school,
insomuch that they treated no kind of disease without
them. A great deal has also been recorded con-
cerning the powers of medicaments, as in the works
of Zeno or of Andreas or of Apollonius, surnamed
Mys. On the other hand, Asclepiades dispensed
with the use of these for the most part, not without
reason; and since nearly all medicaments harm the
stomach and contain bad juices, he transferred all
his treatment rather to the management of the
actual diet. But while in most diseases that is the
more useful method, yet very many illnesses attack
our bodies which cannot be cured without medicaments. This before all things it is well to recognize,
that all branches of medicine are so connected
together, that it is impossible to separate off any

3

3 eo nomen trahant, a quo plurimum petunt. Ergo
et illa, quae victu curat, aliquando medicamentum
adhibet, et illa, quae praecipue medicamentis
pugnat, adhibere etiam rationem victus debet,
quae multum admodum in omnibus corporis malis
proficit.

Sed cum omnia medicamenta proprias facultates
habeant, ac simplicia saepe opitulentur, saepe mixta,
non alienum videtur ante proponere et nomina et
vires et mixturas eorum (*capp.* i–xxv), qui minor
ipsas nobis curationes exsequentibus mora sit.

**1.** Sanguinem supprimunt atramentum sutorium,
quod Graeci chalcanthon appellant, chalcitis, acacia,
et ex aqua Lycium, tus, aloe, cummi, plumbum
combustum, porrum, herba sanguinalis; creta vel
Cimolia vel figularis, misy; frigida aqua, vinum,
acetum; alumen Melinum, squama et ferri et aeris
[atque huius quoque duae species sunt, alia tantum
aeris, alia rubri aeris].

**2.** Glutinant vulnus murra, tus, cummi, praecipueque acanthinum; psylleum, tragacantha, carda-
momon, bulbi, lini semen, nasturcium; ovi album,
gluten, icthyocolla; vitis alba, contusae cum testis
suis cocleae, mel coctum; spongia vel ex aqua
frigida vel ex vino vel ex aceto expressa; ex iisdem
lana sucida; si levis plaga est, etiam aranea.

Reprimunt alumen et scissile, quod σχιστόν
vocatur, et liquidum; Melinum, auripigmentum,
aerugo, chalcitis, atramentum sutorium.

4

one part completely, but each gets its name from the treatment which it uses most. Therefore, both that which treats by dieting has recourse at times to medicaments, and that which combats disease mainly by medicaments ought also to regulate diet, which produces a good deal of effect in all maladies of the body.

But since all medicaments have special powers, and afford relief, often when simple, often when mixed, it does not seem amiss beforehand to state both their names and their virtues and how to compound them, that there may be less delay when we are describing the treatment itself.[a]

**1.** The following suppress bleeding: Blacking which the Greeks call chalcanthon, copper ore, acacia, and lycium with water, frankincense, lign-aloe, gums, lead sulphide, leek, polygonum; Cimolian chalk or potter's clay, antimony sulphide; cold water, wine, vinegar; alum from Melos, iron and copper scales [and of this last there are two kinds, one from ordinary copper, the other from red copper].

**2.** The following agglutinate a wound: myrrh, frankincense, gums, especially gum arabic; flea-wort, tragacanth, cardamon, bulbs, linseed, nasturtium; white of egg, glue, isinglass; white vine, snails pounded with their shells, cooked honey, a sponge squeezed out of cold water or out of wine or out of vinegar; unscoured wool squeezed out of the same; if the wound is slight, even cobwebs.

The following subdue inflammation: alum, both split alum called schiston, and alum brine; quince oil, orpiment, verdigris, copper ore, blacking.

---

[a] For a list of the drugs given and the probable identification of those which are doubtful see Introduction to vol. II.

# CELSUS

**3.** Concoqunt et movent pus nardum, murra, costus, balsamum, galbanum, propolis, sturax, turis et fuligo et cortex, bitumen, pix, sulpur, resina, sebum, adeps, oleum.

**4.** Aperiunt tamquam ora in corporibus, quod stomun Graece dicitur, cinnamomum, balsamum, panaces; iuncus quadratus, puleium et flos albae violae, bdella, galbanum, resina terebenthina et pinea, propolis, oleum vetus; piper, pyrethrum, chamaepitys, uva taminia; sulpur, alumen, rutae semen.

**5.** Purgant aerugo, auripigmentum, quod arsenicon a Graecis nominatur [huic autem et sandaracae in omnia eadem vis, sed validior est squama aeris], pumex; iris, balsamum, sturax, tus, turis cortex, resina et pinea et terebenthina liquida, oenanthe; lacerti stercus, sanguis columbae et palumbi et 2 hirundinis; Hammoniacum, bdellium [quod in omnia idem quod Hammoniacum potest, sed valentius est habrotonum], ficus arida, coccum Cnidium, scobis eboris, omphacium, radicula; coagulum, sed maxime leporinum [cui eadem quae ceteris coagulis facultas, sed ubique validior est], fel, vitellus crudus, cornu cervinum, gluten taurinum, mel crudum; misy, chalcitis; crocum, uva taminia; habrotonum, spuma argenti, galla, squama aeris, lapis haematites, minium, costum, sulpur, pix cruda; sebum, adeps, oleum; ruta, porrum, lenticula, ervum.

**6.** Rodunt alumen liquidum, sed magis rotundum,

---

*a* These drugs were intended to open the pores (stomata of Erasistratus) at the ends of veins, and so to relieve congestion; for stomata, see vol. I. pp. 10, 392.

**3.** The following mature abscessions and promote suppuration: nard, myrrh, costmary, balsam, galbanum, propolis, storax, frankincense, both the soot and the bark, bitumen, pitch, sulphur, resin, suet, fat, oil.

**4.** The following open, as it were, mouths in our bodies, called in Greek στομοῦν:[a] cinnamon, balsam, all-heal; rush-root, pennyroyal, white violet flowers, bdellium, galbanum, turpentine and pine-resin, propolis, old olive-oil; pepper, pyrethrum, ground pine thistle, black bryony berries, sulphur, alum, rue seed.

**5.** The following have a cleansing effect: verdigris, orpiment, called by the Greeks arsenicon [now this has the same property as sandarach, but copper scales are stronger], pumice; orris root, balsam, storax, frankincense, frankincense bark, pine-resin and liquid turpentine, vine-flowers; lizard dung, blood of pigeon and wood pigeon and swallow: ammoniacum, bdellium [which has the same virtue as ammoniacum, but southernwood is more powerful], dry fig, Cnidian berry, powdered ivory, omphacium, radish; rennet, especially of the hare [which has the same faculty as other rennet but is far more active], ox-bile, uncooked yolk of egg, burnt stagshorn, ox-glue, raw honey, antimony sulphide, copper ore; saffron, black bryony berries, southernwood, litharge, oak-gall, haematite, minium, costmary, sulphur, crude pitch, suet, fat, oil, rue, leek, lentil, bitter vetch.

**6.** The following are erodents:[b] alum brine, especially when made from round alum, verdigris, copper

---

[b] *Rodere—exedere—adurere*—The substances given in sections 6–8 are divided into these three classes according to the severity of their action upon the tissues.

7

CELSUS

aerugo, chalcitis, misy, squama aeris, sed magis rubri,
aes combustum, sandaraca, minium Sinopicum;
galla, balsamum, murra, tus, turis cortex, galbanum,
resina terebenthina umida, piper utrumque, sed
rotundum magis, cardamomum; auripigmentum,
2 calx, nitrum et spuma eius; [apii semen], narcissi
radix, [omphacium], alcyonium, [oleum ex amaris
nucibus], alium, mel crudum, vinum, lentiscus,
squama ferri, fel taurinum, scamonia, uva taminia,
cinnamomum, styrax, cicutae semen, omphacium,
apii semen, resina, narcissi semen, fel, nuces amarae
oleumque earum, atramentum sutorium, chrysocolla,
veratrum, cinis.

7. Exedunt corpus acaciae sucus, hebenus, aerugo,
squama aeris, chrysocolla, cinis, cinis Cyprius,
nitrum, cadmia, spuma argenti, hypocistis, diphryges,
sal, auripigmentum, sulpur, cicuta, sandaraca, salamandra, [alcyoneum], aeris flos, chalcitis, atramentum sutorium, ochra, calx, [acetum], galla,
alumen, lac caprifici vel lactucae marinae, quae
tithymallos a Graecis appellatur, alcyoneum, fel,
turis fuligo, spodium, lenticula, mel, oleae folia,
marrubium, lapis haematites et Phrygius et Assius et
scissilis, misy, vinum, acetum.

8. Adurunt auripigmentum, atramentum sutorium, chalcitis, misy, aerugo, calx, charta combusta,
sal, squama aeris, faex combusta, murra, stercus et
lacerti et columbae et palumbi et hirundinis, piper,
coccum Cnidium, alium, diphryges, lac utrumque,
quod proxime [capite supra] comprehensum est,
veratrum et album et nigrum, cantharides, corallium,
pyrethrum, tus, salamandra, eruca, sandaraca, uva
taminia, chrysocolla, ochra, alumen scissile, ovillum
stercus, oenanthe.

8

ore, antimony sulphide, copper scales, especially from red copper, calcined copper, sandarach, minium from Sinope; oak-galls, balsam, myrrh, frankincense, frankincense bark, galbanum, liquid turpentine, pepper of both kinds but especially the round, cardamon; orpiment, lime, soda and its scum; [parsley seed], narcissus root, [omphacium], coral, [oil of bitter almonds], garlic, uncooked honey, wine, mastich, iron scales, ox-bile, scammony, black bryony berries, cinnamon, storax, hemlock seed, omphacium, parsley seed, resin, narcissus seed, bile, bitter almonds and their oil, blacking, chrysocolla, hellebore, ash.

**7.** The following are exedents : acacia juice, ebony, verdigris, copper scales, chrysocolla, ash, cyprus ash, soda, cadmia, litharge, hypocistis, slag, salt, orpiment, sulphur, hemlock, sandarach, salamander-ash, [coral], flowers of copper, copper ore, blacking, ochre, lime, [vinegar], oak-gall, alum, milk of the wild fig, or of sea spurge which the Greeks call tithymallos, coral, bile, frankincense, spode, lentil, honey, olive leaves, horehound, haematite stone, Phrygian, Assian and ironschist, antimony sulphide, wine, vinegar.

**8.** The following are caustics : orpiment, blacking, copper ore, antimony sulphide, verdigris, lime, burnt papyrus-ash, salt, copper scales, burnt wine-lees, myrrh, dung of lizard and pigeon and wood pigeon and swallow, pepper, Cnidian berry, garlic, slag, both the milks mentioned in the previous chapter, hellebore both white and black, cantharides, coral, pyrethrum, frankincense, salamander-ash, rocket, sandarach, black bryony berries, chrysocolla, ochre, split alum, sheep's dung, vine-flower buds.

**9.** Eadem fere crustas ulceribus tamquam igne
adustis inducunt, sed praecipue chalcitis, utique si
cocta est, flos aeris, aerugo, auripigmentum, misy, et
id quoque magis coctum.

**10.** Crustas vero has resolvit farina triticea cum
ruta vel porro, aut lenticula, cui mellis aliquid
adiectum est.

**11.** Ad discutienda vero ea, quae in corporis parte
aliqua coierunt, maxime possunt habrotonum,
helenium, amaracus, alba viola, mel, lirium, sampsychus Cyprius, lac, sertula Campana, serpullum,
cupressus, cedrus, iris, viola purpurea, narcissus, rosa,
crocum, passum, iuncus quadratus, nardum, cinnamomum, casia, Hammoniacum, cera, resina, uva
taminia, spuma argenti, styrax, ficus arida, tragori-
ganus, lini et narcissi semen, bitumen, sordes ex
gymnasio, pyrites lapis aut molaris, crudus vitellus,
amarae nuces, sulpur.

**12.** Evocat et educit ladanum, alumen rotundum,
hebenus, lini semen, omphacium, fel, chalcitis, bdellium, resina terebenthina et pinea, propolis, ficus
arida decocta, stercus columbae, pumex, farina lolii,
grossi in aqua cocti, elaterium, lauri bacae, nitrum,
sal.

**13.** Levat id, quod exasperatum est, spodium,
hebenus, cummi, ovi album, lac, tragacanthum.

**14.** Carnem alit et ulcus implet resina pinea,
ochra Attice vel Scyrice, cera, buturum.

**15.** Molliunt aes combustum, terra Eretria,
nitrum, papaveris lacrima, Hammoniacum, bdellion,
cera, sebum, adeps, oleum, ficus arida, sesamum,

---

<sup>a</sup> What is scraped off the skin by the *strigil* after exercise.

<sup>b</sup> *i.e.* they draw out collections of matter and bring them to
the surface; ἐπισπαστικὰ φάρμακα, p. 17.

**9.** The foregoing generally induce scabs on ulcerations almost as when burnt by a cautery, but most of all copper ore—especially after being heated —copper flowers, verdigris, orpiment, antimony sulphide, and that also more after being heated.

**10.** But such scabs are loosened by wheat flour with rue or leek or lentils, to which some honey has been added.

**11.** The following, again, are most powerful to disperse whatever has collected in any part of the body: southernwood, elecampane, marjoram, white violet, honey, lily, Cyprian marjoram, milk, melilot, thyme, oil of cypress, cedar-oil, iris, purple violet, narcissus, rose, saffron, raisin wine, angular rush, nard, cinnamon, casia, ammoniacum, wax, resin, black bryony berries, litharge, storax, dry fig, goat's marjoram, linseed, narcissus seed, bitumen, sordes[a] from the gymnasium, pyrites or millstone, raw yolk of egg, bitter almonds, sulphur.

**12.** The following are epispastics[b]: ladanum, round alum, ebony, linseed, omphacium, ox-bile, copper ore, bdellium, turpentine and pine-resin, propolis, dried fig cooked, pigeons' dung, pumice, darnel meal, unripe figs cooked in water, elaterium, laurel berries, soda, salt.

**13.** The following relieve any irritated part: oxide of zinc, ebony, gum, white of egg, milk, tragacanth.

**14.** The following make the flesh grow, and fill in ulcerations: pine-resin, ochre from Attica or Scyros, wax, butter.

**15.** The following are emollients: calcined copper, Eretrian earth, soda, poppy-tears, ammoniacum, bdellium, wax, suet, soft fat, oil, dried fig, sesamum,

sertula Campana, narcissi et radix et semen, rosae
folia, coagulum, vitellus crudus, amarae nuces,
medullae omnes, stibi, pix, coclea cocta, cicutae
semen, plumbi recrementum (σκωρίαν μολύβδου
Graeci vocant), panaces, cardamomum, galbanum,
resina, uva taminia, styrax, iris, balsamum, sordes
ex gymnasio, sulpur, buturum, ruta.

**16.** Cutem purgat mel, sed magis si est cum
galla vel ervo vel lenticula vel marrubio vel iride vel
ruta vel nitro vel aerugine.

**17.** Expositis simplicibus facultatibus dicendum
est, quemadmodum misceantur, quaeque ex his fiant.
Miscentur autem varie, neque huius ullus modus est,
cum ex simplicibus alia demantur, alia adiciantur,
iisdemque servatis ponderum ratio mutetur. Itaque
cum facultatium materia non ita multiplex sit,
innumerabilia mixturarum genera sunt: quae
conprehendi si possent, tamen esset supervacuum.
B Nam et idem effectus intra paucas compositiones sunt,
et mutare eas cuilibet cognitis facultatibus facile est.
Itaque contentus iis ero, quas accepi velut nobilissi-
mas. In hoc autem volumine eas explicabo, quae
vel desiderari in prioribus potuerunt, vel ad eas
curationes pertinent, quas protinus hic compre-
hendam, sic ut tamen quae magis communia sunt,
C simul iungam: si qua singulis vel etiam parvis
adcommodata sunt, in ipsorum locum differam. Sed
et ante sciri volo, in uncia pondus denarium septem

melilot, narcissus root and seed, rose-leaves, curd, raw yolk of egg, bitter almonds, marrow of any kind, antimony sulphide, pitch, snails boiled, hemlock seed, lead-slag which the Greeks call σκωρία μολύβδου, all-heal, cardamon, galbanum, resin, black bryony berries, storax, iris, balsam, gymnasium sordes, sulphur, butter, rue.

**16.** The following cleanses the skin: honey, but better if mixed with galls or bitter vetch or lentil or horehound or iris or rue or soda or verdigris.

**17.** The powers of medicaments when unmixed having been set out, we have to say how they may be mixed together, and what are the compositions so made. Now they are mixed in various ways and there is no limit to this, since some simples may be omitted, others added, and when the same ingredients are used the proportion of their weights may be changed. Hence though there are not so very many substances having medicinal powers, there are innumerable kinds of mixtures; and, even if all of them could be included, yet this would be needless. For the same effects are produced by but a few compositions, and to vary these is easy to anyone who knows their powers. Therefore I shall content myself with those I have heard of as the best known. Now in this book I will set forth those compositions which may have been required in the previous treatments or which pertain to those treatments which I am going shortly to mention here, so that I may bring together at the same time compositions which are more generally used: those that are applicable to a particular disease, or even to a few, I shall mention in their appropriate places. But I wish to make clear in advance that our uncia has the weight

esse, unius deinde denarii pondus dividi a me in sex
partes, id est sextantes, ut idem in sextante denarii
habeam, quod Graeci habent in eo, quem obolon
appellant. Id ad nostra pondera relatum paulo plus
dimidio scripulo facit.

2   Malagmata vero atque emplastra pastillique, quos
trochiscos Graeci vocant, cum plurima eadem habeant,
differunt eo, quod malagmata maxime ex odoribus[1]
eorumque etiam surculis, emplastra pastillique
magis ex quibusdam metallicis fiunt; deinde malagmata contusa abunde mollescunt: nam super
integram cutem iniciuntur: laboriose vero conteruntur ea, ex quibus emplastra pastillique fiunt, ne
B laedant vulnera, cum inposita sunt. Inter emplastrum autem et pastillum hoc interest, quod emplastrum utique liquati aliquid accipit, in pastillo
tantum arida medicamenta aliquo umore iunguntur.
Tum emplastrum hoc modo fit: arida medicamenta
per se teruntur, deinde mixtis iis instillatur aut
acetum aut si quis alius non pinguis umor acces-
surus est, et ea rursus ex eo teruntur. Ea vero, quae
liquari possunt, ad ignem simul liquantur, et si quid
C olei misceri debet, tum infunditur. Interdum etiam
aridum aliquod ex oleo prius coquitur: ubi facta
sunt, quae separatim fieri debuerunt, in unum omnia
miscentur. At pastilli haec ratio est: arida medica-

---

[1] *There is a variant reading* floribus.

---

[a] For the approximate conversion of the weights and measures
to the metric system and for a list of symbols and fractions,
see Introduction to vol. II.

[b] Malagma (μαλάσσειν to soften), a poultice; emplastrum
(ἔμπλαστον sc. φάρμακον), a plaster; pastillum (τροχίσκος), a

of seven denarii, next that I divide one denarius by weight into six parts, namely, sextantes; so that I have in the sextans of a denarius the same weight as the Greeks have in what they call an obolus. That being reduced to our weight, makes the obolus a little more than half a scripulus.[a]

Now emollients and plasters and pastils [b] which the Greeks call trochiscoi, whilst they have much in common, differ in this, that emollients are made chiefly from essences of flowers and even from their shoots, plasters and pastils rather from certain metallic materials: again, the emollients if crushed become quite soft enough; for they are applied over intact skin; the materials out of which plasters and pastils are made are rubbed together laboriously in order that they may not irritate wounds when they are applied to them. But between a plaster and a pastil there is this difference: a plaster must contain some liquefied ingredient, in a pastil only dry materials are used, combined together by a little fluid. Then a plaster is made in this way: dry medicaments are rubbed down separately, then when they have been mixed, either vinegar is dropped in or any other liquid free from fat that is at hand, and these ingredients are rubbed together again. The materials capable of being liquefied are melted all together over the fire, and if there is to be any admixing of oil, it is then poured in. A dry ingredient is even sometimes boiled in oil beforehand: when what should be done separately has been accomplished, all are mixed together. But the making of pastils, on the other hand, is this: dry medicaments

ball or disc-shaped pill or tabloid which could be swallowed or applied externally.

CELSUS

menta contrita umore non pingui, ut vino vel aceto,
coguntur, et rursus coacta inarescunt, atque ubi
utendum est, eiusdem generis umore diluuntur.
Tum emplastrum imponitur, pastillus inlinitur, aut
alicui molliori, ut cerato, miscetur.

**18.** His cognitis, primum malagmata subiciam,
quae fere non sunt refrigerandi sed calfaciendi causa
reperta. Est tamen, quod refrigerare possit, ad
calidas podagras aptum. Habet gallae et im-
maturae et alterius, coriandri seminis, cicutae,
lacrimae aridae, cummis, singulorum plenum acetabulum; cerati eloti, quod πεπλυμένον Graeci vocant,
selibram.

Reliqua fere calefaciunt. Sed quaedam digerunt
materiam, quaedam extrahunt, quae ἐπισπαστικά
vocantur; pleraque certis magis partibus membro-
rum adcommodata sunt.

2    Si materia extrahenda est, ut in hydropico, in
lateris dolore, in incipiente abscessu, in suppura-
tione quoque mediocri, aptum est id, quod habet
resinae aridae, nitri, Hammoniaci, galbani, singulorum pondo; cerae pondo. Aut in quo haec sunt:
aeruginis rasae, turis, singulorum P. ✳ II; Hammoniaci salis P. ✳ VI; squamae aeris, cerae, singulorum P. ✳ VIII; resinae aridae P. ✳ XII; aceti
cyathus. Idem praestat cumini farina cum struthio
et melle.

3    Si iecur dolet, id in quo est balsami lacrimae
P. ✳ XII; costi, cinnamomi, casiae corticis, murrae,
croci, iunci rotundi, balsami seminis, iridis Illyricae,
cardamomi, amomi, nardi, singulorum P. ✳ XVI.

---

[a] For podagra cf. vol. I. Appendix (p. 463).
[b] πεπλυμένον sc. κηρωτόν.

16

which have been rubbed together are mixed by the aid of a liquid free from fat, such as wine or vinegar and the mixture is dried again, and when required for use, dissolved in a liquid of the same kind. Further, a plaster is laid on, a pastil is smeared on, or is mixed with something softer such as a cerate.

18. Premising the above, I will speak first of emollients, almost all of which were invented, not for the purpose of cooling but for heating. There is, however, one kind which can cool, being suitable for hot podagras.[a] It is a cupful of oak-galls, unripe or otherwise, coriander seed, hemlock, dried poppytears, and gum, of each 63 c.cm.; of washed cerate called by the Greeks πεπλυμένον,[b] 168 grms.

Almost all the rest are heating. But some disperse the diseased matter, some extract it and are called epispastic;[c] most are designed rather for particular parts of the body.

If diseased matter has to be extracted, as in the case of a dropsy, pleurisy, incipient abscession, also in cases of moderate suppuration, the following emollient is suitable which contains: dried resin, soda, ammoniacum, galbanum, 336 grms. each, wax 336 grms. Or that one which contains: scrapings of verdigris and frankincense, each 8 grms., ammoniac salt 24 grms., copper scales, wax, each 32 grms., dried resin 48 grms., 42 c.cm. of vinegar. Cumin meal with soap-wort and honey serves the same purpose.

If there is pain in the liver[d] apply the emollient which consists of balsam tears 48 grms., costmary, cinnamon, casia bark, myrrh, saffron, round rush, balsam seeds, Illyrian iris, cardamon, amomum, nard,

---

[c] ἐπισπαστικά φάρμακα, p. 10 note b.   [d] IV. 15. 1.

CELSUS

Quibus adicitur nardum [unguentum], donec cerati crassitudo sit. Et huius quidem recentis usus est: si vero servandum est, resinae terebenthinae P. ✳ XVI, cerae P. ✳ X ex vino leni contunduntur, tum eo miscentur.

4 At si lienis torquet, glandis, quam balanon μυρεψικήν Graeci vocant, cortex et nitrum paribus portionibus contunduntur, respergunturque aceto quam acerrimo. Ubi cerati crassitudinem habet, linteo ante in aqua frigida madefacto inlinitur et sic inponitur, supraque farina hordeacea inicitur: sed manere ibi non amplius sex horis debet, ne lienem consumat; satiusque est id bis aut ter fieri.

5 Commune autem et iocineri et lieni et abscessibus et strumae, parotidibus, articulis, calcibus quoque suppurantibus aut aliter dolentibus, etiam concoctioni ventris Lysias composuit ex his: opopanacis, styracis, galbani, resinae, singulorum P. ✳ II; Hammoniaci, bdelli, cerae, sebi taurini, iridis aridae P. ✳ IIII; cachryos acetabulo, piperis granis XL; quae contrita irino unguento temperantur.

6 Ad laterum autem dolores compositio est Apollophanis, in qua sunt resinae terebenthinae, turis fuliginis, singulorum P. ✳ IIII; bdelli, Hammoniaci, iridis, sebi vitulini aut caprini a renibus, visci, singulorum P. ✳ IIII. Haec autem eadem omnem dolorem levant, dura emolliunt, mediocriter calfaciunt.

7 Ad idem [latus] Andreae quoque malagma est, quod etiam resolvit, educit umorem, pus maturat,

---

a IV. 16. 1.
b i.e. by burning the skin over it.

18

each 64 grms. To these is added nard ointment until
the consistency is that of a cerate. And this is
for use whilst fresh; but if it is to be kept, turpentine resin 64 grms., and wax 40 grms., are pounded
up together in mild wine, and then mixed with the
above.

But if there is acute pain of the spleen [a] the rind
of the nut, called by the Greeks βάλανος μυρεψική,
and soda are pounded together in equal proportions
and sprinkled with sharpest vinegar; when of the
consistency of a cerate this is spread on lint
previously moistened in cold water, and so applied,
with barley-meal dusted over it; but it should not
be kept on longer than six hours, lest it consume the
spleen; [b] it is better to apply it two or three times.

Lysias compounded an emollient equally useful
for the liver and spleen and for abscesses and
scrofulous tumours, for parotid swellings and joints,
for heels suppurating or otherwise painful, even
for promoting digestion, from the following: opopanax,
storax, galbanum, resin, each 8 grms., ammoniacum,
bdellium, wax, beef suet, dried iris, each 16 grms.,
cachry, 63 c.cm., and 40 peppercorns, all pounded
with iris ointment to the right consistency. [c]

Again, for pains in the sides there is the composition of Apollophanes: turpentine-resin and frankincense soot, each 16 grms., bdellium, ammoniacum, iris,
calf's or goat's kidney-suet, mistletoe juice, each 16
grms. This composition relieves pain of all kinds,
softens indurations, and is moderately heating.

The emollient of Andreas is for like use; and it
also relaxes, draws out humour, matures pus, and

---

[c] Galen, *De Compositione Medicamentorum*, XIII. 343, quot-
ing from Asclepiades, gives the same prescription.

CELSUS

ubi id maturum est, cutem rumpit, ad cicatricem
perducit. Prodest impositum minutis maioribusque
abscessibus, item articulis ideoque et coxis et pedibus
dolentibus: item, si quid in corpore conlisum est,
reficit; praecordia quoque dura et inflata emollit,
ossa extrahit, ad omnia denique valet, quae adiuvare
B calor potest. Id habet cerae P. ✳ I; visci, sycamini,
quam alias sycomorum vocant, lacrimae, singulorum
P. ✳ I; piperis et rotundi et longi, Hammoniaci
thymiamatis, bdelli, iridis Illyricae, cardamomi,
amomi, xylobalsami, turis masculi, murrae, resinae
aridae, singulorum P. ✳ X; pyrethri, cocci Cnidi,
spumae nitri, salis Hammoniaci, aristolociae Creticae,
radicis ex cucumere agresti, resinae terebenthinae
liquidae, singulorum P. ✳ XX. Quibus adicitur
unguenti irini, quantum satis est ad ea mollienda
atque cogenda.

8 Praecipuum vero est ad resolvenda, quae astricta
sunt, mollienda, quae dura sunt, digerenda, quae
coeunt, id, quod ad Polyarchum auctorem refertur.
Habet iunci quadrati, cardamomi, turis fuliginis,
amomi, cerae, resinae liquidae pares portiones.

9 Aliud ad eadem Nilei: croci magmatis, quod quasi
recrementum eius est, P. ✳ IIII; Hammoniaci
thymiamatis, cerae, singulorum P. ✳ XX. Ex quibus duo priora ex aceto teruntur, cera cum rosa
liquatur, et tum omnia iunguntur.

10 Proprie etiam dura emollit id, quod Moschi esse
dicitur. Habet galbani unciam; turis fuliginis
P. =; cerae, Hammoniaci thymiamatis trientes; picis
aridae P. II; aceti heminas tres.

---

*a* The residuum of saffron, after extracting the oil.
    *b* Galen, *De Comp. Med.*, XIII. 182.

when it is matured ruptures the skin, and brings a
scar over. It is applied with advantage to abscesses,
both small and large, likewise to joints and so both
to the hips and feet when painful; further, it repairs
any part of the body that is contused; also softens
the praecordia when hard and swollen; draws outwards splinters of bone—in short, is of service in
all cases which heat can benefit. It is composed of
wax 4 grms., mistletoe juice, and tears of sycaminus,
also called sycomorus, 4 grms. each, round and long
pepper, ammoniacum for fumigation, bdellium,
Illyrian iris, cardamon, amomum balsam wood, male
frankincense, myrrh, dried resin, 40 grms. each,
pyrethrum, Cnidian berries, scum of soda, ammoniac
salt, Cretan aristolochia, wild cucumber root, liquid
turpentine and resin, 80 grms. each, to which is
added a sufficiency of iris ointment to give it proper
consistency.

A special emollient for relaxing parts constricted,
for softening parts indurated, and for dispersing any
collection is ascribed to Polyarchus. It contains
square rush, cardamon, frankincense soot, amomum,
wax and liquid resin in equal quantities.

Another emollient for the same purpose is that of
Nileus: crocomagma,[a] which is as it were saffron-lees,
16 grms., ammoniacum for fumigating, and wax, 80
grms. each. Of these the first two are rubbed up
in vinegar, the wax is liquefied by melting in rose-
oil, and then all are mixed together.[b]

Especially useful for softening induration is an
emollient said to have been invented by Moschus.
It contains galbanum 28 grms., frankincense soot 56
grms., wax and ammoniacum for fumigation, 112
grms. each, dried pitch 672 grms., vinegar 750 c.cm.

11    Fertur etiam ad digerenda, quae coeunt, sub auctore Medio, quod habet cerae P. = ; panacis P. S. ; squamae aeris, aluminis rotundi, item scissilis, singulorum P. I ; plumbi combusti P. I S.

12    Ad eadem Pantaenus utebatur calcis P. S. ; sinapis contriti, item faeni Graeci, aluminis, singulorum P. I ; sebi bubuli P. II S.

13    Ad strumam multa malagmata invenio. Credo autem, quo peius id malum est minusque facile discutitur, eo plura esse temptata, quae in personis

14 varie responderunt.—Andrias auctor est, ut haec misceantur : urticae seminis P. ✳ I ; piperis rotundi, bdelli, galbani, Hammoniaci thymiamatis, resinae aridae, singulorum P. ✳ IIII ; resinae liquidae, cerae, pyrethri, piperis longi, lactucae marinae seminis, sulpuris ignem non experti, quod apyron

B vocatur, pares portiones. Hoc autem quod Niconis est : faecis aridae aceti, spumae nitri, salis Hammoniaci, sinapis, cardamomi, radicis ex cucumere silvestri, resinae, singulorum P. ✳ VIII ; quae ex leni vino contunduntur.

15    Expeditius ad idem fit, quod habet visci, simini stercoris, resinae, sulpuris ignem non experti pares portiones ; et in quo est sulpuris P. ✳ I, lapidis quem pyriten vocant P. ✳ IIII, cumini acetabulum. Item in quo est lapidis eiusdem pars una, sulpuris duae partes, resinae terebenthinae partes tres.

16    Arabis autem cuiusdam est ad strumam et orientia tubercula, quae phymata vocantur, quod haec digerit. Habet murrae, salis Hammoniaci, turis, resinae et liquidae et aridae, croci magmatis, cerae,

We have also one ascribed to Medius for dispersing collections of matter. It contains wax 56 grms., panax 168 grms., copper scales, round alum, split alum, 336 grms. each, calcined lead 504 grms.

Pantaenus used for the same purpose, quicklime 168 grms., pounded mustard, also fenugreek and alum, 336 grms. each, ox-suet 840 grms.

For scrofulous tumour I find many emollients. Now I think that the worse this disease, and the less easy its dispersal, the more have been the remedies tried, with results varying according to the several patients. Andrias invented the following: nettle-seed 4 grms., round pepper, bdellium, galbanum, ammoniacum for fumigation, dried resin, 16 grms. each, with equal parts of liquid resin, wax, pyrethrum, long pepper, seed of sea spurge, unheated sulphur, which is called apyron. Nicon's emollient contains dried vinegar lees, soda-scum, ammoniac salt, mustard, cardamon, wild cucumber root, resin, 32 grms. each. These are pounded up together in mild wine.[a]

A more active emollient for the same purpose contains mistletoe juice, ape's dung, resin, untreated sulphur, equal parts; another emollient contains sulphur 4 grms., the stone called pyrites 16 grms., and 63 c.cm. of cumin. In another are pyrites one part, sulphur two parts, turpentine resin three parts.

An emollient, the invention of a certain Arab, serves to disperse scrofulous swelling, and the sprouting small tumours which are called phymata. It contains myrrh, ammoniac salt, incense, resin both liquid and dried, crocomagma, wax, 4 grms. each,

[a] For another prescription see V. 18. 26.

singulorum P. ✳ I; lapidis eius quem pyriten vocant
P. ✳ IIII; quibus quidam adiciunt sulpuris P. II.[1]

17    Est etiam proficiens in struma et in iis tuberibus,
quae difficiliter concocuntur, et in iis, quae carcinode
vocantur, quod ex his constat: sulpuris P. ✳ II;
nitri P. ✳ IIII, murrae P. ✳ VI, fuliginis turis P. Ꞡ.,[2]
salis Hammoniaci P. = , cerae P. I.

18    Protarchus autem ad parotidas eaque tubercula,
quae melicerides [favi] vel phymata nominantur,
item mala ulcera pumicis, resinae pineae liquidae,
turis fuliginis, spumae nitri, iridis, singulorum
P. ✳ VIII cum cerae P. ✳ VIIII miscebat, hisque
olei cyathum et dimidium adiciebat.

19    At adversus panum, . . .[3] tum primum orientem,
quod phygetron Graeci vocant, et omne tuberculum,
quod phyma nominatur, miscetur ocra quae Attice
nominatur cum duabus partibus similae, hisque cum
tunduntur subinde mel instillatur, donec malagmatis
crassitudo sit.

20    Discutit etiam omne tuberculum, quod phyma
vocatur, id quod habet calcis, nitri spumae, piperis
rotundi, singulorum P. ✳ I; galbani P. ✳ II; salis
P. ✳ IIII, quae excipiuntur cerato ex rosa facto.

21    Supprimitque omne quod abscedit id, in quo est
galbani, fabae fresae, singulorum P. ✳ I; murrae,
turis, ex radice capparis corticis, singulorum P. ✳
IIII. Satisque omnia abscedentia digerit murex
combustus et bene contritus, aceto subinde adiecto.

---

[1] *Marx keeps to the MSS. P. II = 672 grms. Caesarius,
followed by Daremberg, emends to P. ✳ II = 8 grms. This is
the usual quantity prescribed and is the amount given in* § 17.

[2] *Sign of* dextans denarii—*i.e.* $\frac{10}{12}$ *of a denarius : this only
occurs here.*

[3] *Marx conjectures that the words* cum omnem *have fallen out,
and this text is translated.*

the stone called pyrites 16 grms., to which some add sulphur 672 grms.

There is also an emollient efficacious for scrofulous swellings, and for those boils which are slow to come to a head, also for those which are called carcinode. It contains sulphur 8 grms., soda 16 grms., myrrh 24 grms., frankincense soot 3·3 grms., ammoniac salt 56 grms., wax 336 grms.

Protarchus, for parotid swellings, and for those small tumours which are named melicerides [favi] or phymata, and for bad ulcerations, mixed together: pumice, liquid pine-resin, frankincense soot, sodascum, iris, each 32 grms., along with wax 36 grms., to which are added 63 c.cm. of oil.

But against panus [a] at any stage and when incipient, the condition called by the Greeks phygetron, and against any small tumour called phyma, the ochre named Attic is mixed with equal parts of wheat flour, and whilst these are being stirred together, honey is dropped in until the consistency is that of an emollient.

Also all the small tumours called phymata are dispersed by an emollient containing quicklime, sodascum, round pepper, each 4 grms., galbanum 8 grms., salt 16 grms., which are taken up in a cerate made of rose oil.

Any abscession [b] is suppressed by galbanum and crushed beans, each 4 grms., myrrh, frankincense, caper root bark, each 16 grms. And calcined murex [c] well pounded, with vinegar gradually added, is sufficient to disperse an abscession when forming.

---

[a] πᾶνος, πῆνος, a superficial abscess in a hair follicle.
[b] I. 88, note.
[c] I. 204, note.

22 At si satis sanguis subit, recte imponitur quod
adversus phymata quoque potest. Constat ex his:
bdelli, styracis, Hammoniaci, galbani, resinae aridae
et liquidae pineae, item ex lentisco, turis, iridis,
singulorum P. ✻ II.

23 Carcinode vero phymata commode his leniuntur:
galbani, visci, Hammoniaci, resinae terebenthinae,
†[1] in, singulorum P. ✻ I; sebi taurini P. S.; faecis
combustae quam maxima portione, dum id siccius
non faciat quam esse malagma oportet.

24 Quod si facie contusa livor subcruentus est, haec
compositio nocte et die imposita tollit: aristolochiae,
thapsiae, singulorum P. ✻ II; bdelli, styracis,
Hammoniaci thymiamatis, galbani, resinae aridae
et ex lentisco liquidae, turis masculi, iridis Illuricae,
cerae, singulorum P. ✻ IIII. Idem faba quoque
imposita proficit.

25 Sunt etiam quaedam malagmata, quae anastomotica Graeci vocant, quoniam aperiendi vim habent.
Quale est, quod ex his constat: piperis longi, spumae
nitri, singulorum P. ✻ II; erysimi P. ✻ IIII, quae
cum melle miscentur. Idoneaque etiam strumae
aperiendae sunt. Eius generis est . . .[2] vehementi-
usque ex his est id, quod habet calcis P. ✻ IIII;
piperis grana VI; nitri, cerae, singulorum P. ✻ XII;
mellis P. =; olei heminam.

---

[1] *Marx conjectures that the corrupt* in (*omitted by some MSS.*)
*may represent* anesi = anise.
[2] *Marx notes that some words have fallen out here.*

---

*a* Celsus probably means that when enough blood has been
lost either naturally or by venesection the treatment described
should follow; but some translators think he is describing an
extravasation of blood and Constantine adds *plus* before *satis*

But if sufficient blood comes up,[a] it is right to apply a remedy which is also useful against phymata. It consists of the following ingredients : bdellium, storax, ammoniacum, galbanum, pine-resin liquid and dried, also lentiscus-resin, frankincense, iris, 8 grms. each.

But the phymata called carcinoid are relieved by the following : galbanum, mistletoe juice, ammoniacum, turpentine-resin, 4 grms. each, beef-suet 168 grms., of burnt wine-lees as large an amount as can be added without making the mass too dry for an emollient.

But if after a blow on the face there is discolouration and bruising, the following prescription applied night and day takes it away : aristolochia and thapsia, each 8 grms., bdellium, storax, ammoniacum for fumigation galbanum, dried resin, liquid from lentiscus-resin, male frankincense, Illyrian iris wax, each 16 grms. The application of bean-meal also has the same effect.

There are certain emollients called by the Greeks anastomotica, because they have the property of opening the pores.[b] Of these one contains long pepper and soda-scum, each 8 grms., hedge mustard 16 grms., these are mixed together with honey. They are also suitable for scrofulous tumours. Of this class is . . . a yet more powerful one of this kind is that which consists of lime16 grms., 6 peppercorns ; soda and wax, each 48 grms., honey 56 grms., and 250 c.cm. of oil.

and believes that excessive loss of blood (through venesection) is referred to, comparing II. 10. 18. Cf. vol. I. p. 164, on blood-letting.
    [b] p. 6, note a.

26   Niconis quoque est quod resolvit, aperit, purgat.
Habet alcyoneum, sulpur, nitrum, pumicem paribus
portionibus, quibus tantum picis et cerae adicitur,
ut fiat cerati crassitudo.

27   Ad spissa[1] autem Aristogenis fit ex his: sulpuris
P. ✳ I; resinae terebenthinae, nitri spumae, et ex
scilla partis interioris, plumbi eloti, singulorum
P. ✳ II; turis fuliginis P. ✳ VIII; ficus aridae quam
pinguissimae, sebi taurini, singulorum P. ✳ VIII;
cerae P. ✳ XII; iridis Macedonicae P. ✳ VI; sesami
fricti acetabulum.

28   Maximeque nervis et articulis malagma convenit.
Igitur Euthyclei est ad articulos, et ad omnem
dolorem et ad vesicae, et ad recenti cicatrice con-
tractos articulos, quas ancylas Graeci nominant, quod
habet: fuliginis turis acetabulum; resinae tantundem; galbani sine surculis sescunciam; Hammoniaci,
bdelli . . .[2] P. ✳ III . . . singulorum P. = ; cerae P. S.
Ad eosdem digitos iridis, Hammoniaci, galbani, nitri,
singulorum P. ✳ XIIII; resinae liquidae P. ✳ VI;
cerae P. ✳ XVI.

29   Ad dolores articulorum Sosagorae: plumbi combusti, papaveris lacrimae, corticis hyoscyami, styracis,
peucedani, sebi, resinae, cerae, pares portiones.

30   Chrysippi: resinae liquidae, sandaracae, piperis,
singulorum P. ✳ XII; quibus cerae paululum adicitur.

31   Clesiphontis: cerae Creticae, resinae terebenthinae,
nitri quam ruberrumi, singulorum P. S., olei cyathi

---

[1] *Some MSS. read* ossa.
[2] *Marx notes that* singulorum *has fallen out after* bdelli;
*and that there is a further loss of words after* P. ✳ III. *Daremberg
omitted* P. ✳ III. *The prescription then read* amonniacum *and*
bdellium *of each 56 grms. as in the following sentence.* (*Cf. list
of apothecaries' signs, Introduction to vol. II.*)

There is also a prescription of Nicon which relaxes, opens and cleans. It contains coral, sulphur, soda, and pumice, equal parts, to which pitch and wax are added to the consistency of a cerate.

Again, for the hard parts there is the emollient of Aristogenes made from the following: sulphur 4 grms., turpentine-resin, soda-scum, the inner part of a squill-bulb, washed lead, 8 grms. each, frankincense soot 32 grms., the ripest figs and beef-suet, 32 grms. each, wax 48 grms., Macedonian iris 24 grms., parched sesame 63 c.cm.

And most of all is an emollient suitable for sinews and joints. Thus there is that of Euthycleus, suitable for joints and for any kind of pain, including that of the bladder, and for joints contracted by recent scarring which the Greeks call ancylae [a]: it consists of frankincense soot 63 c.cm., of resin the same, galbanum without stalks 42 grms., ammoniacum and bdellium, of each 12 grms. . . . of each 56 grms., wax 168 grms. Another for similar pain in the fingers contains ammoniacum, galbanum, and soda, each 56 grms., liquid resin 24 grms., wax 64 grms.

The emollient of Sosagoras for pain in joints contains calcined lead, poppy tears, hyoscyamus-bark, storax, sulphurwort, suet, resin and wax, equal parts.

That of Chrysippus contains liquid resin, sandarach, pepper, 48 grms. each, to which a little wax is added.

That of Clesiphon [b] consists of Cretan wax, turpentine resin, the reddest soda, 168 grms. each, and

---

[a] ἀγκύλαι, stiffened joints.
[b] Galen, *De Comp. Med.*, XIII. 936.

tres. Sed id nitrum ante per triduum instillata aqua teritur, et cum sextario eius incoquitur, donec omnis umor consumatur. Potest vero ea compositio etiam ad parotidas, phymata, strumam omnemque coitum umoris emolliendum.

32 Ad articulos fici quoque aridi partem nepetae mixtam vel uvam taminiam sine seminibus cum puleio recte aliquis imponit.

33 Eadem podagrae praesidio sunt. Sed ad eam fit Aristonis quoque, quod habet: nardi, cinnamomi, casiae, chamaeleontis, iunci rotundi, singulorum P. ✳ VIII; sebi caprini ex irino liquati P. ✳ XX; iridis P. ✳ I, quae in aceto quam acerrimo iacere per xx dies debet. Idem autem etiam recentia phymata doloresque omnes discutit.

34 At Theoxenus ad pedum dolores sebi a renibus partem tertiam, salis partes duas miscebat, hisque membranulam inlitam imponebat, tum superiniciebat Hammoniacum thymiama in aceto liquatum.

35 At Numenius podagram ceterosque articulos induratos hoc molliebat: habrotoni, rosae aridae, papaveris lacrimae, singulorum P. ✳ III; resinae terebenthinae P. ✳ IIII; turis, spumae nitri, singu- lorum P. ✳ VIII; iridis, aristolochiae, singulorum P. ✳ XII; cerae[1] P. III; quibus adicitur cedri cyathus I, olei laurei cyathi III, olei acerbi sextarius.

36 Si quando autem in articulis callus increvit, Dexius docuit inponere calcis P. ✳ IIII; cerussae P. VIII; resinae pineae P. ✳ XX; piperis grana XXX; cerae P. = ; quibus, dum contunduntur, hemina vini lenis instillatur.

---

[1] *Daremberg emends to* $P$ ✳ $III = 12$ *grms. as the amount given,* 1 *kilogram, seems much too large.*

126 c.cm. of oil. But this soda is pounded up beforehand over a period of three days, water being added
drop by drop, and then boiled in half a litre of water
until all fluid has gone. This composition too can
be applied to parotid swellings, phymata, scrofulous
tumours, and to soften any collection of humour.

Some apply to joints with good effect part of a
dried fig mixed with catmint; or black bryony
berries without the seeds, with pennyroyal.

The same are good for podagra. But for this
there is also Ariston's emollient which consists of nard,
cinnamon, casia, chameleon, angular rush, 32 grms.
each, goat's suet in liquid iris oil 80 grms., iris which
should have been steeped in the sharpest vinegar
for 20 days, 4 grms.: this emollient also disperses
recent phymata and pain of all sorts.

But Theoxenus for pain in the feet mixed one part
of kidney-suet with two parts of salt and applied a
thin membrane smeared with these, then poured
over it ammoniacum for fumigation dissolved in
vinegar.

But Numenius used to soften podagra and all cases
of indurated joints with an emollient consisting
of southernwood, dried rose-leaves and poppy-tears,
12 grms. each, turpentine-resin 16 grms., frankincense
and soda-scum, 32 grms. each, iris and aristolochia,
48 grms. each, wax 1 kilogram, to which is added of
cedar-oil 42 c.cm., of laurel-oil 126 c.cm., of bitter
olive-oil 500 c.cm.

If at any time callus has formed in joints, Dexius
advised an application of lime 16 grms., white lead
32 grms., pine-resin 80 grms., 30 peppercorns, wax
56 grms. While these are being pounded together
250 c.cm. of mild wine is dropped in.

**19.** Ex emplastris autem nulla maiorem usum praestant, quam quae cruentis protinus vulneribus iniciuntur: enhaema Graeci vocant. Haec enim reprimunt inflammationem, nisi magna vis eam concitat, atque illius quoque impetum minuunt; tum glutinant vulnera, quae id patiuntur, cicatricem isdem inducunt. Constant autem ex medicamentis non pinguibus, ideoque alipe[ne] nominantur.

B  Optimum ex his est quod barbarum vocatur. Habet aeruginis rasae P. ✳ XII; spumae argenti P. ✳ XX; aluminis, picis aridae, resinae pineae aridae, singulorum P. ✳ I; quibus adiciuntur olei et aceti singulae heminae.

2  Alterum ad idem, quod Coacon vocant, habet spumae argenti P. ✳ C; resinae aridae tantundem: sed spuma prius ex tribus olei heminis coquitur. His duobus emplastris color niger est, qui fere talis fit ex pice atque resina: at ex bitumine nigerrimus, ex aerugine aut aeris squama viridis, ex minio ruber, ex cerussa albus.

3  Paucae admodum compositiones sunt, in quibus aliquid mixturae varietas novat. Ergo id quoque nigrum est, quod basilicon nominatur. Habet panacis P. ✳ I; galbani P. ✳ II; picis et resinae. singulorum P. ✳ X; olei dimidium cyathum.

4  At, quia perviride est, zmaragdinum appellatur in quo sunt: resinae pineae P. ✳ III; cerae P. ✳ I; aeruginis P. S.; turis fuliginis P. =; olei tantundem; aceti, quo fuligo et aerugo in unum cogantur.

---

[a] ἔναιμον φάρμακον Hippocrates III. 352 (*On Joints*, LXIII. 33).

[b] ἀλιπής without grease.

[c] See V. **26.** 23 f. Foreign remedies are to be generally avoided, but this was an exception.

**19.** Among the plasters none render greater service than those for immediate application to bleeding wounds, which the Greeks call enhaema.[a] For these repress inflammation, unless a severe cause excites it, and even then they lessen its attack; further, they agglutinate wounds which allow of it, and induce a scar in them. But as the plasters consist of medicaments which are not greasy, they are named alipe.[b]

The best of these is the plaster called barbarum.[c] It contains scraped verdigris 48 grms., litharge 80 grms., alum, dried pitch, dried pine-resin, 4 grms. each, to which is added oil and vinegar 250 c.cm. each.

Another one called Coacon,[d] used for the same purpose, consists of litharge 400 grms., dried resin the same, but the litharge should be first boiled in three-quarters of a litre of oil. In these two plasters the colour is black, which is the colour generally produced by the pitch-resin, but the blackest is from bitumen, green from verdigris or copper scales, red from minium, white from white-lead.

There are very few compositions in which diversity of ingredients makes any change.[e] Hence that plaster which is called basilicon is also black. It consists of all-heal 4 grms., galbanum 8 grms., pitch and resin, 40 grms. each, oil 20 c.cm.

But, because it is bright green, a plaster is called emerald-like which contains pine-resin 12 grms., wax 4 grms., verdigris 168 grms., frankincense soot 56 grms., oil the same, and vinegar enough to combine into one the soot and verdigris.

[d] Κωακός, "belonging to Cos" (the home of Hippocrates).
[e] *i.e.* in the black colour due to the pitch-resin: *zmaragdinum* is an exception.

33

5    Est etiam coloris fere rufi, quod celeriter ad cicatricem vulnera perducere videtur. Habet turis P. ✻ I; resinae P. ✻ II; squamae aeris P. ✻ IIII; spumae argenti P. ✻ XX; cerae P. ✻ C, olei heminam.

6    Praeterea est quam ῥάπτουσαν a glutinando vocant. Constat ex his: bituminis, aluminis scissilis P. ✻ IIII; spumae argenti P. ✻ XL; olei veteris hemina.

7    Praeterea sunt quaedam generis eiusdem, quae, quia capitibus fractis maxime conveniunt, cephalica a Graecis nominantur. Philotae compositio habet: terrae Eretriae, chalcitidis, singulorum P. ✻ IIII; murrae, aeris combusti, singulorum P. ✻ X; icthyocollae [singulorum] P. ✻ VI; aeruginis rasae, aluminis rotundi, misy crudi, aristolochiae, singulorum P. ✻ VIII; squamae aeris P. ✻ X; turis masculi P. ✻ II; cerae P. I; rosae et olei acerbi ternos cyathos; aceti quantum satis est, dum arida ex eo conteruntur.

8    Aliud ad idem viride: aeris combusti, squamae aeris, murrae, icthyocollae, singulorum P. ✻ VI; misy crudi, aeruginis rasae, aristolochiae, aluminis rotundi, singulorum P. ✻ VIII; cerae P. ✻ I, olei hemina, aceti quod satis sit.

9    Puri autem movendo non aliud melius quam quod expeditissimum est: tetrapharmacon a Graecis nominatur. Habet pares portiones cerae, picis, resinae, sebi taurini, si id non est, vitulini.

10    Alterum ad idem enneapharmacum nominatur, quod magis purgat. Constat ex novem rebus: cera melle, sebo, resina, murra, rosa, medulla vel cervina

---

ᵃ ῥάπτουσα (σύνθεσις) a composition which "sews up" the wound.

ᵇ Galen, *De Comp. Med.*, XIII. 745.

34

There is also one, almost red in colour, which is found to bring wounds rapidly to a scar. It contains incense 4 grms., resin 8 grms., copper scales 16 grms., litharge 80 grms., wax 400 grms, oil 250 c.cm.

As well, there is one called rhaptousa,[a] because it agglutinates, consisting of bitumen and split alum 16 grms., litharge 160 grms., and 250 c.cm. of old oil.

There are also some plasters of the same class, called by the Greeks cephalica, because they are especially suitable for broken heads. That of Philotas [b] has the following composition: Eretrian earth and chalcitis, 16 grms. each, myrrh and calcined copper 40 grms. each, isinglass 24 grms. [each], scraped verdigris, round alum, crude antimony sulphide and aristolochia, 32 grms. each, copper scales 40 grms., male frankincense 8 grms., wax 336 grms., rose-oil and bitter olive-oil, 125 c.cm. each, and sufficient vinegar to rub up the ingredients while keeping them dry.

A green plaster for the same purpose consists of calcined copper, copper scales, myrrh and isinglass, 24 grms. each, crude antimony sulphide, scraped verdigris, aristolochia and round alum, 32 grms. each, wax 4 grms., oil 250 c.cm., and as much vinegar as is required.

But for promoting suppuration there is nothing better than the plaster called by the Greeks tetra-pharmacon, which acts very quickly. It contains wax, pitch, resin and bull's suet, or, if that is not at hand, veal-suet, in equal proportions.

Another for the same purpose is named enneaphar-macum, which is more for cleaning wounds. It has nine ingredients: wax, honey, suet, resin, myrrh.

vel vitulina vel bubula, oesypo, buturo. Quorum
ipsorum quoque pondera paria miscentur.

11  Sunt autem quaedam emplastra, quibus utriusque
rei facultas est, quae si [1] . . . singula habenda sunt,
meliora sunt: sed in copia reicienda sunt, iis potius
adhibitis, quae proprie id, quod eo tempore opus est,
consecuntur. Exempli causa duo proponam.

Est igitur ad vulnera Attalium, quod habet:
squamae aeris P. ✱ XVI; turis fuliginis P. ✱ XV;
Hammoniaci tantundem; resinae terebenthinae
liquidae P. ✱ XXV; sebi taurini tantundem; aceti
heminas tres, olei sextarium.

B   At inter ea, quae fracto capiti accommodantur,
habent quidam id, quod ad auctorem Iudaeum
refertur. Constat ex his: salis P. ✱ IIII; squamae
aeris rubri, aeris combusti, singulorum P. ✱ XII;
Hammoniaci thymiamatis, turis fuliginis, resinae
aridae. singulorum P. ✱ XVI; resinae Colophoniacae,
cerae, sebi vitulini curati, singulorum P. ✱ XX;
aceti sesquicyatho, olei minus cyatho. τεθεραπευμένα
Graeci appellant, quae curata vocant, cum ex sebo
puta omnes membranulae diligenter exemptae sunt
[ex alio medicamento].

12  Sunt etiam quaedam emplastra nobilia ad extrahendum. Quae ipsa quoque ἐπισπαστικά nominantur; quale est quod, quia lauri bacas habet,
dia daphnidon appellatur. In eo est resinae tere-

---

[1] *Marx thinks the text is corrupt and that there is a consider-*
*able lacuna after* si; *he suggests the following:* . . . quae si-
<mul et pus movent et glutinant. Neque tamen eis quae
imposita ad> '*which are both suppurative and agglutinant.*
*And these are not better than those which are to be applied for the*
*given purpose.*'

---

[a] The grease from unwashed wool, cf. Galen, X. 965.

# BOOK V. 19. 10–12

rose-oil, deer or calf or ox marrow, oesypum,[a] butter;
equal weights of which are mixed together.[b]

Now there are certain plasters which produce both
effects [c] which if . . . they are to be applied for both
purposes are better; but if there is a choice these
are to be rejected, and those plasters rather are to
be selected which especially effect what is needed
at the time. I will mention two as examples.

There is the plaster of Attalus for wounds, which
contains copper scales 64 grms., frankincense soot 60
grms., ammoniacum the same; liquid turpentine
100 grms., bull-suet the same amount; vinegar
three-quarters of a litre, oil half a litre.

But among those suitable for broken heads, some
include the one which is ascribed to Iudaeus. It is
composed of salt 16 grms., red copper scales and
calcined copper, 48 grms. each, ammoniacum for fumigation, frankincense soot and dried resin, 64 grms.
each, Colophon resin, wax and prepared calf's suet,
80 grms. each, vinegar 65 c.cm., less than 40 c.cm.
of oil. The Greeks call tetherapeumena, what we
call prepared, when, for instance, from suet all
membranous particles are carefully removed, and so
in the case of other medicaments.

There are besides certain plasters noteworthy for
extracting, and these too are named epispastic; [d] for
instance, that called dia daphnidon,[e] because it contains laurel berries. In it there are terebinth-resin

---

[b] Both the 4-ingredient and the 9-ingredient plasters are
often mentioned later, *e.g.* by Galen, *De Comp. Med.*, XII.
328.

[c] *i.e.* suppuration and cleaning.

[d] See p. 10, note *b*.

[e] διὰ δαφνίδων, containing laurel (δάφνη) berries, Galen, *De
Comp. Med.*, XIII. 979.

37

benthinae P. ✳ X; nitri, cerae, picis aridae, bacarum
lauri, singulorum P. ✳ XX; olei paulum. Quotiens
autem bacam aut nucem aut simile aliquid posuero,
scire oportebit, antequam expendatur, ei summam
pelliculam esse demendam.

13  Aliud eodem nomine, quod puri quoque movendo
est: sebi vitulini, Hammoniaci thymiamatis, picis,
cerae, nitri, bacarum lauri, resinae aridae, aristolochiae, pyrethri pares portiones.

14  Praeter has est Philocratis, quod habet: salis
Hammoniaci P. ✳ VII; aristolochiae P. ✳ VIII;
cerae, resinae terebenthinae, fuliginis turis, singulorum P. ✳ XV; spumae argenti P. ✳ XXXII,
quibus, ut pus quoque moveant, iridis P. ✳ IIII et
galbani P. ✳ VI adiciuntur.

15  Optimum tamen ad extrahendum est id, quod a
similitudine sordium rhypodes Graeci appellant.
Habet murrae, croci, iridis, propolis, bdelli, capitulorum Punici mali, aluminis et scissilis et rotundi,
misy, chalcitis, atramenti sutorii cocti, panacis, salis
Hammoniaci, visci, singulorum P. ✳ IIII; aristolochiae P. ✳ VIII; squamae aeris P. ✳ XVI; resinae
terebenthinae P. ✳ LXXV; cerae et sebi vel
taurini vel hircini, singulorum P. ✳ C.

16  Hecataeo quoque auctore emplastrum generis
eiusdem fit ex his: galbani P. ✳ II; fuliginis turis
P. ✳ IIII; picis P. ✳ VI; cerae et resinae terebenthinae singulorum P. ✳ VIII; quibus paululum
irini unguenti miscetur.

17  Valensque ad idem emplastrum viride Alexandrinum est. Habet aluminis scissilis P. ✳ VIII; salis
Hammoniaci P. ✳ VIII =; squamae aeris P. ✳ XVI;
murrae, turis, singulorum P. ✳ XVIII; cerae P. ✳
CL; resinae Colophoniacae aut pineae P. ✳ CC; olei
heminam, aceti sextarium.

38

40 grms., soda, wax, dried pitch, laurel-berries, 80 grms. each, with a little oil. But whenever I mention a berry or nut or the like, it should be understood that the outer husk is to be removed before weighing.

Another of the same name which also promotes suppuration, contains calf-suet, ammoniacum for fumigation, pitch, wax, soda, laurel-berries, dried resin, aristolochia and pellitory, equal parts.

There is also that of Philocrates, which consists of ammoniac salt 28 grms., aristolochia 32 grms., wax, turpentine resin, frankincense soot, 60 grms. each, litharge 128 grms., to which is added, in order to promote suppuration, iris 16 grms., and galbanum 24 grms.

The best as an extractive, however, is that called by the Greeks rhypodes, from its resemblance to dirt. It contains myrrh, crocus, iris, propolis, bdellium, pomegranate heads, alum both split and round, antimony sulphide, copper ore, boiled blacking, all-heal, ammoniacum salt, mistletoe juice, 16 grms. each, aristolochia 32 grms., copper scales 56 grms., turpentine resin 300 grms., wax and ox or he-goat's suet, 400 grms. each.

The plaster invented by Hecataeus is of the same class, and is composed of galbanum 8 grms., frankincense soot 16 grms., pitch 24 grms., wax and turpentine-resin, 32 grms. each, with which is mixed a little iris ointment.

Efficacious for the same purpose is the green Alexandrian plaster. It consists of split alum 32 grms., ammoniac salt 32·66 grms., copper scales 64 grms., myrrh and frankincense 72 grms., wax 600 grms., Colophon or pine resin 800 grms., oil 250 c.cm., vinegar half a litre.

18    Quaedam autem sunt emplastra exedentia, quae
septa Graeci vocant; quale est id, quod habet resinae
terebenthinae, fuliginis turis, singulorum P. =;
squamae aeris P. ✻ I; ladani P. ✻ II; aluminis
tantundem; spumae argenti [singulorum] P. ✻ IIII.
19    Exest etiam vehementer corpus atque ossa quoque
resolvit et supercrescentem carnem coercet id, quod
habet spumae argenti, squamae aeris uncias singulas;
nitri ignem non experti, lapidis Assii, aristolochiae P.
sextantes; cerae, resinae terebenthinae, turis, olei
veteris, atramenti sutorii, salis Hammoniaci P. S.;
aeruginis rasae P. bessem; aceti scilliti heminam;
vini Aminaei tantundem.
20    Sunt etiam adversus morsus quaedam adcommodata, quale est Diogeni nigrum, quod habet:
bituminis, cerae, resinae pineae aridae, singulorum
P. ✻ XX; spumae argenti P. ✻ C; olei sextarium.
Aut in quo sunt squamae aeris P. ✻ IIII; cerussae
et aeruginis rassae, singulorum P. ✻ VIII; Hammoniaci P. ✻ XII; cerae, resinae pineae, singulorum
P. ✻ XXV; spumae argenti P. ✻ C; olei sextarium.
Aut in quo sunt squamae aeris P. ✻ XIIII; galbani
P. ✻ VI; cerussae et aeruginis rasae, singulorum
P. ✻ VIII; Hammoniaci P. ✻ XII; cerae, resinae
pineae, singulorum P. ✻ XXXV . . .[1] spuma argenti
concoquitur.
21    Rubrum quoque emplastrum, quod Ephesium
vocatur, huc aptum est.  Habet resinae terebenthinae
P. ✻ II; galbani P. ✻ IIII; minii Sinopici P. ✻ VI;
turis fuliginis P. ✻ VI; cerae P. ✻ VIII; spumae
argenti P. ✻ XXXVI; olei veteris heminam.

    [1] *Marx suggests that* ex quo *has fallen out before* spuma;
*Targa would emend to* spumae argenti P ✻ C: olei sextarium
in quo concoquitur.

Some plasters, called by the Greeks septa,[a] eat away flesh; one such contains turpentine-resin and frankincense soot, each 56 grms., copper scales 4 grms., ladanum 8 grms., alum the same amount, litharge 16 grms.

The following prescription is even violent in its action on soft tissue, and also causes exfoliation of bone and keeps down fungating flesh: litharge and copper scales 28 grms. each, unheated soda, Assos stone, aristolochia, 56 grms. each, wax, turpentine resin, incense and old oil, blacking and ammoniac salt, 168 grms. each, scraped verdigris 224 grms., vinegar of squills 250 c.cm., Aminaean wine the same amount.

There are also some suitable for bites; one of these is the black plaster of Diogenes, which contains bitumen, wax, dried pine-resin, each 80 grms., litharge 400 grms., oil half a litre. Another consists of copper scales 16 grms., white-lead and scraped verdigris, each 32 grms., ammoniacum 48 grms., wax and pine resin, each 100 grms., litharge 400 grms., oil half a litre. Or there is that in which there are copper scales 56 grms., galbanum 24 grms., white-lead and scraped verdigris, each 32 grms., ammoniacum 48 grms., wax and pine-resin, each 140 grms. cooked with litharge.

The red plaster called Ephesian is likewise suited for this purpose. It contains turpentine-resin 8 grms., galbanum 16 grms., minium from Sinope 24 grms., frankincense soot 24 grms., wax 32 grms., litharge 144 grms., old olive-oil 250 c.cm.

---

[a] This word is used by Aristotle (*H.A.* VIII. **29**. 607a. 3) of a drug that erodes flesh, σηπτικὸν φάρμακον, though its usual meaning was rotten, decomposed (of food); cf. Hippocrates, *Diseases* (L) VI. 451.

22 Item id, quod ex his constat; squamae aeris, turis fuliginis, singulorum P. ✳ IIII; galbani P. ✳ VI; salis Hammoniaci P. ✳ XII = ; cerae P. ✳ XXV; olei tribus heminis. Haec autem aliis quoque recentioribus vulneribus recte imponuntur.

23 Sunt etiam alba lenia (leuca Graeci vocant) fere non gravibus vulneribus accommodata, praecipueque senilibus. Quale est quod habet: cerussae P. ✳ XXXII; sebi vitulini curati et cerae, singulorum P. ✳ XLVIII; olei heminas tres; ex quibus ea cerussa coquitur.

24 Aliud quod habet cerussae P. ✳ XX; cerae P. ✳ XXXV, olei heminam, aquae sextarium. Quae quotiens adiciuntur cerussae vel spumae argenti, scire licet illa ex his coquenda esse. Est autem ea percandida compositio quae supra posita est, ideoque elephantine nominatur.

25 Lenia quoque quaedam emplastra sunt, quas liparas fere Graeci nominant; ut id, quod habet mini P. ✳ IIII; spumae argenti P. ✳ XXV; cerae et adipis suillae, singulorum P. ✳ XXXVII; vitellos quattuor.

26 Alia compositio generis eiusdem: cerae, resinae terebenthinae, singulorum P. ✳ VI; cerussae P. ✳ VIII; spumae argenti, plumbi recrementi (σκωρίαν μολύβδου Graeci vocant), singulorum P. ✳ XX; cicini olei et murtei singulorum heminae.

27 Tertia, quae ad auctorem Archagathum refertur: misy cocti, aeris combusti, singulorum P. ✳ IIII; cerussae coctae P. ✳ VIII; resinae terebenthinae P. ✳ X; spumae argenti P. ✳ VI.

There is another similar one which consists of
copper scales and frankincense soot, each 16 grms.,
galbanum 24 grms., ammoniac salt 48·66 grms.,
wax 100 grms., olive-oil 750 c.cm. These plasters,
however, may be also usefully applied to more
recent wounds.

There are also soothing white plasters, called by the
Greeks leuca, fitted in general for wounds which are
not severe, especially in old people. Such is that
containing white-lead 128 grms., prepared calf's
suet, and wax, each 192 grms., olive-oil 750 c.cm.,
with which the white-lead is boiled.

Another consists of white-lead 80 grms., wax 140
grms., olive-oil 250 c.cm., water half a litre. Whenever these liquids are added to white lead or
litharge, it is understood that those drugs are to be
boiled up in the liquids. But the above composition
being of a glistening white appearance is called ivory
plaster.

There are also some soothing plasters, commonly
called liparae [a] by the Greeks, such as that containing
minium 16 grms., litharge 100 grms., wax and lard,
each 148 grms., with the yolk of 4 eggs.

Another composition of the same sort contains
wax and turpentine-resin, each 24 grms., white-lead
32 grms., litharge and lead-slag, called by the Greeks
σκωρία μολύβδου, each 80 grms., castor-oil and myrtle-
oil, each 250 c.cm.

A third, said to have been invented by Archagathus,
contains boiled antimony sulphide and calcined
copper, each 16 grms., boiled white-lead 32 grms.,
turpentine-resin 40 grms., litharge 24 grms.

---

[a] Greasy plasters; the opposite of ἀλιπῆ ἔμπλαστρα, p. 32,
note b.

28 Etiamnum generis eiusdem: spumae argenti,
cerae, adipis suillae, singulorum P. ✳ XXVII; vitelli
cocti IIII; rosae hemina. Aut: ceràti ex oleo
myrteo facti partes tres; adipis suillae pars quarta;
paulum ex plumbi recremento. Aut: spumae
argenti selibra, ex olei hemina et aquae marinae
altera cocta, donec bullire desierit, cui paulum cerae
sit adiectum. Aut: pares portiones cerae, sebi,
stibis, spumae argenti, cerussae.

**20.** Pastilli quoque facultates diversas habent.
Sunt enim ad recentia vulnera glutinanda sananda-
que apti; qualis est qui habet chalcitis, misy, spumae
nitri, floris aeris, gallae, aluminis scissilis modice
cocti, singulorum P. ✳ I; aeris combusti, capitulorum mali Punici, singulorum P. ✳ III. Hunc
oportet diluere aceto, ac sic, ubi vulnus glutinandum
est, inlinere. At si nervosus aut musculosus is locus
est, commodius est cerato miscere, sic ut illius VIII
partes, nona huius sit.

B Alius ad idem constat ex his: bituminis, aluminis
scissilis, singulorum P. ✳ I; aeris combusti P. ✳ IIII;
spumae argenti P. ✳ XI; olei sextario.

2 Sed longe Polyidi celeberrimus est, sphragis autem
nominatur; qui habet aluminis scissilis P. ✳ I =;
atramenti sutorii P. ✳ II; murrae P. ✳ V; aloes
tantundem; capitulorum Punici mali, fellis taurini,
singulorum P. ✳ VI; quae contrita vino austero
excipiuntur.

3 Ad ulcera sordida et nigritiem in auribus, naribus,
obscenis partibus, inflammationesque eorum: chryso-
collae P. ✳ I; atramenti sutori, aluminis scissilis,

Yet another of the same class consists of litharge, wax and lard, each 108 grms., yolk of 4 eggs boiled, rose-oil 250 c.cm. Another consists of a cerate made with myrtle-oil three parts, lard a fourth part, and a small quantity of lead-slag. Alternatively : litharge 168 grms., olive-oil 250 c.cm., and an equal quantity of sea water, boiled, to which, when off the boil, a little wax may be added. Or : wax, suet, antimony sulphide, litharge and white-lead, equal parts.

**20.** Pastils have also divers faculties. For some are suitable for agglutinating and making the scar upon recent wounds : such as that containing copper ore, antimony sulphide, soda-scum, flowers of copper, oak-galls, split alum moderately boiled, each 4 grms., calcined copper and pomegranate-heads, each 12 grms. It should be dissolved with vinegar, and so smeared on for agglutinating a wound. But if the part wounded involves sinews or muscles, it is better to mix the pastil with a cerate, eight parts of the former to nine of the latter.

Another for the same purpose is composed of bitumen and split alum, each 4 grms., calcined copper 16 grms., litharge 44 grms., oil half a litre.

But the pastil of Polyides [a] called the " seal " is by far the most celebrated. It contains split alum 4·66 grms., blacking 8 grms., myrrh 20 grms., lign aloes the same, pomegranate heads and ox-bile, 24 grms. each ; these are rubbed together and taken up in dry wine.

For foul ulcerations and gangrene in the ears, nostrils and genitals, and their inflammatory complications, take chrysocolla 4 grms., blacking and split

---

[a] Also referred to by Galen, *De Compositione Medicamentorum*, Bk. V. 12 XIII. 834.

CELSUS

singulorum P. ✳ II; halicaccabi corticis P. ✳ IIII;
mini P. ✳ VI; spumae argenti P. ✳ XII; cerussae
P. ✳ XVI; quae ex aceto et coguntur et, ubi utendum
est, diluuntur.

4 Andronis vero est ad uvam inflammatam, ad
naturalia sordida, etiam cancro laborantia: gallae,
atramenti sutorii, murrae, singulorum P. ✳ I; aristolochiae, aluminis scissilis, singulorum P. ✳ II; capitulorum Punici mali P. ✳ XXV; ex passo coacta, et
cum usus exigit, aceto vel vino diluta, prout valentius
aut lenius vitium est, cui medendum est.

5 Proprie autem ad ani fissa, vel ora venarum
fundentia sanguinem, vel cancrum: aeruginis P. ✳
II; murrae P. ✳ IIII; cummis P. ✳ VIII; turis
P. ✳ XII; stibis, lacrimae papaveris, acaciae, singulorum P. ✳ XVI. Quae ex vino et teruntur et in
ipso usu deliquantur.

6 Expellere autem ex vesica cum urina calculum
videtur haec compositio: casiae, croci, murrae, costi,
nardi, cinnamomi, dulcis radicis, balsami, hyperici
pares portiones conteruntur, deinde vinum lene
instillatur, et pastilli fiunt, qui singuli habeant
P. ✳ =, hique singuli cotidie mane ieiuno dantur.

**21.** Haec tria compositionum genera [id est,
quae in malagmatibus, pastillis emplastrisque sunt]
maximum praecipueque varium usum praestant.
Sed alia quoque utilia sunt, ut ea, quae feminis
subiciuntur: pessos Graeci vocant. Eorum haec
proprietas est: medicamenta composita molli lana
excipiuntur, eaque lana naturalibus conditur.

---

[a] Canker means septic and gangrenous forms of inflammation, rather than what is now called cancer. Cf. vol. I.
p. 88 n.; and vol. III. Appendix, p. 589 ff.
[b] pessaries; for prescriptions see p. 49.

46

alum 8 grms. each, winter cherry bark 16 grms., minium 24 grms., litharge 48 grms., cerussa 64 grms.; these are both compounded with vinegar and dissolved for use with the same.

The pastil of Andron is for inflammation of the uvula, and for the genitals when foul, and even when affected by canker.[a] It contains oak-galls, blacking, and myrrh, 4 grms. each, aristolochia and split alum, 8 grms. each, pomegranate-heads 100 grms., compounded with raisin wine, and when required for use dissolved in vinegar or wine, according as the disease to be treated is more severe or milder.

But the following is appropriate for anal fissures, for bleeding piles, or for canker, verdigris 8 grms., myrrh 16 grms., gum 32 grms., frankincense 48 grms., antimony sulphide, poppy tears and acacia, 64 grms. each. These are both pounded up in wine and for actual use are dissolved in the same.

The following prescription is efficacious to expel stones from the bladder along with the urine; casia, crocus, myrrh, costmary, nard, cinnamon, liquorice root, balsamum and hypericum juice, equal parts; these are rubbed together, then mild wine is poured on, and pastils are made, each weighing 0·66 grm.; one of them is given every morning on an empty stomach.

**21.** These three classes of compositions [emollients, pastils and plasters], have very wide and varied uses. But there are other useful compositions, such as those which are introduced into women from below, the Greeks call them pessoi.[b] Their characteristic is that the component medicaments are taken up in soft wool, and this wool is inserted into the genitals.

B    Ad sanguinem autem evocandum Cauneis duabus adicitur nitri P. ✳ S = ; aut alii semen conteritur, adicitur murrae paululum, et unguento Susino miscetur ; aut cucumeris silvestris pars interior ex lacte muliebri diluitur.

2    Ad vulvam molliendam ovi vitellus et foenum Graecum et rosa et crocum temperantur. Aut elateri P. ✳ = ; salis tantundem ; uvae taminiae P. ✳ VI melle excipiuntur.

3    Aut Boetho auctore croci, resinae terebenthinae, singulorum P. ✳ IIII ; murrae P. ✳ = = ; rosae P. ✳ I ; sebi vitulini P. ✳ I = ; cerae P. ✳ II miscentur.

4    Optuma autem adversus inflammationes vulvae Numenii compositio est, quae habet : croci P. ✳ = — ; cerae P. ✳ I ; buturi P. ✳ VIII ; adipis anserini P. ✳ XII ; vitellos coctos duos, rosae minus cyatho.

5    Si vero infans intus decessit, quo facilius eiciatur, malicorium ex aqua terendum eoque utendum est.

6    Si concidere vitio locorum mulier solet, cocleae cum testis suis comburendae conterendaeque, deinde his mel adiciendum est.

7    Si non comprehendit, adeps leonina ex rosa mollienda est.

**22.** Quaedam autem mixturae medicamentorum sunt, quibus aridis neque coactis utimur, sic ut inspergamus, aut cum aliquo liquido mixta inlinamus. Quale est ad carnem supercrescentem exedendam, quod habet : squamae aeris, fuliginis turis, singulorum P. ✳ I ; aeruginis P. ✳ II. Haec autem eadem cum melle purgant ulcera, cum cera inplent.

---

[a] hysterical fits, cf. IV. **27.** 1 (vol. I. p. 446).

48

A pessary for inducing menstruation contains soda 2·65 grms., added to two Caunean figs; or garlic seeds are pounded, a little myrrh added, and these are mixed with Susine lily ointment; or the pulp of a wild cucumber is diluted in woman's milk.

To mollify the womb a yolk of egg, fenugreek, rose-oil and saffron are mixed together. Or elaterium 0·66 grm., the same quantity of salt, and black bryony berries 24 grms. are taken up with honey.

The pessary invented by Boethus consists of saffron and turpentine resin, 16 grms. each, myrrh 1·33 grms., rose-oil 4 grms., calf's suet 4·66 grms., wax 8 grms., mixed together.

But against inflammations of the womb, the composition of Numenius is the best; it consists of saffron 1 grm., wax 4 grms., butter 32 grms., goose-fat 48 grms., 2 yolks of egg boiled, and of rose-oil less than 40 c.cm.

If the foetus is dead, to render its expulsion more easy, pomegranate rind should be rubbed up in water and so used.

If a woman is liable to fits[a] owing to genital disease, snails are to be burnt with their shells, and pounded up together; then honey added to them.

If a woman does not conceive, lion's fat is to be softened by rose-oil.

22. Now, some mixtures of medicaments are used dry, without being combined, so that they are dusted or smeared on after some liquid has been mixed with them. Such is the prescription to eat away fungous flesh, which contains copper scales and frankincense soot, 4 grms. each, verdigris 8 grms. But when combined with honey this compound cleans ulcers, when with wax it fills them up. Also antimony

Misy quoque et galla, si paribus portionibus misceantur, corpus consumunt; eaque vel arida inspergere licet vel excepta cadmia inlinere.

2 Putrem vero carnem continet neque ultra serpere patitur et leniter exest mel vel cum lenticula vel cum marrubio vel cum oleae foliis ante ex vino decoctis. Item sertula Campana in mulso cocta, deinde contrita; aut calx cum cerato; aut amarae nuces cum alio, sic ut huius pars tertia sit, paulumque his croci adiciatur. Aut quod habet spumae argenti P. ✳ VI; cornu bubuli combusti P. ✳ XII; olei murtei et vini
B cyathos ternos. Aut quod ex his constat: floris Punici mali, atramenti sutorii, aloes, singulorum P. ✳ II; aluminis scissilis, turis, singulorum P. ✳ IIII; gallae P. ✳ VIII; aristolochiae P. ✳ X. Vehementius idem facit etiam adurendo auripigmentum cum chalcitide et aut nitro aut calce aut charta combusta: item sal cum aceto. Vel ea compositio, quae habet: chalcitidis, capitulorum Punici mali, aloes, singulorum P. ✳ II; aluminis scissilis, turis, singulorum P. ✳ IIII; gallae P. ✳ VIII; aristolochiae P. ✳ X; mellis quantum satis sit ad ea cogenda.
C Vel cantharidum P. ✳ I; sulpuris P. ✳ I; lolii P. ✳ III; quibus adicitur picis liquidae quantum satis est ad iungendum. Vel chalcitis quoque cum resina et ruta mixta; aut cum eadem resina diphryges; aut uva taminia cum pice liquida. Idem vero possunt et faecis vini combustae et calcis et nitri pares portiones; vel aluminis scissilis P. ✳ = =; turis, sandaracae, nitri, singulorum P. ✳ I; gallae P. ✳ VIII; aristolochiae P. ✳ X; mellis quantum satis sit.

---

[a] Made of *terra cadmia* from Cyprus, which contained oxide of zinc.

sulphide and oak-galls, if they are mixed in equal proportions, corrode flesh. We may either sprinkle this
mixture on dry or take it up in cadmian *ᵃ* ointment
and smear it on.

Honey mixed with lentils or with horehound or
with olive leaves previously boiled in wine holds in
check putrid flesh, prevents its further spread, and
is a mild corrosive. The same is the action of
melilot, boiled in honey wine, then pounded up;
or lime with cerate; or bitter almonds with garlic
in the proportion of three to one, with the addition
of a little saffron. Or the composition containing
litharge 24 grms., burnt ox-horn 48 grms., myrtle-
oil and wine, 125 c.cm. of each. Or that mixture
which consists of pomegranate flowers, blacking and
lign-aloes, 8 grms. each, split alum and frankincense
16 grms., oak-galls 32 grms., aristolochia 40 grms.
Stronger as a corrosive is that compounded by cal-
cining orpiment with copper ore, and with either
soda or lime or burnt papyrus; salt with vinegar is
similar. Or that composition which contains copper
ore, pomegranate heads, lign-aloes, 8 grms. each, split
alum and frankincense, 16 grms. each, oak-galls 32
grms., aristolochia 40 grms., with sufficient honey to
combine them. An alternative is the composition
containing cantharides 4 grms., sulphur 4 grms.,
darnel 12 grms., to which is added enough liquid
pitch to combine them. Or also that composed of
copper ore mixed with resin and rue; or slag similarly
with resin; or black bryony berries with liquid pitch.
The same property too belongs both to burnt wine-
lees and lime and soda, equal parts, or to split alum,
1·33 grms., frankincense, sandarach and soda, 4 grms.
each, oak-galls 32 grms., aristolochia 40 grms., and
as much honey as is required.

3   Est etiam Herae compositio, quae habet murrae, chalcitidis, singulorum P. ✳ II; aloes, turis, aluminis scissilis, singulorum P. ✳ IIII; aristolochiae, gallae inmaturae, singulorum P. ✳ VIII; malicori contriti P. ✳ X.

4   Est Iudaei, in qua sunt calcis partes duae; nitri quam ruberrumi pars tertia, quae urina inpuberis pueri coguntur, donec strigmenti crassitudo sit. Sed subinde is locus, cui id inlinitur, madefaciendus est.

5   At Iollas chartae combustae, sandaracae, singulorum P. ✳ I; calcis P. ✳ II; auripigmenti tantundem miscebat.

6   Si vero ex membrana, quae super cerebrum est, profluit sanguis, vitellus combustus et contritus inspergi debet: si alio loco sanguinis profluvium est, auripigmenti, squamae aeris, singulorum P. ✳ I; sandaracae P. ✳ II; marmoris cocti P. ✳ IIII inspergi debet. Eadem cancro quoque obsistunt. Ad inducendam cicatricem: squamae aeris, turis fuliginis, singulorum P. ✳ II; calcis P. ✳ IIII. Eadem increscentem quoque carnem coercent.

Timaeus autem ad ignem sacrum, ad cancrum his utebatur: murrae P. ✳ II: turis, atramenti sutori, singulorum P. ✳ III; sandaracae, auripigmenti, squamae aeris, singulorum P. ✳ IIII; gallae P. ✳ VI; cerussae combustae P. ✳ VIII. Ea vel arida inspersa vel melle excepta idem praestant.

8   Sternumenta vero vel albo veratro vel struthio coiecto in nares excitantur, vel his mixtis: piperis, veratri albi, singulorum P. ✳ =; castorei P. ✳ ⟨⟩; spumae nitri P. ✳ I; struthi P. ✳ IIII.

9   Gargarizationes autem aut levandi causa fiunt aut

---

ᵃ p. 10, note a.

There is also the compound of Heras which contains myrrh and copper ore, 8 grms. each, lign-aloes, frankincense, split alum, 16 grms., aristolochia and immature oak-galls, 32 grms. each, pomegranate rind pounded 40 grms.

The compound of Iudaeus contains lime two parts; the reddest soda one part, mixed with the urine of a young boy to the consistency of strigil scrapings.[a] But the place on which it is smeared should from time to time be moistened.

Then the compound of Iollas consists of burnt papyrus and of sandarach, 4 grms. each, lime 8 grms., mixed with the same quantity of orpiment.

But if there is haemorrhage from the membrane covering the brain, a yolk of egg which has been charred and then pounded should be scattered on; for haemorrhage elsewhere orpiment and copper scales, 4 grms. each, sandarach 8 grms., calcined marble 16 grms., should be dusted on. The same also checks canker. To induce scarifying, copper scales and frankincense soot, 8 grms. each, lime 16 grms. The same also counters fungous flesh.

Also Timaeus used the following for ignis sacer and for canker: myrrh 8 grms., frankincense and blacking, 12 grms. each, sandarach, orpiment, copper scales, 16 grms. each, oak-galls 24 grms., burnt white-lead 32 grms. This is either scattered on dry or has the same effect when taken up in honey.

Sneezing too is excited by putting up the nose either white veratrum or soapwort; or the following mixture: pepper and white veratrum, 0·66 grm. each, castoreum 1 grm., soda-scum 4 grms., soapwort 16 grms.

Now gargles are used as emollients or as repres-

reprimendi aut evocandi. Levant lac, cremor vel
tisanae vel furfurum: reprimit aqua, in qua vel
lenticula vel rosa vel rubus vel Cotoneum malum vel
palmulae decoctae sunt. Evocant sinapi, piper.

23. Antidota raro sed praecipue interdum necessaria sunt, quia gravissimis casibus opitulantur.
Ea recte quidem dantur conlisis corporibus, vel per
ictus, vel ubi ex alto deciderunt, vel in viscerum,
laterum, faucium, interiorumque partium doloribus.
Maxime autem desideranda sunt adversus venena,
vel per morsus vel per cibos aut potiones nostris
corporibus inserta.

B     Unum est, quod habet lacrimae papaveris P. ✳ = ;
acori, malabathri P. ✳ V; iridis Illyricae, cummi,
singulorum P. ✳ II; anesi P. ✳ III; nardi Gallici,
foliorum rosae aridorum, cardamomi, singulorum P. ✳
IIII; petroselini P. ✳ IIII = (vel folii P. ✳ V);
casiae nigrae, silis, bdelli, balsami seminis, piperis
albi, singulorum P. ✳ V = ; styracis P. ✳ V = ;
murrae, opopanacis, nardi Syri, turis masculi, hypocistidis suci, singulorum P. ✳ VI; castorei P. ✳ VI;
costi, piperis albi, galbani, resinae terebenthinae,
croci, floris iunci rotundi, singulorum P. ✳ VI= — ;
dulcis radicis P. ✳ VIII = — ; quae vel melle vel
passo excipiuntur.

2     Alterum, quod Zopyrus regi Ptolemaeo dicitur
composuisse atque ambrosian nominasse, ex his
constat: costi, turis masculi, singulorum P. ✳ = = ;
piperis albi P. ✳ = — ; floris iunci rotundi P. ✳ II;

---

*a* Stimulant and aromatic substances mixed with honey
and wine. Celsus mentions three only, with 30, 10, and 37
ingredients respectively. These ingredients would comfort
patients suffering from the conditions described, and the

sives or to draw out humour. As emollients, milk, pearl-barley or bran gruel; as repressants, a decoction of lentils or rose-leaves or blackberries or quinces or of dates. Mustard and pepper draw out humour.

**23.** Antidotes [a] are seldom needed, but are at times important because they bring aid to the gravest cases. They are appropriately administered for bodily contusions, either from blows or in cases of a fall from a height, or for pain in the viscera, sides, fauces, or internal parts.[b] But they are chiefly necessary against poisons introduced into our bodies through bites or food or drink.

One consists of poppy-tears 0·66 grm., sweet flag and malabathrum, 20 grms. each, Illyrian iris and gum, 8 grms. each, anise 12 grms., Gallic nard, dried rose-leaves and cardamons, 16 grms. each, parsley 16·66 grms. (or trifolium 20 grms.), black casia, seseli, bdellium, balsam seed, white pepper, 20·66 grms. each, storax 20·66 grms., myrrh, opopanax, Syrian nard, male frankincense and hypocistis juice, 24 grms. each, castoreum 24 grms., costmary, white pepper, galbanum, turpentine, resin, crocus, flowers of round rush 25 grms., liquorice root 33 grms., which are taken up in honey or in raisin wine.

Alternatively there is that which Zopyrus [c] is said to have composed for a King Ptolemy, and to have called it ambrosia, consisting of the following: costmary and male frankincense, 1·33 grms. each, white pepper 1 grm., flowers of round rush 8 grms.,

remedy could be administered repeatedly in small doses. The first and third include a small quantity of poppy juice. There is no other narcotic or poisonous ingredient.

[b] V. **26**. 24 C.

[c] Galen, *Antidotes*, II. 17. XIV. 205.

cinnamomi P. ✳ III; casiae nigrae P. ✳ IIII; croci
Cilici P. ✳ IIII = —; murrae, quam stacten
nominant, P. ✳ V; nardi Indici P. ✳ V = —.
Quae singula contrita melle cocto excipiuntur;
deinde ubi utendum est, id quod Aegyptiae fabae
magnitudinem impleat, in potione vini diluitur.

3    Nobilissimum autem est Mithridatis, quod cottidie
sumendo rex ille dicitur adversus venenorum pericula
tutum corpus suum reddidisse. In quo haec sunt:
costi P. ✳ = = —; acori P. ✳ V; hyperici, cummi,
sagapeni, acaciae suci, iridis Illyricae, cardamomi,
singulorum P. ✳ II; anesi P. ✳ III; nardi Gallici,
gentianae radicis, aridorum rosae foliorum, singulorum P. ✳ IIII; papaveris lacrimae, petroselini,
singulorum P. ✳ IIII = —; casiae, silis, lolii, piperis
longi, singulorum P. ✳ V =; styracis P. ✳ V = —;
B castorei, turis, hypocistidis suci, murrae, opopanacis,
singulorum P. ✳ VI; malabathri folii P. ✳ VI;
floris iunci rotundi, resinae terebenthinae, galbani,
dauci Cretici seminis, singulorum P. ✳ VI =; nardi,
opobalsami, singulorum P. ✳ VI = —; thlaspis
P. ✳ VI = —; radicis Ponticae P. ✳ VII; croci,
zingiberis, cinnamomi, singulorum P. ✳ VII = —.
Haec contrita melle excipiuntur, et adversus venenum, quod magnitudinem nucis Graecae impleat, ex
vino datur. In ceteris autem adfectibus corporis pro
modo eorum vel quod Aegyptiae fabae vel quod ervi
magnitudinem impleat, satis est.

    **24.** Acopa quoque utilia nervis sunt. Quale est,
quod habet floris iunci rotundi P. ✳ II = =; costi,
iunci quadrati, lauri bacarum, Hammoniaci, cardamomi, singulorum P. ✳ IIII = —; murrae, aeris
combusti, singulorum P. ✳ VII; iridis Illyricae,
cerae, singulorum P. ✳ XIIII; Alexandrini calami,

cinnamon 12 grms., black casia 16 grms., Cilician saffron 17 grms., myrrh called stacte 20 grms., Indian nard 21 grms. Each ingredient is ground up separately, and they are taken up in boiled honey; then at the time of using, a quantity the size of an Egyptian bean is dissolved in a draught of wine.

But the most famous antidote is that of Mithridates,[a] which that king is said to have taken daily and by it to have rendered his body safe against danger from poison. It contains costmary 1·66 grms., sweet flag 20 grms., hypericum, gum, sagapenum, acacia juice, Illyrian iris, cardamon, 8 grms. each, anise 12 grms., Gallic nard, gentian root and dried rose-leaves, 16 grms. each, poppy-tears and parsley, 17 grms. each, casia, saxifrage, darnel, long pepper, 20·66 grms. each, storax 21 grms., castoreum, frankincense, hypocistis juice, myrrh and opopanax, 24 grms. each, malabathrum leaves 24 grms., flower of round rush, turpentine-resin, galbanum, Cretan carrot seeds, 24·66 grms. each, nard and opobalsam, 25 grms. each, shepherd's purse 25 grms., rhubarb root 28 grms., saffron, ginger, cinnamon, 29 grms. each. These are pounded and taken up in honey. Against poisoning, a piece the size of an almond is given in wine. In other affections an amount corresponding in size to an Egyptian bean is sufficient.

**24.** Acopa[b] again are useful for neuralgia. Of these there is one which consists of the flower of the round rush, 9·33 grms. each, costmary, square rush, laurel berries, ammoniacum, cardamons, 17 grms. each, myrrh and calcined copper 28 grms., Illyrian iris and wax 56 grms., Alexandrian flag,

[a] Galen, *Antidotes*, II. 1. XIV. 108.
[b] ἄκοπα φάρμακα. Anodyne salves, IV. **31**. 8 (vol. I. p. 460).

iunci rotundi, aspalathi, xylobalsami, singulorum
P. ✳ XXVIII; sebi P. ✳ I; unguenti irini cyathum.
2   Alterum, quod euodes vocant, hoc modo fit: cerae
P. = —; olei tantundem; resinae terebenthinae ad
nucis iuglandis magnitudinem simul incocuntur;
deinde infusa in mortario teruntur, instillaturque
subinde quam optumi mellis acetabulum, tum irini
unguenti et rosae terni cyathi.
3   Enchrista autem Graeci vocant liquida, quae
inlinuntur. Quale est, quod fit ad ulcera purganda
et inplenda, maxime inter nervos, paribus portionibus
inter se mixtis: buturi, medullae vitulinae, sebi
vitulini, adipis anserinae, cerae, mellis, resinae terebenthinae, rosae, olei cicini. Quae separatim omnia
liquantur, deinde liquida miscentur, et tum simul
teruntur. Et hoc quidem magis purgat: magis
vero emollit, si pro rosa cyprus infunditur.
4   Et ad sacrum ignem: spumae argenti P. ✳ VI;
cornu bubuli combusti P. ✳ XII conteruntur, adiciturque invicem vinum et id quod specialiter sil
vocatur, et murteum donec utriusque terni cyathi
coiciantur.
25. Catapotia quoque multa sunt, variisque
de causis fiunt. Anodyna vocant, quae somno
dolorem levant; quibus uti, nisi nimia necessitas
urget, alienum est: sunt enim ex vehementibus
medicamentis et stomacho alienis. Potest tamen
etiam ad concoquendum, quod habet papaveris
lacrimae, galbani, singulorum P. ✳ I; murrae,
castorei, piperis, singulorum P. ✳ II. Ex quibus,
quod ervi magnitudinem habet, satis est devorasse.

---

a ἔγχριστα φάρμακα, liniments.
b Cf. V. 28. 4.

round rush, aspalathus and balsam wood, 112 grms. each, suet 4 grms., iris ointment 42 c.cm.

Another called euodes is prepared as follows: wax 84 grms., oil the same quantity, and turpentine-resin, the size of a walnut, are boiled together, then pounded in a mortar, and into this is gradually dropped 63 c.cm. of the best honey, and then iris ointment and rose-oil, 125 c.cm. of each.

Now enchrista is the Greek name for liquid applications.[a] Of these one is used for cleaning and filling up ulcers, especially those about sinews. It is composed of a mixture of equal parts of butter, calf's marrow, calf's suet, goose-fat, wax, honey, turpentine-resin, rose-oil and castor-oil. These are all liquefied separately, then the liquids are mixed and stirred up together. And the above is more for cleaning up wounds; it is more of an emollient if instead of the rose-oil, cyprus-oil is poured in.

And for ignis sacer [b] take litharge 24 grms., burnt ox-horn 48 grms., are rubbed up together, adding by turns wine, especially that which is called sil,[c] and myrtle-oil until 125 c.cm. of each is mixed in.

**25.** Pills are also numerous, and are made for various purposes. Those which relieve pain through sleep are called anodynes; unless there is over-whelming necessity, it is improper to use them; for they are composed of medicaments which are very active and alien to the stomach. There is one, however, which actually promotes digestion; it is composed of poppy-tears and galbanum, 4 grms. each, myrrh, castory, and pepper, 8 grms. each. Of this it is enough to swallow an amount the size of a vetch.

---

[c] Vinum siliatum (vol. I. p. 498) flavoured with seseli, meadow saxifrage.

2     Alterum stomacho peius, ad somnum valentius, ex his fit: mandragorae P. ✳ = — ; apii seminis, item hyoscyami seminis, singulorum P. ✳ IIII; quae ex vino teruntur. Unum autem eiusdem magnitudinis, quae supra (1) posita est, abunde est sumpsisse.

3     Sive autem capitis dolores sive ulcera sive lippitudo sive dentes . . .[1] sive spiritus difficultas sive intestinorum tormenta sive inflammatio vulvae est, sive coxa sive iecur aut lienis aut latus torquet, sive vitio locorum aliqua prolabitur et ommutescit, occurrit

B dolori per quietem eiusmodi catapotium: silis, acori, rutae silvestris seminis, singulorum P. ✳ I; castorei, cinnamomi, singulorum P. ✳ II; papaveris lacrimae, panacis radicis, mandragorae malorum aridorum,[2] iunci rotundi floris, singulorum P. ✳ II = — ; piperis grana LVI. Haec per se contrita, rursus instillato subinde passo, simul omnia teruntur, donec crassitudo sordium fiat. Ex eo paululum aut devoratur, aut aqua diluitur et potui datur.

4     Quin etiam silvestris papaveris, cum iam ad excipiendam lacrimam maturum est, manipellus qui manu conprehendi potest, in vas demittitur, et superinfunditur aqua, quae id contegat, atque ita coquitur. Ubi iam bene manipellus is coctus est ibidem[3] expressus proicitur; et cum eo umore passi par mensura miscetur, infervescitque, donec crassitudinem

B sordium habeat. Cum infrixit, catapotia ex eo fiunt ad nostrae fabae magnitudinem, habentque usum multiplicem. Nam et somnum faciunt vel per se

---

[1] *Marx supplies* male habent *after* dentes, *and this is translated.*

[2] *Marx punctuates* mandragorae, malorum aridorum *but cf. vol. I. p. 296* (III. **18.** 12) mandragorae mala.

[3] *Marx thinks there is a lacuna here and* (referring to Scribonius Largus, Comp. Med. 73) *supplies* exprimitur et

Another, worse for the stomach, but more soporific, consists of mandragora 1 grm., celery-seed and hyoscyamus seed, 16 grms. each, which are rubbed up after soaking in wine. One of the same size mentioned above is quite enough to take.

But whether there is headache or ulceration or ophthalmia or toothache or difficulty in breathing or intestinal gripings or inflammation of the womb or pain in the hips or liver or spleen or ribs, or, whether owing to genital trouble, a woman collapses speechless, a pill of the following kind counteracts pain by producing sleep: saxifrage, sweet flag, wild rue seed, 4 grms. each, castory and cinnamon 8 grms., poppy-tears, panax root, dried mandrake apples, flowers of the round rush, 9 grms. each, and 56 peppercorns. These are first pounded separately, then rubbed up all together, whilst gradually adding raisin wine until the mixture is of the consistency of sordes.[a] A small quantity is either swallowed or dissolved in water and taken as a draught.

Or take a good handful of wild poppy-heads when just ripe for collecting the juice and put into a vessel and boil with water sufficient to cover it. When this handful has been well boiled there, after being squeezed out it is thrown away; and with its juice is mixed an equal quantity of raisin wine, and heated until of the consistency of sordes. When the mixture has cooled, pills are formed, the size of our beans; they are used in many ways. For they procure sleep

---

[a] Cf. p. 10, note a.

---

in aliud vas umor *after* ibidem, *it is squeezed out and its juice poured into another vessel. Other editors (including Daremberg) leave the text as it stands.*

61

adsumpta vel ex aqua data, et aurium dolores levant, adiectis exiguo modo rutae suco[1] ac passo, et tormina supprimunt ex vino liquata, et inflammationem vulvae coercent mixta cerato ex rosa facto, cum paulum his croci quoque accessit; et ex aqua fronti inducta pituitam in oculos decurrentem tenent.

5 Item si vulva dolens somnum prohibet, croci P. ✻ = =; anesi, murrae, singulorum P. ✻ I; papaveris lacrimae P. ✻ III; cicutae seminis P. ✻ VIII miscentur excipiunturque vino vetere, et quod lupini magnitudinem habet in tribus cyathis aquae diluitur.    Id tamen in febre periculose datur.

6 Ad iecur sanandum nitri P. ✻ = —; croci, murrae, nardi Gallici, singulorum P. ✻ I melle excipiuntur, daturque quod Aegyptiae fabae magnitudinem habeat.

7 Ad lateris dolores finiendos piperis, aristolochiae, nardi, murrae pares portiones.

8 Ad thoracis nardi P. ✻ I; turis, casiae, singulorum P. ✻ III; murrae, cinnamomi, singulorum P. ✻ VI; croci P. ✻ VIII; resinae terebenthinae P. ✻ = —; mellis heminae tres.

9 Ad tussim Athenionis: murrae, piperis, singulorum P. ✻ =; castorei, papaveris lacrimae, singulorum P. ✻ I. Quae separatim contusa postea iunguntur, et ad magnitudinem fabae nostrae bina catapotia mane, bina noctu dormituro dantur.

10 Si tussis somnum prohibet, ad utrumque Heraclidis Tarentini: croci P. ✻ =; murrae, piperis longi, costi, galbani, singulorum P. ✻ = —; cinnamomi, castorei, papaveris lacrimae, singulorum P. ✻ I.

---

[1] *So v. d. Linden.   Marx keeps the MS.* suci ac passi; *one MS. has* sucis.

whether taken as they are or in water; they relieve earache when a little rue-juice and raisin wine are added; when dissolved in wine they relieve gripings, and when mixed with cerate of rose-oil with the addition of a little saffron they relieve inflammation of the womb; also when smeared upon the forehead mixed with water they check the flow of phlegm into the eyes.

Again, if inflammation of the womb prevents sleep take saffron 1·33 grms., anise and myrrh, 4 grms. each, poppy-tears 12 grms., hemlock seed 32 grms. These are mixed together, and taken up in old wine, and a pill the size of a lupin is dissolved in 125 c.cm. of water. It is dangerous, however, to give it when there is fever.

For the relief of pain in the liver soda 1 grm., saffron, myrrh, Gallic nard, 4 grms. each, are taken up in honey, and a pill the size of an Egyptian bean administered.

A pill to stop pain in the side is made of pepper, aristolochia, nard, and myrrh in equal parts.

A pill for pain in the chest is made from nard 4 grms., frankincense and casia, 12 grms. each, myrrh and cinnamon, 24 grms. each, saffron 32 grms., turpentine-resin 1 grm., honey three-quarters of a litre.

The pill of Athenion for cough contains myrrh and pepper, 0·66 grm. each, castory and poppy-tears, 4 grms. each; these are rubbed down separately, then together, and two pills, the size of our bean, are given in the morning and two at bed-time.

If cough prevents sleep the pill of Heracleides of Tarentum relieves both; it contains saffron 0·66 grm., myrrh, long pepper, costmary, galbanum, 1 grm. each, cinnamon, castory and poppy-tears, 4 grms. each.

11 Quod si purganda ulcera in faucibus tussientibus
sunt, panacis, murrae, resinae terebenthinae, singulorum P. uncia; galbani P. ✳ = ; hysopi P. ✳ = —
conterenda sunt, hisque hemina mellis adicienda, et
quod digito excipi potest, devorandum est.

12 Colice vero Cassi ex his constat: croci, anesi,
castorei, singulorum P. ✳ III; petroselini P. ✳ IIII;
piperis et longi et rotundi, singulorum P. ✳ V;
papaveris lacrimae, iunci rotundi, murrae, nardi, singulorum P. ✳ VI; quae melle excipiuntur. Id
autem et devorari potest et ex aqua calida sumi.

13 Infantem vero mortuum aut secundas expellit
aquae potio, cui salis Hammoniaci P. ✳ I, aut cui
dictamni Cretici P. ✳ I adiectum est.

14 Ex partu laboranti erysimum ex vino tepido
ieiunae dari debet.

15 Vocem adiuvat turis P. ✳ I in duobus cyathis vini
datum.

16 Adversus urinae difficultatem piperis longi, castorei,
murrae, galbani, papaveris lacrimae, croci, costi
unciae singulae; styracis, resinae terebenthinae
pondo sextantes, melabsinthi cyathus. Ex quibus ad
magnitudinem fabae Aegyptiae et mane et cenato
dari debet.

17 Arteriace vero hoc modo fit: casiae, iridis, cinnamomi, nardi, murrae, turis, singulorum P. ✳ I; croci
P. ✳ I = — ; piperis grana XXX ex passi tribus
sextariis decocuntur, donec mellis crassitudo his fiat.
Aut croci, murrae, turis, singulorum P. ✳ I coiciuntur
in passi eundem modum, eodemque modo decocuntur. Aut eiusdem passi heminae tres usque eo

---

ᵃ Cf. Galen, *De Comp. Med.*, IX. 4, XIII. 276

But if ulcers of the throat causing cough are to be
cleaned, panax, myrrh and turpentine-resin, 28 grms.
each, galbanum 0·66 grm., hyssop 1 grm. are rubbed
together, and 250 c.cm. of honey added to them
and as much swallowed as can be taken up on the
finger.

The pill[a] of Cassius for colic contains saffron, anise,
castory, 12 grms. each, parsley 16 grms., pepper both
long and round, 20 grms. each, poppy-tears, round
rush, myrrh, nard, 24 grms. each; these are taken
up in honey. It may be either swallowed as it is or
dissolved in hot water.

A draught for the expulsion of a dead foetus or
placenta consists of ammoniac salt 4 grms., or of
Cretan dittany 4 grms. in water.

In difficult labour hedge mustard in tepid wine
should be administered on an empty stomach.

The voice is strengthened by frankincense 4 grms.
in two cups of wine.

For difficult micturition long pepper, castory, myrrh,
galbanum, poppy-tears, saffron, costmary, 28 grms.
each; storax and turpentine-resin, 56 grms. each,
honey with absinth 42 c.cm. Of this an amount the
size of an Egyptian bean should be taken in the
morning and after dinner.

A medicine[b] for the windpipe is prepared as
follows: casia, iris, cinnamon, nard, myrrh, frankincense, 4 grms. each; saffron 1 grm.; and 30 peppercorns boiled in a litre and a half of raisin wine until
of the consistency of honey. Or, saffron, myrrh,
frankincense, 4 grms. each, similarly boiled in raisin
wine to the same consistency. Or 750 c.cm. of raisin

[b] ἀρτηριακὴ, sc. ἰατρεία, cf. Pliny, N.H. XXIII. 7. 71.

coquuntur, donec extracta inde gutta indurescat;
eo adicitur tritae casiae P. ✳ I.

**26.** Cum facultates medicamentorum proposuerim,
genera, in quibus noxa corpori est, proponam. Ea
quinque sunt : cum quid extrinsecus laesit, ut in vulneribus (*capp.* xxvi, xxvii) ; cum quid intra se ipsum
corruptum est, ut in cancro (*cap.* xxviii) ; cum quid
innatum est, ut in vesica calculus ; cum quid increvit,
ut vena, quae intumescens in varicem convertitur ;
cum quid deest, ut cum curta pars aliqua est.

B     Ex his alia sunt, in quibus plus medicamenta, alia,
in quibus plus manus proficit. Ego dilatis iis, quae
praecipue scalpellum et manum postulant (*libb.*
VII, VIII), nunc de iis dicam, quae maxime medicamentis egent. Dividam autem hanc quoque curandi
partem sicut priorem (III. 1, 3 ; I. 4, 1) et ante dicam
de iis, quae in quamlibet partem corporis incidunt,
tum de iis, quae certas partes infestant (VI. 1 *seqq.*).
Incipiam a vulneribus.

C     In his autem ante omnia scire medicus debet, quae
insanabilia sint, quae difficilem curationem habeant,
quae promptiorem. Est enim prudentis hominis
primum eum, qui servari non potest, non adtingere,
nec subire speciem . . . [1] eius, ut occisi, quem sors
ipsius interemit ; deinde ubi gravis metus sine certa

---

[1] *Marx suggests :* speciem <iactatoris sed negare fieri
posse curationem> ' *not to risk the appearance of a boaster,
but to say there is no hope of saving one.*'

---

       [a] V. 26, 27.            [b] V. 28. 2.
       [c] VII. 26, 27.          [d] VII. 22.

wine are boiled until a drop, if taken out, solidifies; thereupon pounded casia 4 grms. is added.

**26.** Now that I have set out the properties of the medicaments, I will explain the classes of lesions harmful to the body: there are five; when something from without causes the lesion, as in the case of wounds;[a] when some internal part has become corrupted, as in the case of canker;[b] when some new formation has occurred, such as a stone in the bladder;[c] when something has grown bigger, as when a vein swells up and is converted into a varix;[d] when there is some defect, as when some part has been mutilated.[e]

In some of these medicaments are more effectual, in others surgery. Postponing those conditions which demand in particular the scalpel and surgical treatment,[f] I will speak now of those which chiefly require medicaments. As I have done before,[g] I shall divide this part of treatment, and speak first of those lesions which may occur in any part of the body,[h] then of those which attack particular parts.[i] I shall begin with wounds.

In this connexion, however, a practitioner should know above all which wounds are incurable, which may be cured with difficulty, and which more readily. For it is the part of a prudent man first not to touch a case he cannot save, and not to risk the appearance of having killed one whose lot is but to die;[j] next, when there is grave fear without, however, absolute

---

[a] VII. 9. 1.　　　　　Cf. Books VII, VIII.
[g] I. 4. 1, III. 1. 3.　　[h] V. 26–28.　　[i] VI. 1–19.
[j] The text as it stands cannot be translated, but the general sense is as given above. For a suggested restoration, see critical note.

tamen desperatione est, indicare necessariis pericli-
tantis in difficili spem esse, ne, si victa ars malo fuerit,
D vel ignorasse vel fefellisse videatur. Sed ut haec pru-
denti viro conveniunt, sic rursus histrionis est parvam
rem adtollere, quo plus praestitisse videatur. Obli-
garique aecum est confessione promptae rei, quo
curiosius etiam circumspiciat, ne, quod per se exiguum est, maius curantis neglegentia fiat.

2    Servari non potest, cui basis cerebri, cui cor, cui
stomachus, cui iocineris portae, cui in spina medulla
percussa est, cuique aut pulmo medius aut ieiunum
aut tenuius intestinum aut ventriculus aut renes
vulnerati sunt; cuive circa fauces grandes venae vel
arteriae praecisae sunt.

3    Vix autem ad sanitatem perveniunt, quibus ulla
parte aut pulmo aut iocineris crassum aut membrana,
quae continet cerebrum, aut lienis aut vulva aut
vesica aut ullum intestinum aut saeptum transversum vulneratum est. Ii quoque in praecipiti
sunt, in quibus usque ad grandes intusque conditas
venas in alis vel poplitibus mucro desedit. Periculosa etiam vulnera sunt, ubicumque venae maiores
sunt, quoniam exhaurire hominem profusione san-
B guinis possunt. Idque evenit non in alis tantum
atque poplitibus, sed etiam in iis venis, quae ad anum
testiculosque perveniunt. Praeter haec malum
vulnus est, quodcumque in alis vel feminibus vel
inanibus locis vel in articulis vel inter digitos est;
item   quodcumque   musculum   aut   nervum   aut

despair, to point out to the patient's relatives that hope is surrounded by difficulty, for then if the art is overcome by the malady, he may not seem to have been ignorant or mistaken. But while such steps become a prudent practitioner, it is like a mountebank to exaggerate a small matter in order to enhance his own achievement. It is right to commit himself to a statement that a case is simple in order that he may examine it with even more care for fear a case slight in itself may become worse by negligence on the doctor's part.

It is impossible to save a patient when the base of the brain, the heart, the gullet, the porta of the liver, or the spinal marrow has been pierced; when the middle of the lung, or the jejunum, or the small intestine, or the stomach, or kidneys have been wounded; or when the large blood-vessels and arteries in the region of the throat have been cut.

Again, there is hardly ever recovery when either the lung or the thick part of the liver or the membrane enclosing the brain, or the spleen, womb, bladder, any of the intestines or diaphragm has been wounded in any part. There is also grave danger when the point of a weapon has gone down to the large blood-vessels deeply seated in the armpits or hams. Also wounds are dangerous wherever the blood-vessels are larger, because they may exhaust the patient by profuse bleeding. This occurs not only in the armpits and hams, but also in those blood-vessels which go to the anus and testicles. Moreover, a wound is a bad one whenever it is in the armpits or in the thighs or in hollow places or in joints or between the fingers; also whenever a muscle

69

arteriam aut membranam aut os aut cartilaginem
laesit. Tutissimum omnium, quod in carne est.

4 Et haec quidem loco vel peiora vel mitiora sunt.
Modo vero periculum facit, quodcumque magnum est.

5 Aliquid etiam in vulneris genere figuraque est.
Nam peius est, quod etiam conlisum quam quod
tantum discissum est, adeo ut acuto quoque quam
retunso telo vulnerari commodius sit. Peius etiam
vulnus est, ex quo aliquid excisum est, exve quo caro
alia parte abscisa alia dependet. Pessimaque plaga
curva est: tutissima quae lineae modo recta est;
quo deinde propius huic illive figurae vulnus est, eo
vel deterius vel tolerabilius est.

6 Quin etiam confert aliquid et aetas et corpus et
vitae propositum et anni tempus; quia facilius
sanescit puer vel adulescens quam senior, valens
quam infirmus; neque nimis tenuis neque nimis
plenus, quam si alterum ex his est; integri habitus
quam corrupti, exercitatus quam iners, sobrius et
temperans quam vino venerique deditus. Oportunis-
simumque curationi tempus vernum est, aut certe
neque fervens neque frigidum, siquidem vulnera
et nimius calor et nimium frigus infestant, maxime
tamen horum varietas; ideoque perniciosissimus
autumnus est.

7 Sed pleraque ex vulneribus oculis subiecta sunt;
quorundam ipsae sedes indices sunt, quas alio loco (IV.
1, 1 seqq.) demonstravimus, cum positus interiorum
partium ostendimus. Verum tamen quia quaedam
vicina sunt, interestque vulnus in summa parte sit

---

*a* e.g. if the wound is in the intestine, though it cannot be
seen, the escape of faeces indicates its position. For the
description of the internal organs, cf. vol. I. p. 384.

or sinew or artery or membrane or bone or cartilage is injured. The safest of all is a wound in the flesh.

The above wounds are severer or slighter according to their situations. Still, whenever it is large, a wound makes for danger.

The class of wound and its shape are also important. For a contused wound is worse than one simply incised, hence it is better to be wounded by a sharp weapon than by a blunt one. A wound is worse also if a piece is cut out, or if the flesh is cut away in one part and hanging free in another. A curved wound is worst, a straight linear one safest; hence a wound is more or less serious, according as it approximates to the former or to the latter shape.

Again, both age and constitution and mode of life and the season have also some influence; for a boy or young adult heals more readily than does an old man; one who is strong than a weak man; a man who is not too thin or too fat than one who is either of these; one of sound habit than of unsound; one who takes exercise than a sluggard; one who is sober and temperate than one addicted to wine and venery. And the most opportune time for healing is the spring, or at any rate when the weather is neither cold nor hot, for wounds are harmed by excessive heat and excessive cold, but most of all by variations of these; hence autumn is the most pernicious season.

Now most wounds are open to view; some are inferred from their situation,[a] which we have pointed out elsewhere when indicating the positions of the internal parts. Since, however, some of these wounds are near at hand, and it is of importance whether the wound is superficial or has penetrated inwards,

71

an penitus penetraverit, necessarium est notas subicere, per quas, quid intus actum sit, scire possimus, et ex quibus vel spes vel desperatio oriatur.

8 Igitur corde percusso sanguis multus fertur, venae elanguescunt, color pallidissimus, sudores frigidi malique odoris tamquam inrorato corpore oriuntur, extremisque partibus frigidis matura mors sequitur.

9 Pulmone vero icto spirandi difficultas est; sanguis ex ore spumans, ex plaga ruber; simulque etiam spiritus cum sono fertur; in vulnus inclinari iuvat; quidam sine ratione consurgunt. Multi si in ipsum vulnus inclinati sunt, loquntur, si in aliam partem, obmutescunt.

10 Iocineris autem vulnerati notae sunt multus sub dextra parte praecordiorum profusus sanguis; ad spinam reducta praecordia; in ventrem cubandi dulcedo; punctiones doloresque usque ad iugulum iunctumque ei latum scapularum os intenti; quibus nonnumquam etiam bilis vomitus accedit.

11 Renibus vero percussis dolor ad inguina testiculosque descendit; difficulter urina redditur, eaque aut haec cruenta aut cruor fertur.

12 At liene icto sanguis niger a sinistra parte prorumpit; praecordia cum ventriculo ab eadem parte indurescunt; sitis ingens oritur; dolor ad iugulum sicut iocinere vulnerato venit.

13 At cum vulva percussa est, dolor inguinibus et

---

[a] Proemium 75. Vol. I. p. 40.
[b] For the various meanings of praecordia, cf. vol. I. p. 100 note a, and index.

it is necessary to state the signs by which it is possible to recognize what has happened inside, and from which follow either hope or despair.[a]

Now when the heart is penetrated, much blood issues, the pulse fades away, the colour is extremely pallid, cold and malodorous sweats burst out as if the body had been wetted by dew, the extremities become cold and death quickly follows.

But when the lung is pierced there is difficulty in breathing; frothy blood escapes from the mouth, red blood from the wound; and at the same time breath is drawn with a noise; to lie upon the wound affords relief; some stand up without any reason. Many speak if they have been laid upon the wound; if upon the opposite side they become speechless.

Symptoms that the liver has been wounded are that considerable haemorrhage occurs from under the right part of the hypochondria;[b] the hypochondria are retracted towards the spine; the patient is eased by lying on his belly; stabbing pains spread upwards as high as the clavicle and its junction with the scapula; to which, not infrequently, also bilious vomiting is added.

When the kidneys have been penetrated, pain spreads down to the groin and testicles; urine is passed with difficulty, and it is either bloodstained or actual blood clot is passed.

But when the spleen has been pierced, black blood flows out from the left side; the hypochondria on that side together with the stomach become hard; great thirst comes on; pain extends to the clavicle as when the liver has been wounded.

But when the womb has been penetrated, there is

73

coxis et feminibus est; sanguinis pars per vulnus,
pars per naturale descendit; vomitus bilis insequitur.
Quaedam obmutescunt, quaedam mente labuntur,
quaedam sui conpotes nervorum oculorumque dolore
urgeri se confitentur, morientesque eadem, quae
corde vulnerato, patiuntur.

14  Sin cerebrum membranave eius vulnus accepit,
sanguis per nares, quibusdam etiam per aures exit;
fereque bilis vomitus insequitur. Quorundam sensus
optunduntur, appellatique ignorant; quorundam
trux vultus est; quorundam oculi quasi resoluti huc
atque illuc moventur; fereque tertio vel quinto die
delirium accedit; multorum etiam nervi distenduntur. Ante mortem autem plerique fascias,
quibus caput deligatum est, lacerant ac nudum
vulnus frigori obiciunt.

15  Ubi stomachus autem percussus est, singultus et
bilis vomitus insequitur; si quid cibi vel potionis
adsumptum est, ea redditur cito. Venarum motus
elanguescunt, sudores tenues oriuntur, per quos
extremae partes frigescunt.

16  Communes vero ieiuni intestini et ventriculi
vulnerati notae sunt: nam cibus et potio per vulnus
exeunt; praecordia indurescunt; nonnumquam bilis
per os redditur. Intestino tantum sedes inferior
est. Cetera intestina icta vel stercus vel odorem
eius exhibent.

17  Medulla vero, quae in spina est, discussa nervi
resolvuntur aut distenduntur; sensus intercidit;
interposito tempore aliquo sine voluntate inferiores

pain in the groins and hips and thighs; blood passes downwards in part through the wound, in part by the vagina; bilious vomiting follows. Some become speechless, some are mentally disturbed, others whilst composed in mind complain of pain in their sinews and eyeballs, and when dying they suffer like those wounded in the heart.

When the brain or its membrane has been wounded, blood escapes through the nostrils, in some also through the ears; and generally bilious vomiting follows. Some lose their senses and take no notice when spoken to; some have a wild look; in some the eyes move from side to side as if they were out of control; generally on the third or fifth day delirium supervenes; many have also spasm of sinews. Again, before death many tear off the bandages with which their head has been bound up, and expose the bared wound to cold.

But when the gullet has been penetrated, hiccough and bilious vomiting follow; if any food or drink is swallowed, it is returned at once; pulsation of the blood-vessels fades away; thin sweat breaks out, following which the extremities become cold.

The signs when the small intestine and the stomach have been wounded are the same; for food and drink come out through the wound; the hypochondria become hard, sometimes bile is regurgitated through the mouth. Only in the case of the intestine the situation of the wound is lower down. All other intestinal wounds cause the emission of faeces or a faecal odour.

When the marrow which is within the spine has been crushed, there is either paralysis or spasm of sinews; sensation is interrupted; after some time there is

partes vel semen vel urinam vel etiam stercus
excernunt.

18 At si saeptum transversum percussum est, praecordia susum contrahuntur; spina dolet; spiritus
rarus est; sanguis spumans fertur.

19 Vesica vero vulnerata dolent inguina: quod super
pubem est, intenditur; pro urina sanguis, at ex ipso
vulnere urina descendit. Stomachus adficitur: itaque
aut bilem vomunt, aut singultiunt; frigus et ex eo
mors sequitur.

20 His cognitis etiamnum quaedam alia noscenda ad
omnia vulnera ulceraque, de quibus dicturi sumus,
pertinentia. Ex his autem exit sanguis, sanies, pus.
Sanguis omnibus notus est: sanies est tenuior hoc,
varie crassa et glutinosa et colorata. Pus crassis-
simum albidissimumque, glutinosius et sanguine et
sanie. Exit autem sanguis ex vulnere recenti aut
iam sanescente, sanies [est] inter utrumque tempus,
B pus ex ulcere iam ad sanitatem spectante. Rursus
et sanies et pus quasdam species Graecis nominibus
distinctas habent. Est enim quaedam sanies, quae
vel hidros[a] vel melitera[b] nominatur; est pus, quod
elaeodes[c] appellatur. Hidros tenuis, subalbidus ex
malo ulcere exit, maximeque ubi nervo laeso inflammatio secuta est. Melitera crassior et gluti-
C nosior, subalbida, mellique albo subsimilis. Fertur
haec quoque ex malis ulceribus, ubi nervi circa
articulos laesi sunt, et inter haec loca maxime ex
genibus. Elaeodes tenue, subalbidum, quasi unc-
tum, colore atque pinguitudine oleo albo non dis-

---

[a] ἱδρώς, sweat, but other editors read ἰχώρ = sanies, cf.
Hipp. III. 44 (*Head wounds* XIX.).
[b] μελιτηρός honey-like.
[c] Like olive oil (ἔλαιον).

involuntarily evacuation from the parts below of either semen or urine or even faeces.

But if the diaphragm has been penetrated, the praecordia are contracted upwards; the spine is painful; breathing is laboured; frothy blood escapes.

When the bladder has been wounded, the groins are painful; the hypogastrium becomes tense; blood is passed, instead of urine, the urine being discharged from the actual wound. The gullet is affected, and so the patients either vomit bile or hiccough. Coldness and after that death follows.

Even when these facts are known, there are still some other things to be learnt about wounds and ulcerations in general, of which we will now speak. From wounds, then, there comes out blood, or sanies, or pus. Blood everybody knows; sanies is thinner than blood, varying both in thickness and stickiness and colour. Pus is the thickest and whitest, more sticky than either sanies or blood. Now blood comes out from a fresh wound or from one which is already healing, sanies between these two periods, pus from an ulceration already beginning to heal. Again, the Greeks distinguish by name different kinds of sanies and pus. For there is a kind of sanies which is named either hidros[a] or melitera;[b] there is pus which is called elaeodes.[c] Hidros is thin, whitish, and comes from a bad ulceration, especially when inflammation has followed upon a wound of a sinew. Melitera is thicker, stickier and whitish, something like honey. It is likewise discharged from bad ulcerations, when sinews near to joints have been wounded, and among such places especially from the knees. Elaeodes is thin, whitish, fatty, in colour and fattiness not unlike white olive-oil; it appears

CELSUS

simile; apparet in magnis ulceribus sanescentibus. Malus autem est sanguis nimium aut tenuis aut crassus, colore vel lividus vel niger, aut pituita mixtus aut varius: optimus calidus, ruber, modice

D crassus, non glutinosus. Itaque protinus eius vulneris expedita magis curatio est, ex quo sanguis bonus fluxit. Itemque postea spes in iis maior est, ex quibus melioris generis quaeque proveniunt. Sanies igitur mala est multa, nimis tenuis, livida aut pallida aut nigra aut glutinosa aut mali odoris, aut quae ipsum ulcus et iunctam ei cutem erodit: melior est non multa, modice crassa, subrubicunda aut subalbida.

E Hidros autem peior est multus, crassus, sublividus aut subpallidus, glutinosus, ater, calidus, mali odoris: tolerabilior est subalbidus, qui cetera omnia contraria prioribus habet. Melitera autem mala est multa et percrassa: melior, quae tenuior et minus copiosa est. Pus inter haec optimum est; sed id quoque peius est multum, tenue, dilutum, magisque si ab initio tale est; itemque si colore sero simile, si pallidum, si lividum, si faeculentum est; praeter haec, si male

F olet, nisi tamen locus hunc odorem excitat. Melius est, quo minus est, quo crassius, quo albidius; itemque si leve est, si nihil olet, si aequale est: modo tamen convenire et magnitudini vulneris et tempori debet. Nam plus ex maiore, plus nondum solutis inflammationibus naturaliter fertur. Elaeodes quoque peius est multum, et parum pingue: quo minus eius, quoque id ipsum pinguius, eo melius est.

in large ulcerations when they are healing. Blood
is bad when it is too thin or too thick, livid or black
in colour, or mixed with phlegm or variable; it is
best when hot, red, moderately thick, and not sticky.
Consequently from the first the treatment is more
expeditious in the case of a wound from which good
blood has flowed. Also later there is more hope in
the case of wounds from which all the discharges are
of the better kind. Thus sanies is bad when profuse,
too thin, livid, or pallid or black or sticky or
malodorous or when it erodes either the ulceration
itself or the skin adjoining it; it is better when
not profuse, moderately thick, reddish or whitish.
But hidros is worse when it is profuse, thick, somewhat livid or pallid, sticky, black, hot, malodorous;
it is less serious when whitish, and when all the
rest of its characteristics are the opposite of the
foregoing. Melitera again is bad when profuse and
very thick; better for being thinner and less copious.
Amongst these discharges pus is the best; but it
is likewise worse when profuse, thin, watery, and the
more so if it is such from the beginning; and also
if it is in colour like whey, if pallid, or livid, or like
wine-lees; if, besides, it is malodorous, unless,
however, it is the part which causes this odour.
It is better, the smaller the quantity, the thicker
and whiter; also if it is bland, odourless, uniform;
none the less it should correspond in quantity with
the size and age of the wound. For naturally there
is more discharge, the larger the wound, still more
when inflammation has not yet subsided. Elaeodes
also is worse when large in quantity and but little
fatty, the less in quantity and the more fatty the
better.

21    Quibus exploratis, ubi aliquis ictus est qui servari potest, protinus prospicienda duo sunt : ne sanguinis profusio neve inflammatio interemat. Si profusionem timemus, quod ex sede vulneris et ex magnitudine eius et ex impetu ruentis sanguinis intellegi potest, siccis linamentis vulnus inplendum est, supraque imponenda spongia ex aqua frigida expressa

B  ac manu super conprimenda. Si parum sic sanguis conquiescit, saepius linamenta mutanda sunt, et si sicca parum valent, aceto madefacienda sunt. Id vehemens ad sanguinem subprimendum est ; ideoque quidam id volneri infundunt. Sed alius rursus metus subest, ne nimis valenter ibi retenta materia magnam inflammationem postea ˙moveat. Quae res efficit, ut neque rodentibus medicamentis neque adurentibus et ob id ipsum inducentibus crustam sit utendum, quamvis pleraque ex his sanguinem supprimunt ; sed, si semel ad ea decurritur, iis potius, quae mitius

C  idem efficiunt. Quod si illa quoque profluvio vincuntur, venae quae sanguinem fundunt adprehendendae, circaque id quod ictum est duobus locis deligandae intercidendaeque sunt, ut et in se ipsae coeant, et nihilo minus ora praeclusa habeant. Ubi ne id quidem res patitur, possunt ferro candenti aduri. Sed etiam satis multo sanguine effuso ex eo loco, quo neque nervus neque musculus est, ut puta in fronte vel superiore capitis parte, commodissimum tamen est cucurbitulam admovere a diversa parte, ut illuc sanguinis cursus revocetur.

After these matters have been investigated, when a man has been wounded who can be saved, there are in the first place two things to be kept in mind: that he should not die from haemorrhage or inflammation. If we are afraid of haemorrhage which can be judged both from the position and size of the wound and from the force of the flowing blood, the wound is to be filled with dry lint, and over that a sponge applied, squeezed out of cold water, and pressed down by the hand. If the bleeding is not checked thus, the lint must be changed several times, and if it is not effective when dry, it is to be soaked in vinegar. Vinegar is powerful in suppressing a flow of blood; and some, therefore, pour it into wounds. But there is an underlying fear of another kind, that if too much diseased matter is forcibly retained in the wound it will afterwards cause great inflammation. It is on this account that no use is made, either of corrosives or of caustics, owing to the crust they induce, although most of these medicaments suppress bleeding; but if for once recourse is had to them, choose those which have a milder action. But if even these are powerless against the profuse bleeding, the blood-vessels which are pouring out blood are to be seized, and round the wounded spot they are to be tied in two places and cut across between so that the two ends coalesce each on itself and yet have their orifices closed. When circumstances do not even admit of this, the blood-vessels can be burnt with a red-hot iron. But even when there has been considerable bleeding from a place where there is neither sinew nor muscle, such as the forehead or top of the head, it is perhaps best to apply a cup to a distant part, in order to divert thither the course of the blood.

22    Et adversus profusionem quidem in his auxilium
est: adversus inflammationem autem in ipso sanguinis cursu.   Ea timeri potest, ubi laesum est vel os
vel nervus vel cartilago vel musculus, aut ubi parum
sanguinis pro modo vulneris fluxit.   Ergo quotiens
quid tale erit, sanguinem mature subprimere non
oportebit, sed pati fluere, dum tutum erit; adeo ut,
si parum fluxisse videbitur, mitti quoque ex brachio
debeat; utique si corpus iuvenile et robustum et
exercitatum est, multoque magis si id vulnus ebrietas
praecessit.   Quod si musculus laesus videbitur,
praecidendus erit: nam percussus mortiferus est,
praecisus sanitatem recipit.

23    Sanguine autem vel subpresso, si nimius erumpit,
vel exhausto, si per se parum fluxit, longe optimum
est vulnus glutinari.   Potest autem id, quod vel in
cute vel etiam in carne est, si nihil ei praeterea mali
accedit.   Potest caro alia parte dependens, alia
inhaerens, si tamen etiamnum integra est et coniunc-
tione corporis fovetur.   In iis vero, quae glutinantur,
duplex curatio est.   Nam si plaga in molli parte est,
sui debet, maximeque si discissa auris ima est vel
imus nasus vel frons vel bucca vel palpebra vel
B labrum vel circa guttur cutis vel venter.   Si vero in
carne vulnus est hiatque neque in unum orae facile
adtrahuntur, sutura quidem aliena est: inponendae
vero fibulae sunt (ancteras Graeci nominant), quae

---

   *a* Because this exposes the depth of the wound and permits
of discharge and of application.
   *b* *i.e.* sucked out by cupping, cf. vol. I. 166.
   *c* See vol. II. Introduction, p. lxi, *fibula.*

Against bleeding there is help in the foregoing measures, but against inflammation it lies simply in the bleeding itself. Inflammation is to be feared when a bone is injured or sinew or cartilage or muscle, or whenever there is little outflow of blood compared to the wound. Therefore, in such cases, it will not be desirable to suppress the bleeding early, but to let blood flow as long as it is safe; so that if there seems too little bleeding, blood should be let from the arm as well, at any rate when the patient is young and robust and used to exercise, and much more so when a drinking bout has preceded the wound. But if a muscle is seen to be wounded, it will be best to cut it right through; for when stabbed it causes death, when cut through it admits of cure.[a]

Now, when bleeding has been suppressed if excessive, or encouraged[b] when not enough has escaped of itself, then by far the best thing is for the wound to become agglutinated. But this is possible for a wound in the skin, or even in the flesh, if nothing else has occurred to do it harm. Agglutination is possible if flesh is hanging free at one part, whilst attached at another, provided, however, that the flesh is still sound, and has a connexion with the body to feed it. But with wounds which are being agglutinated, there are two treatments. For if the wound is in a soft part, it should be stitched up, and particularly when the cut is in the tip of the ear or the point of the nose or forehead or cheek or eyelid or lip or the skin over the throat or abdomen. But if the wound is in the flesh, and gapes, and its margins are not easily drawn together, then stitching is unsuitable; fibulae[c] (the Greeks call them anteres) are then to be

83

oras, paululum tamen, contrahunt, quo minus lata
postea cicatrix sit. Ex his autem colligi potest, id
quoque, quod alia parte dependens alia inhaerebit,
si alienatum adhuc non est, suturam an fibulam
postulet. Ex quibus neutra ante debet imponi,
quam intus volnus purgatum est, ne quid ibi concreti
C sanguinis relinquatur. Id enim et in pus vertitur,
et inflammationem movet, et glutinari volnus prohibet. Ne linamentum quidem, quod subprimendi
sanguinis causa inditum est, ibi relinquendum est:
nam id quoque inflammat. Conprehendi vero sutura
vel fibula non cutem tantum sed etiam aliquid ex
carne, ubi suberit haec, oportebit, quo valentius
haereat neque cutem abrumpat. Utraque optima
est ex acia molli non nimis torta, quo mitius corpori
insidat, utraque neque nimis rara neque nimis crebra
D inicienda est. Si nimis rara est, non continet; si
nimis crebra est, vehementer adficit, quia quo saepius
acus corpus transuit quoque plura loca iniectum
vinculum mordet, eo maiores inflammationes oriuntur
magisque aestate. Neutra etiam vim ullam desiderat, sed eatenus utilis est, qua cutis ducentem
quasi sua sponte subsequitur. Fere tamen fibulae
latius vulnus esse patiuntur, sutura oras iungit, quae
ne ipsae quidem inter se contingere ex toto debent,
ut, si quid intus umoris concreverit, sit qua emanet.
E Si quod vulnus neutrum horum recipit, id tamen
purgari debet. Deinde omni vulneri primo inpo-

inserted, which draw together the margins to some extent and so render the subsequent scar less broad. Now from the above it can be gathered also whether flesh which is hanging free at one part and attached at another, if it is still capable of juncture, demands suture or fibula. But neither of these should be inserted until the interior of the wound has been cleansed, lest some blood-clot be left in it. For blood clot turns into pus, and excites inflammation, and prevents agglutination of the wound. Not even lint which has been inserted to arrest bleeding should be left in, for this also inflames the wound. The suture or fibula should take up, not only skin but also some of the under-lying flesh, where there is any, that it may hold more firmly, and not tear through the skin. And both are best used with a strand of a soft wool not too closely twisted that it may cause less irritation to the body, and both should be inserted at intervals not too distant or too close. For if the intervals are too distant, the wound is not held together; if too close, it is very hurtful, for the more often the needle transfixes the tissues, and the more places are wounded by the inserted stitches, the worse is the inflammation set up, especially in summer. Neither procedure needs any force, but is useful just so far as the skin follows that which draws it as if of its own accord. Generally, however, fibulae leave the wound wider open, a suture joins the margins together, but these should not be brought actually into contact throughout the whole length of the wound, in order that there may be an outlet for any humour collecting within. If any wound admits of neither of these, it should none the less be cleaned. Hence, upon every

nenda est spongia ex aceto expressa: si sustinere
aliquis aceti vim non potest, vino utendum est.
Levis plaga iuvatur etiam, si ex aqua frigida expressa
spongia inponitur.   Sed ea quocumque modo inposita
est, dum madet, prodest; itaque ut inarescat, non
F est committendum.  Licetque sine peregrinis et
conquisitis et compositis medicamentis vulnus curare.
Sed si quis huic parum confidit, imponere medicamentum debet, quod sine sebo compositum sit ex iis,
quae cruentis vulneribus apta esse proposui (19, 1):
maximeque, si caro est, barbarum;  si nervi vel
cartilago vel aliquid ex eminentibus, quales aures
vel labra sunt, Polyidi sphragidem:  Alexandrinum
quoque viride nervis idoneum est; eminentibusque
G partibus ea, quam Graeci rhaptusam vocant.   Solet
etiam colliso corpore exigua parte findi cutis.   Quod
ubi incidit, non alienum est scalpello latius aperire,
nisi musculi nervique iuxta sunt; quos incidi non
expedit.  Ubi satis diductum est, medicamentum
imponendum est.  At si id, quod collisum est,
quamvis parum diductum est, latius tamen aperiri
propter nervos aut musculos non licet, adhibenda sunt
ea, quae umorem leniter extrahant, praecipueque
ex his id, quod rhypodes vocari proposui (19, 15).
H Non alienum est etiam, ubicumque vulnus grave est,
imposito quo id iuvetur, insuper circumdare lanam
sucidam ex aceto et oleo; vel cataplasma, si mollis is

---

[a] V. 19. 1.        [b] V. 19. 1 B.        [c] V. 20. 2.
[d] V. 19. 17.       [e] V. 19. 6.

86

wound there is to be applied, first a sponge squeezed
out of vinegar; or out of wine if the patient cannot
bear the strength of vinegar. A slight wound is
even benefited if a sponge is applied wrung out of
cold water. But in whatever way it is put on, it is
only of service whilst moist; and so it must not be
allowed to become dry. And a wound can be treated
without foreign and far-fetched and complicated
medicaments. But if any one has not confidence in
this treatment, a medicament should be put on,
which has no suet in its composition, chosen from
those which I have stated to be suitable for bleeding
wounds:[a] and especially, if it is a flesh wound, the
composition called barbarum;[b] if a wound of sinews
or of cartilage or of some projecting part, such as the
ears or lips, the seal of Polyides:[c] the green
composition called Alexandrian[d] is also suitable for
sinews; and that which the Greeks call rhaptousa[e]
for parts which project. When the body is bruised
it is usual also for the skin to be broken to a
small extent. When this occurs, it is not improper
to lay it open more widely with a scalpel, unless
there are muscles and sinews near, as it is inex-
pedient to cut into these. When it has been
sufficiently opened, a medicament is to be put on.
But if the skin over the contusion, although broken
too little, yet must not be laid open more widely on
account of sinews or muscles, then such applications
should be made as gently extract humour, especially that which I have said is called rhypodes.[f]
It is also not inappropriate, when the wound is severe,
after putting on what is beneficial, to lay on over
this, wool saturated with vinegar and oil; or a poultice,

[f] V. 19. 15.

locus est, quod leniter reprimat; si nervosus aut
musculosus, quod emolliat.

24    Fascia vero ad vulnus deligandum lintea aptissima
est eaque lata esse debet, ut semel iniecta non vulnus
tantum sed paululum utrimque etiam oras eius
conprehendat. Si ab altera parte caro magis reces-
sit, ab ea melius adtrahitur; si aeque ab utraque,
transversa conprehendere oras debet; aut si id
vulneris ratio non patitur, media primum inicienda
B est, ut tum in utramque partem ducatur. Sic autem
deliganda est, ut et contineat neque adstringat.
Quod non continetur, elabitur: quod nimis adstrictum est, cancro periclitabitur. Hieme saepius
fascia circumire debet, aestate quotiens necesse est;
tum extrema pars eius inferioribus acu adsuenda est:
nam nodus ulcus laedit, nisi tamen longe est.

C    Illo neminem decipi decet, ut propriam viscerum
curationem requirat: de quibus supra (IV. 14 *seqq.*)
posui. Nam plaga ipsa curanda extrinsecus vel
sutura vel alio medicinae genere est: in visceribus
nihil movendum est, nisi ut, si quid ex iocinere aut
liene aut pulmone dumtaxat extremo dependet,
praecidatur. Alioqui volnus interius ea victus ratio
eaque medicamenta sanabunt, quae cuique visceri
convenire superiore libro (IV. 14 *seqq.*) posui.

25    His ita primo die ordinatis, homo lecto conlo-

---

*a* VIII. **10.** 1 F.   Hippocrates III. 105 (*Fractures* IV.).
*b* V. **26.** 8–19; for *viscera* see vol. I. p. 356.
*c* IV. **14.–17.**–V. **23.** 1 A, **25.** 6, 7.

gently repressant if to a soft part; or emollient to a part where there are sinews or muscles.

The bandage too for binding up a wound is best made of linen, and it should be so wide as to cover in a single turn, not the wound alone but somewhat of its edges on either side. If the flesh has receded more from one edge, the traction is better made from that side. If equally from both, the bandage, put crosswise, should press the margins together; or if the character of the wound does not admit of that, the middle of the bandage is to be applied first, so that it may then be drawn to either side.[a] Moreover, the wound is to be bandaged so that it is held together, yet not constricted. When it is not so held, it gapes; if it is constricted too much, there is a risk of canker. In winter there should be more turns of the bandage, in summer just those necessary; finally, the end of the bandage is to be stitched by means of a needle to the deeper turns; for a knot hurts the wound, unless, indeed, it is at a distance from it.

On the following point no practitioner should be ignorant so that he has to enquire as to the special treatment required for the internal organs, which I have spoken of above.[b] For whilst an external wound is to be treated either by suture, or by some sort of medicine; in the case of the internal organs, nothing is to be moved, unless it be to cut away some bit of liver or spleen or lung which hangs outside. Otherwise internal wounds will be cured by the regulation of diet, and by those medicaments which I have stated in the preceding book to suit each individual organ.[c]

So then, after this has been done on the first day,

candus est; isque, si grave vulnus est, abstinere,
quantum vires patiuntur, ante inflammationem cibo
debet: bibere, donec sitim finiat, aquam calidam;
vel, si aestas est ac neque febris neque dolor est,
B etiam frigidam. Adeo tamen nihil perpetuum est,
sed semper pro vi corporis aestimandum, ut inbecillitas etiam cibum protinus facere necessarium possit,
tenuem scilicet et exiguum, qui tantum sustineat;
multique etiam ex profluvio sanguinis intermorientes
ante ullam curationem vino reficiendi sunt, quod
alioqui inimicissimum vulneri est.

26    Nimis vero intumescere vulnus periculosum; nihil
intumescere periculosissimum est: illud indicium
est magnae inflammationis, hoc emortui corporis.
Protinusque, si mens homini consistit, si nulla febris
accessit, scire licet mature vulnus sanum fore. Ac
ne febris quidem terrere debet, si in magno vulnere,
dum inflammatio est, permanet. Illa perniciosa est,
quae vel levi vulneri supervenit, vel ultra tempus
inflammationis durat, vel delirium movet; vel, si
nervorum rigor aut distentio, quae ex vulnere orta
B est, eam non finit. Vomitus quoque bilis non
voluntarius, vel protinus ut percussus est aliquis, vel
dum inflammatio manet, malum signum est in iis
dumtaxat, quorum vel nervi, vel etiam nervosi loci
vulnerati sunt. Sponte tamen vomere non alienum
est, praecipue iis, quibus in consuetudine fuit: sed
neque protinus post cibum, neque iam inflammatione

90

the patient is to be put to bed; if the wound is
severe, before inflammation sets in, he should
abstain from food, as far as his strength permits:
he should drink warm water until his thirst is
quenched; or, if it is summer and he has neither
fever nor pain, even cold water. There is, however,
in this no standing order, for always account has to be
taken of the bodily strength, since weakness may
render it necessary for him to take food even from
the first, light of course and scanty, just enough to
sustain him; and many who are actually fainting
from loss of blood must, before any treatment, be
resuscitated by wine, which in other cases is most
inimical to a wound.

It is dangerous when a wound swells overmuch;
no swelling at all is the worst danger: the former
is an indication of severe inflammation; the latter
that the part is dead. And from the first if the
patient retains his senses, if no fever follows, we may
recognize that the wound will soon heal. And even
fever should not cause alarm in the case of a large
wound, if it persists whilst there is inflammation.
That fever is harmful which either supervenes upon
a slight wound, or lasts beyond the inflammatory
period, or excites delirium; or which does not put
an end to the rigor or spasm of sinews which has
originated from the wound. Also involuntary bilious
vomiting either immediately after the injury, or during the inflammatory period, is a bad sign only when
sinews or even the neighbourhood of sinews have
been wounded. The induction of a vomit, however,
is not inappropriate, especially in those habituated
to it; provided that this is not done immediately
after food, or just when inflammation has arisen, or

orta, neque cum in superioribus partibus plaga est.

27  Biduo sic vulnere habito, tertio die id aperiundum, detergendaque sanies ex aqua frigida est, eademque rursus inicienda. Quinto iam die, quanta inflammatio futura est, se ostendit. Quo die rursus detecto vulnere considerandus color est. Qui si lividus aut pallidus aut varius aut niger est, scire licet malum vulnus esse; idque quandocumque animadversum est, terrere nos potest. Album aut rubicundum esse ulcus commodissimum est: item
B cutis dura, crassa, dolens periculum ostendit. Bona signa sunt, ubi haec sine dolore tenuis et mollis est. Sed si glutinatur vulnus aut leviter intumuit, eadem sunt inponenda, quae primo fuerunt: si gravis inflammatio est neque glutinandi spes est, ea, quae pus moveant. Iamque aquae quoque calidae necessarius usus est, ut et materiam digerat et duritiam emolliat et pus citet. Ea sic temperanda est, ut manu contingenti iucunda sit, usque adeo adhibenda, donec aliquid ex tumore minuisse coloremque ulceri
C magis naturalem reddidisse videatur. Post id fomentum, si late plaga non patet, inponi protinus emplastrum debet, maximeque si grande vulnus est, tetrapharmacum; si in articulis, digitis, locis cartilaginosis, rhypodes : et si latius hiat, idem illud emplastrum liquari ex irino unguento oportet eoque inlita linamenta disponi per plagam; deinde emplastrum supra dari, et super id sucidam lanam.

---

<sup>a</sup> V. 19. 9.          <sup>b</sup> V. 19. 15.

when the wound is situated in the upper part of the body.

When the wound has been so treated for two days, on the third it should be uncovered, sanies washed away with cold water, and then the same dressing applied again. By the fifth day the extent of inflammation in prospect is apparent. And on that day, when the wound has been uncovered again, its colour must be considered. If it is livid or pallid or patchy or dusky, it can be recognized that the wound is a bad one, and whenever this is observed, it should alarm us. It is best for the wound to be white or rubicund; also if the skin is hardened, thickened, or painful, danger is indicated. Good signs are for the skin to be thin and soft without pain. But if the wound is agglutinating or swollen slightly, the same dressings as at first are to be applied; if there is severe inflammation and no hope of agglutination, then such applications are to be made as promote suppuration. And now the use of hot water as well is a necessity, in order to disperse diseased matter and to soften hardening and bring out pus. The temperature of the water must be pleasant to the hand when put into it, and the affusion is to be continued until the swelling is seen to have diminished and a more natural colour to have returned to the wound. After this fomentation, if the wound is not gaping widely, a plaster should be put on at once, particularly the tetrapharmacum if it is a large wound;[a] in the case of wounds of joints, fingers, cartilaginous places, the plaster rhypodes;[b] if the wound gapes more widely, that same plaster should be liquefied by iris unguent, and lint smeared with this laid all over the wound; upon this put the plaster, and above that greasy wool.

93

Minusque etiam quam primo fasciae adstringendae
sunt.

28    Proprie quaedam in articulis visenda sunt, in
quibus, si praecisi nervi sunt, qui continebant,
debilitas eius partis sequitur. Si id dubium est, et
ex acuto telo plaga est, ea transversa commodior est;
si retuso et gravi, nullum in figura discrimen est.
Sed videndum est, pus supra articulum an infra
nascatur. Si sub eo nascitur albumque et crassum
diu fertur, nervum praecisum credibile est, magisque
quo maiores dolores inflammationesque et quo
B   maturius excitatae sunt. Quamvis autem non
abscisus nervus est, tamen si circa tumor durus
diu permanet, necesse est et diuturnum ulcus
esse et sano quoque eo tumorem permanere;
futurumque est ut tarde membrum id vel exten-
datur vel contrahatur. Maior tamen in extendendo
mora est, ubi recurvato curatio adhibita est, quam in
recurvando eo, quod rectum continuerimus. Con-
locari quoque membrum quod ictum est ratione certa
C   debet. Si glutinandum est, ut superius sit: si in
inflammationibus est, ut in neutram partem incli-
natum sit: si iam pus profluit, ut devexum sit.
Optimum etiam medicamentum quies est: moveri,
ambulare nisi sanis alienum est. Minus tamen is
periculosus, qui in capite vel brachiis quam qui
in inferioribus partibus vulnerati sunt. Minimeque
ambulatio convenit femine aut crure aut pede
D   laborante. Locus, in quo cubabit, tepidus esse

The bandages are to be even less tight than at first.

As to joints, there are certain special points to be noticed, as, if the controlling sinews have been divided, weakness of the part concerned follows. If this is in doubt, and the wound has been made by a sharp weapon, a transverse wound is the more favourable; if by a blunt and heavy weapon, the shape of the wound makes no difference. But it is to be observed whether pus is being formed above the joint or beneath. If it is produced underneath, and thick and white discharge continues for some time, it is probable that a sinew has been cut, and the more so the greater the pains and inflammation, and the earlier these occur. But even though no sinew is divided, yet, if a hard swelling persists for a long while round about, the wound will last a long time and even after healing a swelling will persist; and in future that limb will be bent or stretched out slowly. There is, however, more delay in extending a limb which has been kept bent while treated, than in bending a limb which has been kept straight. Also there should be a definite rule as to position for a limb which has been wounded. If the wound is to be agglutinated, the limb is kept raised; it must not be bent either way if there is still inflammation; if pus is already being discharged it should be hanging down. The best medicament too is rest; movement and walking before healing are adverse. The danger, however, from movement is less for wounds of the head and arms than for the lower limbs. Walking about is least of all suited to an injured thigh or leg or foot. The patient's room should be kept warm.

debebit. Balneum quoque, dum parum vulnus purum est, inter res infestissimas est: nam id et umidum et sordidum reddit, ex quibus ad cancrum transitus esse consuevit. Levis frictio recte adhibetur, sed is partibus, quae longius absunt a vulnere.

29 Inflammatione finita vulnus purgandum est. Et id optime faciunt tincta in melle linamenta, supraque idem emplastrum vel enneapharmacum dandum est. Tum demum vero purum ulcus est, cum rubet, ac nimium neque siccum neque umidum est. At quodcumque sensu caret, quod non naturaliter sentit, quod nimium aut aridum aut umidum est, quod aut albidum aut pallidum aut lividum aut nigrum est, id purum non est.

30 Purgato, sequitur ut impleatur; iamque calida aqua eatenus necessaria est, ut sanies removeatur. Lanae sucidae supervacuus usus est: lota melius circumdatur. Ad implendum autem vulnus proficiunt quidem etiam medicamenta aliqua: itaque ea adhiberi non alienum est, ut buturum cum rosa et exigua mellis parte; aut cum eadem rosa tetra-
B pharmacum; aut ex rosa linamenta. Plus tamen proficit balneum rarum, cibi boni suci, vitatis omnibus acribus, sed iam pleniores: nam et avis et venatio et suilla elixa dari potest. Vinum omnibus, dum febris, inflammatio inest, alienum est: itemque usque cicatricem, si nervi musculive vulnerati sunt; etiam, si alte caro. At si plaga in summa cute generis

---

*a* V. **19**. 9, 10.　　　*b* *infra*, par. 31 B.　　　*c* V. **14**.

Bathing, too, while the wound is not yet clean, is one of the worst things to do; for this makes the wound both wet and dirty, and then there is a tendency for gangrene to occur. It is advantageous to apply light rubbing, but in those parts which are rather far away from the wound.

When the inflammation has ended, the wound must be cleaned. And that is best done by putting on lint soaked in honey, and over it the plaster called tetrapharmacum or that called enneapharmacum.[a] Then at length the wound is really clean when it is red, and neither too dry nor too moist. But a wound is not clean when it lacks sensation, when there is sensation which is not natural, when it is either too dry or too wet, when it is either whitish or pallid or livid or blackish.[b]

When the wound is clean, there follows the growth of new flesh; and now warm water is necessary in order to remove sanies. The use of unscoured wool is superfluous; scoured wool is the better wrapping. But for filling up a wound certain medicaments also are useful;[c] therefore it is not inappropriate to make use of such things as butter with rose-oil and a little honey; or the tetrapharmacum with the said rose-oil, or lint soaked in rose-oil. More beneficial, however, is an occasional bath, a nourishing diet, while avoiding everything acrid, but now somewhat fuller, for both poultry and venison and boiled pork can be given. In all cases, while fever and inflammation are present, wine is inappropriate; also, until the scar is formed, if either sinews or muscles have been wounded; or even if there is a deep flesh wound. But when the wound is of the safer kind, only skin deep, wine if

97

tutioris est, potest non pervetus, modice tamen
C datum, ad implendum quoque proficere. Si quid
molliendum est, quod in nervosis locis musculosisque
necessarium est, cerato quoque super vulnus utendum est. At si caro supercrevit, modice reprimit
siccum linamentum, vehementius squama aeris. Si
plus est, quod tolli opus est, adhibenda sunt etiamnum vehementiora, quae corpus exedunt. Cicatricem post omnia haec commode inducit Lycium ex
passo aut lacte dilutum, vel etiam per se impositum
siccum linamentum.

31   Hic ordo felicis curationis est. Sed quaedam
tamen periculosa incidere consuerunt: interdum
enim vetustas ulcus occupat, induciturque ei callus,
et circum orae crassae livent; post quae quicquid
medicamentorum ingeritur, parum proficit; quod
fere neglegenter curato ulceri supervenit. Interdum vel ex nimia inflammatione, vel ob aestus
inmodicos, vel ob nimia frigora, vel quia nimis
vulnus adstrictum est, vel quia corpus aut senile aut
B mali habitus est, cancer occupat. Id genus a
Graecis diductum in species est, nostris vocabulis
non est.

Omnis autem cancer non solum id corrumpit, quod
occupavit, sed etiam serpit; deinde aliis aliisque
signis discernitur. Nam modo super inflammationem
rubor ulcus ambit, isque cum dolore procedit (erysipelas Graeci nominant); modo ulcus nigrum est,
quia caro eius corrupta est, idque vehementius
etiam putrescendo intenditur ubi vulnus umidum

---

*a* V. 6-8.
*b* For the diseases referred to in sections 31 B-34, see
Appendix, pp. 589 ff.

not too old, given in moderation, can even aid the growth of flesh. If any part is to be softened, which is necessary in the region of sinews and muscles, cerate also is to be used upon the wound. But if flesh fungates, dry lint is a moderate repressant, copper scales a more active one. If more fungation needs to be removed the still more active corrosives are to be employed.[a] After all such applications, lycium dissolved in raisin wine or in milk, or even only an application of dry lint, is useful in inducing a scar.

Such is the procedure of a successful treatment; dangerous complications, however, are wont to occur. Sometimes the wound becomes the seat of chronic ulceration, and it becomes hardened, and the thickened margins are a livid colour; after which whatever medicament is applied is of little service; and this commonly occurs when the wound has been carelessly treated. At times, whether owing to excess of inflammation, or to unusually hot weather, or to excessively cold weather, or because the wound has been bandaged too tightly, or on account of old age, or of a bad habit of body, canker sets in. The Greeks divided this genus into species for which there are no terms in our language.

Now canker,[b] whatever its species, corrupts not only the part it attacks, but it also spreads; next it is distinguished by differing signs. For sometimes a redness, over and above the inflammation, surrounds the wound, and this spreads with pain (the Greeks term it erysipelas); at times the wound is black because its flesh has become corrupted, and this is still more intensified by putrefaction when the wound is moist, and from the black wound is discharged a

99

est et ex nigro ulcere umor pallidus fertur malique
C odoris [est] carunculaeque corruptae: interdum
etiam nervi ac membranae resolvuntur, specillumque
demissum descendit aut in latus aut deorsum, eoque
vitio nonnumquam os quoque adficitur; modo oritur
ea, quam Graeci gangrenam appellant. Priora in
qualibet parte corporis fiunt: hoc in prominentibus
membris, id est, inter ungues et alas vel inguina,
fereque in senibus vel in is, quorum corpus mali
habitus est. Caro in ulcere vel nigra vel livida est,
sed sicca et arida; proxumaque cutis plerumque
subnigris pustulis impletur; deinde ei proxima vel
pallida vel livida, fereque rugosa, sine sensu est;
D ulterior in inflammatione est. Omniaque ea
simul serpunt; ulcus in locum pustulosum, pustulae
in eum, qui pallet aut livet, pallor aut livor in id,
quod inflammatum est, inflammatio in id, quod
E integrum est, transit. Inter haec deinde febris
acuta oritur ingensque sitis: quibusdam etiam
delirium: alii, quamvis mentis suae compotes sunt,
balbutiendo tamen vix sensus suos explicant; incipit
adfici stomachus; fit foedi spiritus ipse odoris. Atque
initium quidem eius mali recipit curationem: ubi
vero penitus insedit, insanabile est; plurimique sub
frigido sudore moriuntur.
32 Ac pericula quidem vulnerum haec sunt. Vetus
autem ulcus scalpello concidendum est, exciden-
daeque eius orae, et, quicquid super eas livet, aeque
incidendum. Si varicula intus est, quae id sanari
prohibet, ea quoque excidenda. Deinde, ubi sanguis

---

ᵃ For *varicula* cf. II. 7. 28. This condition would now be
termed "wound aneurism" and is sometimes met with in war
wounds.

pallid humour, which has a foul odour, and the granulations break down: at times also sinews and membranes undergo dissolution, and when a probe is introduced it passes to the side or downwards, and this lesion not infrequently affects the bone too; sometimes there arises what the Greeks call gangrene. The former varieties occur in any part of the body; gangrene in the extremities, that is, in the nails, armpits or groins, and generally in aged people or in those of a bad habit of body. The flesh in the wound becomes either black or livid, but dry and shrivelled; the skin near it is for the most part occupied by dusky pustules; then the skin around these becomes either pallid or livid, and usually wrinkled, deficient in sensation: farther away from the wound the skin is inflamed. All these things spread simultaneously, the ulceration into the pustules, the pustules into the pallid or livid part, that into the inflamed part, and that again into the sound flesh. Now together with the above an acute fever arises and great thirst: in some also delirium: others, although in their right minds, nevertheless stammer so that they can scarcely explain their feelings; the stomach begins to be affected: even the breath gets a foul odour. This disorder at its commencement admits of treatment; but when thoroughly established it is incurable, and most patients die in a cold sweat.

And such are the dangers following upon wounds. Now a wound when of long standing should be cut with a scalpel, its margins excised, and incisions made at the same time into any livid area surrounding the margins. If there is a small varix *a* inside the wound which hinders healing, it also is to be excised.

emissus novatumque vulnus est, eadem curatio
adhibenda, quae in recentibus vulneribus (§ 23 A)
exposita est. Si scalpello aliquis uti non vult, potest
sanare id emplastrum, quod ex ladano fit, et cum
ulcus sub eo exesum est, id, quo cicatrix inducitur.

33    Id autem, quod erysipelas vocari dixi (§ 31 B),
non solum vulneri supervenire sed sine hoc quoque
oriri consuevit, atque interdum periculum maius
adfert, utique si circa cervices aut caput constitit.
—Oportet, si vires patiuntur, sanguinem mittere ;
deinde imponere simul reprimentia et refrigerantia,
maximeque cerussam solani suco, aut Cimoliam
cretam aqua pluviali exceptam ; aut ex eadem aqua
subactam farinam cupresso adiecta aut, si tenerius
B corpus est, lenticulam. Quicquid inpositum est,
betae folio contegendum et super linteolum frigida
aqua madens inponendum. Si per se refrigerantia
parum proderunt, miscenda erunt hoc modo : sulpuris P. ✻ I ; cerussae, croci singulorum P. ✻
XII S. ; eaque cum vino conterenda sunt, et id
his inlinendum : aut si durior locus est, solani folia
contrita suillae adipi miscenda sunt et inlita linteolo
superinicienda.
C    At si nigrities est nequedum serpit, imponenda sunt
quae carnem putrem lenius edunt, repurgatumque
ulcus sic ut cetera nutriendum est. Si magis putre
est, iamque procedit ac serpit, opus est vehementius
erodentibus. Si ne haec quidem evincunt, aduri

---

ᵃ V. 19. 18.

Then when the blood has been let out and the wound made like a new one, the same treatment is to be adopted as that described for recent wounds. If any one does not want to use the scalpel, healing may be secured by using the plaster made up with ladanum,[a] and, when that has eaten away the ulcer, by the one which induces a scar.[b]

But what I have said is called erysipelas, not only follows upon a wound, but is wont also to arise without a wound, and sometimes brings with it some danger, especially when it sets in about the neck or head. If strength permits, blood should be let; then repressives and refrigerants applied together, particularly white-lead with nightshade juice, or Cimolian chalk with rain-water as an excipient; or flour made into a paste with the same, with cyprus shoots added, or lentil meal if the skin is more delicate. Whatever is put on is to be covered over with beet leaves, and over that with lint wetted with cold water. If refrigerants by themselves have little effect, they are to be combined with the following: sulphur 4 grms., white-lead and saffron, 50 grms. each; and these are pounded up with wine and the place smeared with them: or when the skin is more hardened, nightshade leaves are pounded, mixed with lard, and applied spread on lint.

But if there is a blackening which is not yet spreading, the milder corrosives of putrid flesh are to be put on, and the wound having been thus cleaned out, is cared for like other wounds. If there is more corruption, and it is already spreading, stronger corrosives are needed. If even these are not effective,

[b] V. 14.; 19. 21–28.

locus debet, donec ex eo nullus umor feratur: nam
D quod sanum est, siccum est, cum aduritur. Post
ustionem putris ulceris superponenda sunt, quae
crustas a vivo resolvant: eas escharas Graeci
nominant. Ubi eae exciderunt, purgandum ulcus
maxime melle et resina est: sed aliis quoque purgari
potest, quibus purulenta curantur; eodemque modo
ad sanitatem perducendum est.

34    Gangrenam vero, si nondum plane tenet, sed
adhuc incipit, curare non difficillimum est, utique in
corpore iuvenili; et magis etiam si musculi integri
sunt, si nervi vel laesi non sunt vel leviter adfecti
sunt, neque ullus magnus articulus nudatus est, aut
carnis in eo loco paulum est, ideoque non multum,
quod putresceret, fuit, consistitque eo loco vitium;
B quod maxime fieri in digito potest.—In eiusmodi
casu primum est, si vires patiuntur, sanguinem
mittere; deinde quicquid aridum est et intentione
quadam proximum quoque locum male habet, usque
eo [sanum corpus] concidere. Medicamenta vero,
dum malum serpit, adhibenda nulla sunt, quae pus
movere consuerunt; ideoque ne aqua quidem calida.
Gravia quoque, quamvis reprimentia, aliena sunt;
sed his quam levissimis opus est; superque ea, quae
C inflammata sunt, utendum est refrigerantibus. Si
nihilo magis malum constitit, uri, quod est inter
integrum ac vitiatum locum, debet: praecipueque in
hoc casu petendum non a medicamentis solum sed
etiam a victus ratione praesidium est: neque enim
id malum nisi corrupti vitiosique corporis est. Ergo
primo, nisi inbecillitas prohibet, abstinentia utendum;

---

*a* V. 9.                    *b* V. 5.

the place should be burnt by a cautery until no more
humour escapes from it; for sound flesh is dry when it
is burnt. After the cauterizing of a putrid wound,
such drugs are to be applied as will loosen from the
living flesh the crusts [a] which the Greeks call eschara.
When these have fallen off, the wound is to be cleaned
by honey and resin in particular; but it can also be
cleaned by the other materials with which suppurating wounds are treated [b] and in the same way
brought to healing.

But gangrene, when not yet widespread, but only
beginning, is not very difficult to cure, at any rate
in a young subject; and even more so if muscles
are intact, sinews uninjured or but slightly affected,
and no large joint opened, or if there is little
flesh in the part, and so not much to putrefy, and if
the lesion is limited to one place; and this mostly
happens in a finger. In such a case the first thing to
be done, when strength permits, is to let blood;
then whatever has become dry, and by stretching
out, as it were, is injuring also what is next to it, is
cut away up to this point [the sound tissue]. Whilst
the gangrene is spreading, medicaments which tend
to promote suppuration are not to be applied; and
therefore not even hot water. Weighty dressings
also, although repressant, are unsuitable; but the
lightest are needed; and over the parts which are
inflamed refrigerants are to be used. If the malady
is still not checked, the part between what is sound
and diseased ought to be cauterized; and in such a
case especially assistance is to be sought, not only
from medicaments, but also from a system of diet;
for this malady only occurs in a corrupt and diseased
body. Therefore at first, unless weakness prohibits

deinde danda quae per cibum potionemque alvum ideoque etiam corpus adstringant, sed ea levia. Postea si vitium constitit, inponi super vulnus eadem debent, quae in putri ulcere praescripta sunt (§ 33 C).

D Ac tum quoque ut plenioribus cibis uti licebit ex media materia, sic tamen non nisi alvum corpusque siccantibus; aqua vero pluvia[ti]li frigida. Balneum, nisi iam certa fiducia redditae sanitatis est, alienum est: siquidem emollitum in eo vulnus cito rursus eodem malo adficitur. Solent vero nonnumquam nihil omnia auxilia proficere ac nihilo minus serpere is cancer. Inter quae, miserum sed unicum auxilium est, ut cetera pars corporis tuta sit, membrum, quod paulatim emoritur, abscidere.

35 Hae gravissimorum vulnerum curationes sunt. Sed ne illa quidem neglegenda, ubi integra cute interior pars conlisa est; aut ubi derasum adtritumve aliquid est; aut ubi surculus corpori infixus est; aut ubi tenue sed altum vulnus insedit.

In primo casu commodissimum est malicorium ex vino coquere, interioremque eius partem conterere et cerato miscere ex rosa facto, idque superponere: deinde, ubi cutis ipsa exasperata est, inducere lene medicamentum, quale lipara est.

B Derasso vero detritoque imponendum est emplastrum tetrapharmacum, minuendusque cibus et vinum subtrahendum. Neque id, quia non habebit altiores ictus, contemnendum erit: siquidem ex

---

        [a] VII. 33.        [b] VII. 1.        [c] VII. 2-5.
        [1] λιπαρά, a greasy ointment, cf. V. 19. 25.

it, the patient should fast; after that he should be given light food and drink to tone up the bowels, and so also the body in general. Later if the lesion has been checked, the same things should be put on the wound which were prescribed for putrid ulceration. And it is now also permissible to make use of a fuller diet—foods of the middle class, but only such as dry up the bowels and the body generally; and cold rain-water to drink. The bath is harmful until it is quite certain that soundness has returned; for a wound, if softened in the bath, is quickly again affected by the same malady. But it still happens sometimes that none of these remedies is effectual, and in spite of everything this canker spreads. In such circumstances there is one sad but solitary remedy to secure the safety of the rest of the body, that is to cut away the limb which is gradually dying.[a]

Such are the treatments of the gravest wounds. But there should be no neglect of those in which the skin is intact, but some inner part has been contused; or where something has been scraped or rubbed off:[b] or where a splinter has become fixed in the body, or where the wound is small but deep.[c]

In the first case the best thing is to cook the rind of a pomegranate in wine, and pound up its interior and mix with rose-oil cerate, and so apply it: next, when the skin has been actually abraded, to lay on a soothing medicament such as lipara.[d]

When the skin has been scraped and rubbed off, the plaster tetrapharmacum is to be applied, the food reduced and wine withdrawn. Such wounds are not to be disregarded because deeper structures are uninjured; for often from injuries of this kind

eiusmodi casibus saepe cancri fiunt. Quod si levius
id erit et in parte exigua, contenti esse poterimus
eodem leni medicamento.

Surculum vero, si fieri potest, oportet vel manu
vel etiam ferramento eicere. Si vel praefractus est
vel altius descendit, quam ut id ita fieri possit,
C medicamento evocandus est. Optume autem educit
superinposita harundinis radix, si tenera est, protinus
contrita; si iam durior, ante in mulso decocta;
cui semper mel adiciendum est aut aristolochia cum
eodem melle. Pessima ex surculis harundo est,
quia aspera est: eademque offensa etiam in filice
est. Sed usu cognitum est utramque adversus
alteram medicamentum esse, si contrita superinposita est. Facit autem idem in omnibus surculis,
quodcumque medicamentum extrahendi vim habet.

Idem altis tenuibusque vulneribus aptissimum est.
Priori rei Philocratis, huic Hecataei emplastrum
maxime convenit.

36 Ubi vero in quolibet vulnere ventum ad inducendam cicatricem est, quod perpurgatis iam reple-
tisque ulceribus necessarium est, primum ex aqua
frigida linamentum, dum caro alitur; deinde iam,
cum continenda est, siccum imponendum est, donec
cicatrix inducatur. Tum deligari super album
plumbum oportet quo et reprimitur cicatrix et
B colorem maxime corpori sano similem accipit.
Idem radix silvestris cucumeris praestat, idem
compositio, quae habet: elateri P. ✱ I; spumae

---

ª Cf. p. 39.
 ᵇ It is not certain what this was. Perhaps plumbum album
or candidum=tinstone, a common ingredient of nail polishes.
White lead (basic lead acetate) was called by Celsus *cerussa*
(Gk. ψιμύθιον). See vol. II., Introduction, p. xlviii, *plumbum*.

canker develops. But if the hurt is trifling, and of small extent, we may be content with the same soothing application.

A splinter too, whenever possible, should be extracted either by the hand or even by the help of an instrument. But if the splinter has been broken off or has penetrated too deeply for this to be done, it must be drawn towards the surface by a medicament. The best thing to draw it out is an application of pole-reed root pounded up straight away if soft, but if already rather hard, boiled first in honey wine; to which honey should always be added, or birthwort also with honey. Of splinters the pole-reed is the worst because it is rough; there is the same harmfulness in fern. But by experience it has been learnt that either, when pounded up and applied, serves as a medicament against the other. Any medicament which has an extractive property has the same effect on splinters of all kinds.

The same treatment is best for deep and narrow wounds. The plaster of Philocrates is especially good for the former, that of Hecataeus for the latter.[a]

Whatever the kind of wound, when the time has come for inducing the scar, which must be after the wound has cleaned and filled with new flesh, first lint is applied, wetted by cold water while the flesh is being nourished; afterwards, when it has to be checked, dry lint must be applied until the scar is induced. Then plumbum album [b] should be bandaged on in order to keep down the scar, and to give it a colour as much as possible like sound skin. Wild cucumber root has the same property, so has the prescription containing: elaterium [c] 4 grms., litharge

[c] A preparation made from the juice of wild cucumber.

argenti P. ✳ II; unguenti pondo ✳ IIII. Quae
excipiuntur resina terebenthina, donec emplastri
crassitudo ex omnibus fiat. Ac nigras quoque cicatrices leniter purgant paribus portionibus mixta
aerugo, plumbum elotum, eademque rosa coacta;
sive unguitur cicatrix, quod in facie fieri potest;
sive id ut emplastrum inponitur, quod in aliis partibus
C commodius est. At si vel excrevit cicatrix vel
concava est, stultum est decoris causa rursus et
dolorem et medicinam sustinere. Alioqui res utrique
succurri patitur, siquidem utraque cicatrix exulcerari
scalpello potest. Si medicamentum aliquis mavult,
idem efficiunt compositiones eae, quae corpus exedunt. Cute exulcerata super eminentem carnem
exedentia medicamenta coicienda sunt, super con-
cavam implentia, donec utrumque ulcus sanae cuti
aequetur; et tum cicatrix inducatur.

**27.** Dixi de iis vulneribus, quae maxime per
tela inferuntur. Sequitur, ut de iis dicam, quae
morsu fiunt, interdum hominis, interdum simiae,
saepe canis, nonnumquam ferorum animalium aut
serpentium. Omnis autem fere morsus habet
quoddam virus: itaque si vehemens vulnus est,
cucurbitula admovenda est; si levius, protinus
B emplastrum iniciendum, praecipueque Diogeni.ᵃ Si
id non est, quodlibet ex is, quae adversus morsus
proposui (19, 20 *seqq.*).ᵇ si ea non sunt, viride Alexan-
drinum:ᶜ si ne id quidem est, quodlibet non pingue
ex iis, quae recentibus vulneribus accommodantur.
Sal quoque his, praecipueque ei, quod canis fecit,
medicamentum est, si manus vulneri inponitur

---

ᵃ This ointment is perhaps myrobalanon, cf. IV. **16.** 4 (vol.
I. p. 416), and vol. II., Introduction, p. xxii, *Balanos.*
ᵇ V. **19.** 20–22.     ᶜ V. **19.** 17.

8 grms., unguent 16 grms.[a] These are taken up in turpentine until the whole is of the consistency of a plaster. Further, equal parts of verdigris and washed lead mixed together with rose-oil gently clean black scars; either the scar may be anointed, as can be done on the face; or the above may be applied as a plaster, which is more convenient for other parts of the body. But if the scar is either elevated or depressed, it is foolish, just for the sake of appearance, to submit again to pain and medicinal applications. Else both conditions can be remedied, since either scar can be made into a wound by the use of a scalpel. Or if a medicament is preferred, corrosive compositions have the same effect. After the skin has been wounded, to an elevated cicatrix corrosives are applied, to a depressed one medicaments which make flesh, until the wound, in each case, is on a level with the sound skin; and then the scar is induced.

27. I have spoken of those wounds which are mostly inflicted by weapons. My next task is to speak of those which are caused by the bite, at times of a man, at times of an ape, often of a dog, not infrequently of wild animals or of snakes. For almost every bite has in it poison of some sort. Therefore if the wound is severe, a cup should be applied straightway over it; if slighter a plaster, especially that of Diogenes. If that is not at hand, then one of the others I have recommended against bites;[b] failing such, the green plaster called Alexandrian;[c] if not even that is to be had, then any one which suits recent wounds, so long as it is not greasy. Salt is also a remedy for bites, especially dog-bite, if a hand is then placed over the bite and struck by two

superque id duobus digitis verberatur: exaniat
enim; ac salsamentum quoque recte super id vulnus
deligatur.

2 Utique autem si rabiosus canis fuit, cucurbitula
virus eius extrahendum est; deinde si locus neque
nervosus neque musculosus est, vulnus id adurendum
est: si uri non potest, sanguinem homini mitti non
alienum est. Tum usto quidem vulneri superim-
ponenda quae ceteris ustis sunt: ei vero, quod
expertum ignem non est, ea medicamenta, quae
vehementer exedunt. Post quae nullo novo magis-
terio, sed iam supra (26, 30, 36) posito ulcus erit
B implendum et ad sanitatem perducendum. Quidam
post rabiosi canis morsum protinus in balineum
mittunt ibique patiuntur desudare, dum vires
corporis sinunt, ulcere adaperto, quo magis ex eo
quoque virus destillet; deinde multo meracoque
vino accipiunt, quod omnibus venenis contrarium est.
Idque cum ita per triduum factum est, tutus esse
homo a periculo videtur.

C Solet autem ex eo vulnere, ubi parum occursum
est, aquae timor nasci (hydrophobas Graeci appellant), miserrimum genus morbi, in quo simul aeger
et siti et aquae metu cruciatur; quo oppressis in
angusto spes est. Sed unicum tamen remedium
est, neque opinantem in piscinam non ante ei
provisam proicere. Et si natandi scientiam non
habet, modo mersum bibere pati, modo attollere:
si habet, interdum deprimere, ut invitus quoque
aqua satietur: sic enim simul et sitis et aquae metus

---

<sup>a</sup> V. 26. 30–36.

fingers of the other hand; for this brings out sanies;
and brine-pickle may also be appropriately bandaged
upon such a wound.

But especially if the dog was mad, the poison
must be drawn out by a cup; next, if the wound is
not among sinews and muscles, it must be cauterized;
if it cannot be cauterized, it is not amiss to bleed the
man. After cauterizing, applications are to be put
on as for other burns; if the wound is not cauterized,
such medicaments as are powerful corrosives. After
this the wound should be filled in and brought to
healing, not by any new method, but as already
described above.[a] After the bite of a mad dog some
send the patients at once to the bath, and there let
them sweat as much as their bodily strength allows,
the wound being kept open in order that the poison
may drop out freely from it; then follows the ad-
ministration of much wine, undiluted, which is an
antidote to all poisons. And when this has been
carried out for three days, the patient is deemed to
be out of danger.

But when too little has been done for such a
wound, it usually give rise to a fear of water which
the Greeks call hydrophobia, a most distressing
disease, in which the patient is tortured simultaneously by thirst and by dread of water. In these
cases there is very little hope for the sufferer. But
still there is just one remedy, to throw the patient
unawares into a water tank which he has not seen
beforehand. If he cannot swim, let him sink under
and drink, then lift him out; if he can swim, push
him under at intervals so that he drinks his fill of
water even against his will; for so his thirst and dread
of water are removed at the same time. Yet this

D tollitur. Sed aliud periculum excipit, ne infirmum
corpus in aqua frigida vexatum nervorum distentio
absumat. Id ne incidat, a piscina protinus in oleum
calidum demittendus est. Antidotum autem praecipue id, quod primo loco (23, 1 B) posui, ubi id non
est, aliud, si nondum aeger aquam horret, potui ex
aqua dandum est; et si amaritudine offendit, mel
adiciendum est: si iam is morbus occupavit, per
catapotia sumi potest.

3     Serpentium quoque morsus non nimium distantem
curationem desiderant, quamvis in ea multum
antiqui variarunt, ut in singula anguium genera
singula medendi genera praeciperent aliique alia:
sed in omnibus eadem maxime proficiunt. — Igitur
in primis super vulnus id membrum deligandum est,
non tamen nimium vehementer, ne torpeat; deinde
venenum extrahendum est. Id cucurbitula optume
facit. Neque alienum est ante scalpello circa vulnus
incidere, quo plus vitiati iam sanguinis extrahatur.
B Si cucurbitula non est, quod tamen vix incidere
potest, tum quodlibet simile vas, quod idem possit;
si ne id quidem est, homo adhibendus est, qui id
vulnus exsugat. Neque Hercules scientiam prae-
cipuam habent ii, qui Psylli nominantur, sed au-
daciam usu ipso confirmatam. Nam venenum serpentis, ut quaedam etiam venatoria venena, quibus
Galli praecipue utuntur, non gustu, sed in vulnere
C nocent. Ideoque colubra ipsa tuto estur, ictus eius
occidit; et si stupente ea, quod per quaedam medi-

---

*a* For antidotes see V. **23**. 1 B–3.

*b* An African people celebrated as snake-charmers. Cf.
Lucan IX. 893, *gens unica terras*; *Incolit a saevo serpentum
innoxia morsu / Marmaridae Psylli*; and Suetonius, *Aug.* 17.

procedure incurs a further danger, that a spasm of
sinews, provoked by the cold water, may carry off a
weakened body. Lest this should happen, he must
be taken straight from the tank and plunged into a
bath of hot oil. But as an antidote we should give
especially the one which I put first,[a] when that is
not at hand, another; it is to be given in a draught
of water, if the patient does not dread water yet;
and if the bitterness is objected to, honey is to be
added; if dread of water has already seized him, the
antidote can be swallowed as a pill.

Serpents' bites again need a not very different
treatment, although in this the ancients had very
various methods so that for each kind of snake
some prescribed one special kind of remedy, some
another; but in all it is the same measures
which are the most efficacious. Therefore first the
limb is to be constricted above this kind of wound,
but not too tightly, lest it become numbed; next,
the poison is to be drawn out. A cup does this
best. But it is not amiss beforehand to make
incisions with a scalpel around the wound, in order
that more of the vitiated blood may be extracted.
If there is no cup at hand, although this can hardly
happen, use any similar vessel which can do what
you want; if there is not even this, a man must
be got to suck the wound. I declare there is no
particular science in those people who are called
Psylli,[b] but a boldness confirmed by experience. For
serpent's poison, like certain hunter's poisons, such
as the Gauls in particular use, does no harm when
swallowed, but only in a wound. Hence the snake
itself may be safely eaten, whilst its stroke kills;
and if one is stupefied, which mountebanks effect

camenta circulatores faciunt, in os digitum quis
indidit neque percussus est, nulla in ea saliva noxa
est. Ergo quisquis exemplum Psylli secutus id
vulnus exsuxerit, et ipse tutus erit et tutum hominem
praestabit. Illud [ne intereat] ante debebit ad-
tendere, ne quod in gingivis palatove aliave parte
D oris ulcus habeat. Post haec is homo loco calido
conlocandus est, sic ut id quod percussum erit, in
inferiorem partem inclinetur. Si neque qui exsugat
neque ulla cucurbitula est, sorbere oportet ius anserinum
vel ovillum vel vitulinum et vomere, vivum autem
gallinaceum pullum per medium dividere et protinus
calidum super volnus imponere, sic ut pars interior
corpori iungatur. Facit id etiam haedus agnusve
discissus, et calida eius caro statim super volnus
imposita. Emplastra quoque si qua . . .[1] supra
(19, 20 *seqq.*) conprehensa sunt; aptissimumque est
vel Ephesium vel id, quod ei subiectum est (19, 22).
E Praesensque in aliquo antidoto praesidium est: si
id non est, necessarium est exsorbere potionem meri
vini cum pipere, vel quidlibet aliud quod calori
movendo est, ne umorem intus coire patiatur: nam
maxima pars venenorum frigore interemit. Omnia
etiam urinam moventia, quia materiam extenuant,
utilia sunt.

4    Haec adversus omnes ictus communia sunt. Usus
tamen ipse docuit eum, quem aspis percussit, acetum

---

[1] *Marx suggests that the following words have fallen out after*
si qua ⟨curanti praesto sunt adhibenda quae⟩: *the sentence
would then run,* "*plasters too, if the physician has any of them
at hand, should be applied,*" *etc. Daremberg substitutes* quae
*for* si qua.

---

[a] The text as it stands cannot be translated, though the
general sense is given.

by certain medicaments, and if anyone puts his finger into its mouth and is not bitten, its saliva is harmless. Anyone, therefore, who follows the example of the Psylli and sucks out the wound, will himself be safe, and will promote the safety of the patient. He must see to it, however, beforehand that he has no sore place on his gums or palate or other parts of the mouth. After the suction, the patient should be put into a warm room, in such a position that the part bitten is inclined downwards. If there is no one at hand to suck out the wound, or to cup it, the patient should sip goose or mutton or veal broth and provoke a vomit; further a live chicken should be cut through the middle, and whilst warm applied forthwith over the wound so that its inner part is in contact with the patient's body. It will also do to slaughter a kid or lamb, and immediately to put the hot flesh upon the wound. The plasters also should be applied which have been mentioned above;[a] the most suitable is the Ephesian plaster,[b] or that noted next after it. There is ready help in one of the antidotes; if none is at hand, it is necessary to take in sips a draught of strong wine with pepper, or anything else which will stir up heat, to prevent humour from coagulating internally; for most poisons cause death by cold. All diuretics also are useful, because they dilute the diseased matter.

Such are the general remedies against bites of any kind. Experience has taught, however, that anyone bitten by an asp[c] should in particular drink

---

[b] V. 19. 21.

[c] Coluber aspis. See Galen XIV. 235. His account of Cleopatra's death is closely followed by Shakespeare.

potius bibere debere. Quod demonstrasse dicitur
casus cuiusdam pueri, qui cum ab hac ictus esset et
partim ob ipsum volnus partim ob inmodicos aestus
siti premeretur ac locis siccis alium umorem non
reperiret, acetum, quod forte secum habebat, ebibit
et liberatus est, credo, quoniam id, quamvis refrigerandi vim habet, tamen habet etiam dissu-
pandi; quo fit, ut terra respersa eo spumet. Eadem
ergo vi verisimile est spissescentem quoque intus
umorem hominis ab eo discuti et sic dari sanitatem.
5 In quibusdam etiam aliis serpentibus quaedam
auxilia certa satis nota sunt. Nam scorpio sibi ipse
pulcherrimum medicamentum est. Quidam contritum cum vino bibunt: quidam eodem modo contritum super volnus imponunt: quidam super
prunam eo imposito volnus suffumigant, undique
veste circumdata, ne is fumus dilabatur; tum
B carbonem eius super volnus deligant. Bibere autem
oportet herbae solaris, quam heliotropion Graeci
vocant, semen vel certe folia ex vino. Super volnus
vero etiam furfures ex aceto vel ruta silvatica recte
imponitur vel cum melle sal tostus. Cognovi tamen
medicos, qui a scorpione ictis nihil aliud quam ex
bracchio sanguinem miserunt.
6 Et ad scorpionis autem et aranei ictum alium cum
ruta recte miscentur, ex oleoque contritum superin-
ponitur.
7 At si cerastes aut dipsas aut haemorrhois percussit,

---

*a* Cf. Pliny, *N.H.* XXIII. 1. 27.

*b* Coluber cerastes (κεράστης), the horned viper of the
desert. Aristotle, *H.A.* II. 1.

*c* Coluber vipera, called dipsas because its bite produced
great thirst (δίψα).

*d* Haemorrhois (αίμορροΐς). This snake is unidentified; the

vinegar. The case of a certain boy is said to demonstrate this, for having been thus bitten, partly on account of the bite, and partly owing to excessively hot weather, he was tormented by thirst, and being in a dry place found no other fluid, so he drank the vinegar he chanced to have with him, and was saved. I believe this happened because although vinegar is a refrigerant, it has also the faculty of dissipating. Hence it is that earth sprinkled with it froths.[a] Therefore it is likely that by the same faculty humour which is condensing inside a patient is dissipated by it, and so health is restored.

There are also against certain other reptiles remedies which are well enough known. For the scorpion is itself the best remedy against itself. Some pound up a scorpion and swallow it in wine; some pound it up in the same way and put it upon the wound; some put it upon a brazier and fumigate the wound with it, putting a cloth all round to prevent the escape of the fumes, afterwards they bandage its ash upon the wound. The patient should also drink wine in which have been steeped the seeds, or at any rate the leaves, of the herba solaris, which the Greeks call heliotropion. It is good also to apply to the wound bran soaked in vinegar, or wild rue, or roasted salt with honey. I have known, however, practitioners who merely let blood from the arm of those stung by a scorpion, that and nothing more.

For the sting of a scorpion also, or for that of a spider, it is good to put on garlic mixed with rue and pounded up with oil.

But when cerastes,[b] or dipsas,[c] or haemorrhois[d] has

blood of a man bitten by it lost its coagulability and became widely extravasated.

poli quod Aegyptiae fabae magnitudinem aequet,
arfactum ut in duas potiones dividendum est, sic ut
ei rutae paulum adiciatur. Trifolium quoque et
mentastrum et cum aceto panaces aeque proficiunt.
Costumque et casia et cinnamomum recte per
potionem adsumuntur.

8 Adversus chelydri vero ictum panaces aut laser,
quod sit scrip. III S.[1] [✱I], vel porri sucus cum hemina
vini sumendus est, et edenda multa satureia. Imponendum autem super vulnus stercus caprinum ex
aceto coctum, aut ex eodem hordiacia farina, aut ruta
vel nepeta cum sale contrita melle adiecto. Quod in
eo quoque vulnere, quod cerastes fecit, aeque valet.

9 Ubi vero phalangium nocuit, praeter eam curationem, quae manu redditur, saepe homo demittendus
in solium est; dandusque ei murrae et uvae taminiae
par modus ex passi hemina; vel radiculae semen aut
lolii radix ex vino; et super vulnus furfures ex aceto
coctae; imperandumque, ut is conquiescat.

10 Verum haec genera serpentium et peregrina et
aliquanto magis pestifera sunt, maximeque aestuosis
locis gignuntur. Italia frigidioresque regiones hac
quoque parte salubritatem habent, quod minus
terribiles angues edunt. Adversus quos satis proficit herba Vettonica vel Cantabrica vel centaurios
vel argimonia vel trixago vel personina vel marinae
pastinacae, vel singulae binaeve tritae et cum vino
potui datae . . .[2] sunt et super vulnus impositae.
Illud ignorari non oportet, omnis serpentis ictum et
ieiuni et ieiuno magis nocere; ideoque perniciosis-

---

[1] *Marx brackets* ✱ I (*one denarius, i.e.* 3½ *scruples, or* 4
*grammes*) *as a gloss*; *Targa rejects the whole sentence* quod sit
. . . ✱ I.

[2] *Marx inserts:* datae <vel eodem modo contritae protinus
et terra evulsae>, ' *or pounded in the same way as soon as
they have been dug out of the ground.*'

bitten a man, poley-germander roasted, equal in amount to an Egyptian bean, is divided into two draughts, a little rue being added. Trefoil also and wild mint and allheal-juice, with vinegar, are equally efficacious. Costmary, casia, and cinnamon may appropriately be taken in draughts.

For the bite of a chelydrus,[a] allheal-juice or laser 4 grms., or leek-juice in 250 c.cm. of wine, may be taken, and a quantity of savory eaten. Over the bite either goat's dung, or barley-meal boiled with vinegar should be applied, or rue, or catnip pounded with salt, with honey added. This last is equally efficacious for the bite of a cerastes.

But when a venomous spider has done the harm, in addition to the surgical treatment, the patient should be plunged often into the hot bath; and take equal quantities of myrrh and bryony berries in 250 c.cm. of raisin wine; or radish seeds or darnel root in wine; bran boiled in vinegar is to be put on the wound, and the patient is kept in bed.

But the foregoing classes of reptiles belong to foreign countries, and are especially poisonous, and they are mostly generated in hot countries. Italy and colder countries are healthier in this respect too, for the reptiles they produce are less dangerous. Against them sufficient remedies are betony or convolvulus or centaury or agrimony or germander or burdock or sea parsnip; any one or two of these is pounded up and taken in wine . . . and applied to the bite. It must be remembered that all snake-bites are more harmful when either the reptile or the man is hungry. Hence snakes are most injurious when

---

[a] Coluber natrix ($\chi\acute{\epsilon}\lambda\upsilon\delta\rho\sigma$), the marsh snake.

simae sunt cum incubant, utilissimumque est, ubi
ex anguibus metus est, non ante procedi quam quis
aliquid adsumpsit.

11 Non tam ex facili is opitulari est, qui venenum vel
in cibo vel in potione sumpserunt, primum quia non
protinus sentiunt, ut ab angue icti; ita ne succurrere quidem statim sibi possunt; deinde quia
noxa non a cute sed ab interioribus partibus incipit.
Commodissimum est tamen, ubi primum sensit
aliquis, protinus oleo multo epoto vomere; deinde
ubi praecordia exhausit, bibere antidotum: si id
non est, vel merum vinum.

12 Sunt tamen quaedam remedia propria adversus
quaedam venena, maximeque leviora. Nam si
cantharidas aliquis ebibit, panaces cum . . .[1] contusa
vel galbanum vino adiecto dari, vel lac per se debet.

B Si cicutam, vinum merum calidum cum ruta quam
plurimum ingerendum est; deinde is vomere co-
gendus; posteaque laser ex vino dandum: isque, si
febre vacat, in calidum balneum mittendus; si non
vacat, unguendus ex calfacientibus est. Post quae
quies ei necessaria est.

Si hyoscyamum, fervens mulsum bibendum est, aut
quodlibet lac, maxime tamen asininum.

Si cerussam, ius malvae vel ius glandis ex vino
contritae maxime prosunt.

C Si sanguisuga epota est, acetum cum sale bibendum est. Si lac intus coiit, aut passum aut coagulum
aut cum aceto laser.

Si fungos inutiles quis adsumpsit, radicula aut[2]

---

[1] cum lacte *supplied by Edd.*

[2] *The text is corrupt. Marx suggests :* radicula aut ⟨portu-
laca aut per se⟩ aut cum sale, *etc., and this is translated.*
*Daremberg, comparing Pliny, N.H.* XX. **20. 81** : radicula aut
e posca, aut cum sale et aceto, edenda est.

brooding, and it is of the greatest importance when
there is danger from snakes not to go out before
taking some food.

It is not so easy to render assistance when poison
has been taken in food or drink, first because patients
do not perceive it at once as when bitten by a
snake; and so are unable to afford themselves any
help immediately. Moreover, the mischief starts,
not from the skin, but from within. But the best
thing, as soon as any one has perceived it, is to swallow
a quantity of oil at once and vomit; then, when the
praecordia have been emptied, to drink an antidote;
or failing that undiluted wine.

There are, nevertheless, certain remedies proper
for particular poisons, especially for the milder ones.
If a potion of cantharides has been swallowed,
all-heal pounded in milk should be given or galbanum with the addition of wine, or milk by itself.

If it be hemlock, hot undiluted wine with rue should
be taken in a large quantity, then the patient should
be made to vomit; and after that laser is given in
wine; and if free from fever he should be put into
a hot bath; if not free, he should be anointed with
heating remedies. After this, rest is necessary.

If it be hyoscyamus, honey wine should be drunk
hot, or milk of any kind, especially asses' milk.

If it be white-lead, mallow or walnut juice rubbed
up in wine is best.

If a leech has been swallowed,[a] vinegar with salt
is to be drunk. When milk has curdled inside, either
raisin wine or rennet or laser with vinegar.

If any one has eaten fungi that are not used, a

---

[a] Pliny, *N.H.* XXVIII. **10**. 45.

†pota aut cum sale et aceto edenda est. Ipsi vero
hi et specie quidem discerni possunt ab utilibus et
cocturae genere idonei fieri. Nam sive ex oleo
inferverunt, sive piri surculus cum his infervit,
omni noxa vacant.

13     Adustis quoque locis extrinsecus vis infertur:
itaque sequi videtur, ut de his dicam. Haec autem
optime curantur folio aut lilii aut linguae caninae
aut betae in vetere vino oleoque decoctis; quorum
quidlibet protinus impositum ad sanitatem perducit.
Sed dividi quoque curatio potest in ea, quae mediocriter exedentia reprimentiaque primo et pusulas
prohibeant et summam pelliculam exasperent;
deinde ea, quae lenia ad sanitatem perducant. Ex
prioribus est lenticulae cum melle farina vel myrra
cum vino vel creta Cimolia cum turis cortice contrita
et aqua coacta atque, ubi usus necessitas incidit,
B aceto diluta. Ex insequentibus quaelibet lipara:
sed idonea maxime est, quae vel plumbi recrementum
vel vitellos habet. Est etiam illa adustorum curatio,
dum inflammatio est, impositam habere cum melle
lenticulam: ubi ea declinavit, farinam cum ruta vel
porro vel marrubio, donec crustae cadant; tum
ervum cum melle aut irim aut resinam terebinthinam,
donec ulcus purum sit; novissime siccum linamentum.

**28.** Ab his, quae extrinsecus incidunt, ad ea
veniendum est, quae interius corrupta aliqua cor-
porum parte nascuntur. Ex quibus non aliud
carbunculo peius est. Eius hae notae sunt: rubor
est, superque eum non nimium pusulae eminent,

---

ᵃ V. **19.** 25–28; especially 26 and 28.

radish or purslane is to be eaten alone or with a draught of salt and vinegar. Such fungi may be distinguished from the sorts in use by their appearance, and may be rendered safe by suitable cooking; for when boiled in oil, or along with a pear-tree twig, they lose all their noxious property.

Burns are likewise the product of external violence, and so it seems to follow that I should speak of them here. Now they are best treated by leaves either of lily or of hound's tongue or of beet, boiled in old wine and oil; any one of the above applied at once brings healing. But the treatment can also be divided into: first, a stage of moderately exedent and repressant applications both to check blisters and to roughen the skin; next, a stage of soothing applications for healing. Among the former is lentil meal with honey, or myrrh with wine, or Cimolian chalk pounded up with frankincense bark and mixed with water, and when it has to be used, diluted with vinegar. Subsequent applications include anything that is greasy; but the most suitable is that containing lead slag or yolk of egg.[a] There is also another treatment of burns, namely, while the inflammation lasts, to keep lentil meal and honey on the wound; next, when the inflammation has subsided, flour with rue or with leek or with hore-hound, until the crusts fall off; then vetch meal with honey, or iris ointment or turpentine-resin, until the ulceration is clean, and finally dry lint.

**28.** From those lesions which are due to something from without we come to those which originate from within, when some bodily part has become corrupted. Of these none are worse than carbuncles, the signs of which are: redness, with a few pustules projecting

125

maxime nigrae, interdum sublividae aut pallidae:
in his sanies esse videtur. Infra color niger est:
ipsum corpus aridum et durius quam naturaliter
oportet; circaque quasi crusta est, eaque inflammatione cingitur: neque in eo loco levari cutis potest,
B sed inferiori carni quasi adfixa est. Somnus urguet,
nonnunquam horror aut febris oritur, aut utrunque.
Idque vitium subteractis quasi quibusdam radicibus
serpit, interdum celerius, interdum tardius: supra
quoque procedens inalbescit, dein lividum fit, circum-
que exiguae pustulae oriuntur; et si circa stomachum
faucesve incidit, subito spiritum saepe elidit. — Nihil
melius est quam protinus adurere; neque id grave
est: nam non sentit, quoniam ea caro mortua est;
finisque adurendi est, dum ex omni parte sensus
C doloris est. Tum deinde vulnus sicut cetera adusta
curandum est: sequitur enim sub medicamentis
erodentibus crusta undique a viva carne diducta,
quae trahit secum quicquid corruptum erat; purusque
iam sinus curari potest implentibus. At si in summa
cute vitium est, possunt succurrere quaedam vel
D exedentia tantum vel etiam adurentia. Vis pro
magnitudine adhibenda est. Quodcunque vero
medicamentum impositum est, si satis proficiet,
protinus a vivo corruptam partem resolvit; certaque
esse fiducia potest fore, ut undique vitiosa caro
excidat, qua [huiusce rei medicamen] exest. Si [id
non fit] medicamentum malo vincitur, utique ad

---

*a* Cf. *summam pelliculam* (V. 27. 13). Celsus appears to
distinguish the *epidermis* from the *dermis*.

a little, mostly black, sometimes livid or pallid; their
contents seems to be sanies; the colour underneath
is black; the actual tissue is dry, and harder than
it should be naturally; and round them there is a
sort of crust, and outside that an inflammatory ring;
and there the skin cannot be pinched up, but is as it
were fixed in the underlying flesh. The patient is
somnolent; sometimes there is shivering or fever or
both. And this lesion spreads, sometimes quickly,
sometimes slowly, pushing out a sort of root underneath; on the surface too as it spreads the skin gets
paler, then becomes livid, and a ring of small pustules
arises; and if this occurs in the region of the gullet
or fauces, often it suddenly stops the patient's
breathing. The best thing is to apply a cautery at
once; this is not a severe procedure, because the
patient does not feel it, since the flesh is dead; and
the cauterizing is stopped when pain is felt all over
the lesion. After that the wound is to be treated
like other burns; for under erodent medicaments it
follows that the crust becomes separated on all sides
from the living flesh, and takes off with it whatever
has become corrupted; and the cavity when clean
can be dressed with some preparation to make flesh.
But when the lesion is on the surface of the skin,[a]
it is possible to cure it simply by exedents or at any
rate by caustics. The strength of the remedy
adopted is to be proportionate to the lesion. But
whatever the medicament is, if it is sufficiently
effectual, it forthwith detaches the corrupted part
from the living; we may be confident that wherever
the application works, the diseased flesh everywhere
sloughs off. If the medicament is being mastered
by the disease, certainly there must be no delay in

ustionem properandum est. Sed in eiusmodi casu
abstinendum a cibo, a vino est: aquam liberaliter
bibere expedit. Magisque ea servanda sunt, si
febricula quoque accessit.

2     Non idem periculum carcinoma adfert, nisi im-
prudentia curantis agitatum est. Id vitium fit
maxime in superioribus partibus, circa faciem, nares,
aures, labra, mammas feminarum: † et in ulcere [1]
autem aut splene hoc nascitur. Circa locum aliqua
quasi puncta sentiuntur; isque immobilis, inaequalis
tumet, interdum etiam torpet. Circa eum inflatae
venae quasi recurvantur, haeque pallent aut livent,
nonnunquam etiam in quibusdam delitescunt;
tactusque is locus aliis dolorem adfert, in aliis sensum
B non habet. Et nonnunquam sine ulcere durior aut
mollior est quam esse naturaliter debet: nonnunquam isdem omnibus ulcus accedit. Interdumque
nullam habet proprietatem, interdum simile is est,
quae vocant Graeci condylomata aspritudine quadam
et magnitudine; colorque eius ruber est aut lenticulae similis. Neque tuto feritur: nam protinus
aut resolutio nervorum aut distentio insequitur.
Saepe homo ictus ommutescit, atque eius anima
deficit: quibusdam etiam, si id ipsum pressum est,
C quae circa sunt, intenduntur et intumescunt. Ob
quae pessimum id genus est. Fereque primum id
fit, quod cacoethes a Graecis nominatur; deinde ex

---

[1] *This passage is corrupt: one MS. has* iecore *for* ulcere.
*Marx restores it as follows:* etiam in utero autem aut liene
hoc nascitur, '*this arises also in the womb or the spleen.*'

---

[a] See Appendix, pp. 591–2.
[b] The sense seems to require the mention of some other
internal organ, for a suggested emendation see critical note.

applying the cautery. But in such a case there should be abstinence from food and from wine; it is a good thing to drink water freely. And this should be done all the more when there is feverishness as well.

A carcinoma [a] does not give rise to the same danger unless it is irritated by imprudent treatment. This disease occurs mostly in the upper parts of the body, in the region of the face, nose, ears, lips, and in the breasts of women, but it may also arise in an ulceration,[b] or in the spleen. Around the spot is felt a sort of pricking; there is a fixed, irregular swelling, sometimes there is also numbness. Around it are dilated tortuous veins, pallid or livid in hue; sometimes in certain cases they are even hidden from view; and in some the part is painful to the touch, in others there is no feeling. And at times the part becomes harder or softer than natural, yet without ulcerating; and sometimes ulceration supervenes on all the above signs. The ulceration at times has no special characteristic; at times it resembles what the Greeks call condylomata,[c] both in a sort of roughness and in size; its colour is either red or like that of lentils. It is not safe to give it a blow; for either paralysis or spasm of the sinews follows at once. Often from a blow on it a man loses speech and faints; in some also, if the place is pressed, the parts around become tense and swollen. Then it is the worst kind. And generally the first stage is what the Greeks call cacoethes; [d]

Targa followed by Daremberg deletes the whole sentence as a gloss, pointing out that the spleen is not in "the upper parts."
[c] Knuckle-shaped swellings, VI. 18. 8A, C; VII. 30. 2.
[d] κακοήθης is used by Hippocrates to mean malignant, e.g. Coac. 114, 316, 524, etc.; the word is not found in Celsus except in this chapter.

eo id carcinoma, quod sine ulcere est; deinde ulcus,
ex eo thymium. Tolli nihil nisi cacoethes potest:
reliqua curationibus inritantur; et quo maior vis
adhibita est, eo magis. Quidam usi sunt medicamentis adurentibus, quidam ferro adusserunt,
quidam scalpello exciderunt: neque ulla unquam
medicina profecit, sed adusta protinus concitata sunt
D et increverunt, donec occiderent. Excisa, etiam
post inductam cicatricem, tamen reverterunt et
causam mortis adtulerunt: cum interim plerique
nullam vim adhibendo, qua tollere id malum tempt-
tent, sed imponendo tantum lenia medicamenta,
quae quasi blandiantur, quominus ad ultimam
senectutem perveniant, non prohibentur. Discernere
autem cacoethes, quod curationem recipit, a carci-
nomate, quod non recipit, nemo scite[1] potest sed
E tempore et experimento. — Ergo ubi primum id
vitium notatum est, imponi debent medicamenta
adurentia. Si levatur malum, minuuntur eius indicia,
procedere curatio potest et ad scalpellum et ad
ustionem. Si protinus inritatum est, scire licet iam
carcinoma esse, removendaque sunt omnia acria,
omnia vehementia. Sed si sine ulcere is locus durus
est, imponi ficum quam pinguissimam aut rhypodes
F emplastrum satis est. Si ulcus aequale est, ceratum
ex rosa iniciendum est, adiciendusque ei pulvis ex
contrita testa, ex qua faber ferrarius tinguere
candens ferrum solitus est. Si id nimium supercrevit, temptanda squama aeris est, quae lenissima
ex adurentibus est, eatenus ne quid eminere patiatur;

---

[1] *So Daremburg for the MSS.* scire.

---

[a] For thymium (resembling thyme-flowers) see V. **28**. 14 B–E.
[b] V. **19**. 15.

then from that follows a carcinoma without ulceration; then ulceration, and from that a kind of wart.[a]
It is only the cacoethes which can be removed; the
other stages are irritated by treatment; and the more
so the more vigorous it is. Some have used caustic
medicaments, some the cautery, some excision with
a scalpel; but no medicament has ever given relief;
the parts cauterized are excited immediately to an
increase until they cause death. After excision, even
when a scar has formed, none the less the disease
has returned, and caused death; while at the same
time the majority of patients, though no violent
measures are applied in the attempt to remove the
tumour, but only mild applications in order to soothe
it, attain to a ripe old age in spite of it. No one,
however, except by time and experiment, can have
the skill to distinguish a cacoethes which admits of
being treated from a carcinoma which does not.
Therefore, as soon as the lesion is first noted, caustic
medicaments should be applied. If the disease is
relieved, if its indications are lessened, the treatment
can be advanced to the use of the knife and of the
cautery. If it is irritated at once, we may recognize
that it is already a carcinoma, and that all acrid and
severe remedies are to be avoided. But if the place
is hardened without ulceration, it is enough to put
on a fig of the fattest sort or the plaster called
rhypodes.[b] If there is an ulceration level with the
skin, the rose cerate is to be applied, to which must
be added powder from a crusted earthenware pot,
into which a blacksmith has been accustomed to dip
red-hot iron. If there is a considerable growth upon
it, copper scales, which are the mildest of the caustics,
are to be tried, until they check the tendency to

sed ita, si nihil exacerbavit : si minus, eodem cerato
contenti esse debebimsu.

3    Est etiam ulcus, quod θηρίωμα Graeci vocant.
Id et per se nascitur et interdum ulceri ex alia causa
facto supervenit. Color est vel lividus vel niger,
odor foedus, multus et muccis similis umor. Ipsum ulcus neque tactum neque medicamentum
sentit : prurigine tantum movetur. At circa dolor
est et inflammatio; interdum etiam febris oritur,
B nonnunquam ex ulcere sanguis erumpit. Atque id
quoque malum serpit. Quae omnia saepe intenduntur fitque ex his ulcus, quod phagedainam Graeci
vocant, quia celeriter serpendo penetrandoque
usque ossa corpus vorat. Id ulcus inaequale est,
caeno simile; inestque multus umor glutinosus;
odor intolerabilis, maiorque quam pro modo ulceris
inflammatio. Utrunque, sicut omnis cancer, fit maxime in senibus vel iis, quorum corpora mali habitus
sunt.—Curatio utriusque eadem est, sed in maiore
C malo magis necessaria. Ac primum a victus ratione
ordinandus est, ut quiescat in lectulo, ut primis
diebus a cibo abstineat, aquam quam plurimam
adsumat; alvus quoque ei ducatur; dein post
inflammationem cibum boni suci capiat, vitatis
omnibus acribus; potionis quantum volet, sic ut
interdiu quidem aqua contentus sit, in cena vero
etiam vini austeri aliquid bibat. Non aeque tamen
fame in iis, quos φαγέδαινα urgebit, atque iis, qui

───────────────────────────

ᵃ This word is first found in Celsus. Hippocrates (*Coac.*
459) uses θηρίον. Both words are derived from θήρ (wild
beast) and denote the character of the ulceration.
ᵇ An ' eating ' sore φαγέδαινα (φαγεῖν).

growth; but only so if it is in no wise made worse: when the growth is less prominent we ought to rest content with the rose cerate.

There is also an ulceration which the Greeks call therioma.[a] This may arise spontaneously, and at times it may supervene upon ulceration from another cause. It has either a livid or black colour, a foul odour, and an abundant mucus-like discharge. The ulcer itself is insensitive to touch and applications; there is just disturbance by itching. But around there is pain and inflammation; sometimes even fever is set up, occasionally blood is discharged from the ulceration. This also is a spreading disease. And all these signs often extend, and there results from them an ulcer which the Greeks call phagedaena,[b] because it spreads rapidly and penetrates down to the bones and so devours the flesh. This ulceration is uneven, bog-like; there is a large amount of glutinous discharge; the stench is intolerable, and the inflammation is greater than accords with the extent of the ulceration. Both therioma and phagedaena, like all canker, occur for the most part in the aged or those of a bad habit of body. Both are treated in the same way, but treatment is more necessary in the severer form. Firstly, a regimen must be enforced, so that the patient rests in bed, abstains from food for the first days, drinks very freely of water; also has the bowels moved by a clyster; then, on the subsidence of the inflammation, takes digestible food, avoiding everything acrid; drinks as much as he likes, but for the time being contents himself with water, except that at dinner he may drink a little dry wine. But fasting is not to be used for patients with phagedaena

therioma adhuc habebunt, utendum erit. Et victus
D quidem talis necessarius est. Super ulcus vero
inspergenda arida aloe . . .[1] oenanthe est, et, si
parum proficiet, chalcitis. Ac si quis nervus exesa
carne nudatus est, contegendus ante linteolo est,
ne sub eo medicamento aduratur. Si validioribus
etiamnum remediis opus est, ad eas compositiones
veniendum est, quae vehementius adurunt. Quicquid autem inspergitur, averso specillo infundi debet.
E Superdanda cum melle sunt vel linamenta vel oleae
folia ex vino decocta vel marrubium; eaque linteolo
contegenda in aqua frigida madefacto dein bene
expresso; circaque, qua tumor ex inflammatione est,
imponenda quae reprimant cataplasmata. Si sub his
nihil proficitur, ferro locus aduri debet, diligenter
nervis, si qui apparent, ante contectis. Adustum vel
medicamentis vel ferro corpus primum purgandum,
deinde implendum esse apparere cuilibet ex prioribus
potest.
4 Sacer quoque ignis malis ulceribus adnumerari
debet. Eius duae species sunt: alterum est subru-
bicundum aut mixtum rubore atque pallore exasper-
atumque per pusulas continuas, quarum nulla
† alteri[2] maior est, sed plurimae perexiguae: in his
semper fere pus et saepe rubor cum calore est.
Serpitque id nonnunquam sanescente eo, quod
primum vitiatum est, nonnunquam etiam exulcerato,
ubi ruptis pusulis ulcus continuatur umorque exit,
qui esse inter saniem et pus videri potest. Fit maxime in pectore aut lateribus aut eminentibus partibus,

---

[1] *Marx reads:* aloe <contrita vel> oenanthe *and this is
translated.*
[2] *Most editors add* altera.

to the same extent as for those with therioma. Over
the ulceration too should be dusted dry lign-aloes
pounded up or vine-flower, and if this does no good,
copper ore; and if by erosion of flesh a sinew has
become exposed, it must first be covered by lint, to
prevent the medicament from burning it. If still
stronger remedies are required, then recourse must
be had to more active caustics. But whatever the
medicament to be sprinkled on, it ought to be applied
by means of the flat end of a probe. Over this
should be put either lint soaked in honey or olive-
leaves boiled in wine or horehound; and this is to
be covered over by lint well wrung out of cold
water; the inflammatory swelling around is to be
covered with repressant poultices. If there is no
benefit from these measures, the place should be
burnt with the cautery, exposed sinews being first
carefully covered over. The tissue burnt, whether
by caustic or by the cautery, is first to be cleaned,
then to be filled up with new flesh, as is clear to
anyone from what has been stated before.

Ignis sacer [a] should be counted also among the bad
ulcerations. Of this there are two kinds; one is
reddish or partly red, partly pale and roughened
by a chronic pustulation, the pustules all of about
equal size, but mostly very small: in them there is
nearly always pus and often there is redness with
heat. And sometimes the disease spreads while the
first part attacked is healing; sometimes even after
this is ulcerated, when the pustules have ruptured
and the ulcer continues and a humour is discharged
which appears to be something between sanies and
pus. It attacks chiefly the chest or flanks or

---

[a] See Appendix, p. 590.

B praecipueque in plantis. Alterum autem est in
summae cutis exulceratione, sed sine altitudine,
latum, sublividum, inaequaliter tamen; mediumque
sanescit extremis procedentibus. Ac saepe id, quod
iam sanum videbatur, iterum exulceratur. At circa
proxima cutis, quae vitium receptura est, tumidior
et durior est coloremque habet ex rubro subnigrum.
Atque hoc quoque malo fere corpora seniora temp-
tantur aut quae mali habitus sunt, sed in cruribus
C maxime.—Omnis autem sacer ignis, ut minimum
periculum habet ex iis, quae serpunt, sic prope
difficillime tollitur. Medicamentum eius fortuitum
est uno die febris, quae umorem noxium absumat.
Pus quo crassius et albidius est, eo periculi minus est.
Prodest etiam infra os vulnerum . . . laedi,[1] quo plus
puris exeat et id, quod ibi corruptum corpus est, extrahatur. Sed tamen si febricula accessit, abstin-
D entia, lectulo alvi ductione opus est. In omni vero
sacro igni neque lenibus et glutinosis [cibis], neque
salsis et acribus utendum est, sed iis, quae inter
utrunque sunt, qualis est panis sine fermento,
piscis, haedus, aves, exceptoque apro omnis fere
venatio. Si non est febricula, et gestatio utilis est et
ambulatio et vinum austere et balneum. Atque in
hoc quoque genere potio magis liberalis esse quam
cibus debet. Ipsa autem ulcera si mediocriter
serpunt, aqua calida, si vehementius, vino calido
fovenda sunt; deinde acu pusulae, quaecunque sunt,
aperiendae; tum imponenda ea, quae putrem carnem

---

[1] *The text is corrupt: one MSS. reads* ulcerum *for* vulnerum:
*Marx would insert* cutem scalpello *before* laedi *and this is
translated; other emendations are* infra ulcera locum caedi
(*V. d. Linden*), *and* infra ulcera incidere (*Targa*).

---

[1] See vol. I. pp. 181, 183 note *a*; but the meaning here may
be only riding (*i.e.* being carried about) as opposed to walking.

extremities, particularly the soles of the feet. The second form, again, consists of a superficial ulceration, not going deep, but wide, somewhat livid, yet patchy; while it heals at the centre, it extends at the margins. And often the part which apparently had healed again ulcerates. But the skin around, which is about to be invaded by the disease, becomes more swollen and harder and of a dusky red colour. And it is the aged who are mostly afflicted by this malady too or those with a bad habit of body, but chiefly in the legs. Now all cases of erysipelas, although the least dangerous of the ulcerations which spread, are the most difficult to relieve. A chance remedy for it is a one-day fever which carries off noxious humour. The thicker and the whiter the pus, the less the danger. It is also beneficial to make incisions below the openings of the sores, to let a larger amount of pus escape, and to extract it because the body there is corrupt. If, however, slight fever supervenes, abstinence, rest in bed and a clyster are needed. In erysipelas of all kinds, neither mild and glutinous nor salted and acrid foods should be used, but material of the middle class, such as unleavened bread, fish, kid, poultry and all kinds of game, except wild boar's meat. When there is no feverishness, both rocking[1] and walking are of service, and dry wine and the bath. And in this class of cases drink should be taken more freely than food. But if the ulceration spreads slowly it should be fomented with hot water; if rapidly, with hot wine; then whatever pustules there are must be opened with a needle; afterwards applications are to be made which corrode

E exedunt. Ubi inflammatio sublata ulcusque pur
gatum est, imponi lene medicamentum debet.
In altero autem genere possunt proficere mala
Cotonea in vino cocta atque contrita, potest emplastrum vel Herae vel tetrapharmacum, cui quinta pars
turis adiecta sit, potest nigra hedera ex vino austero
cocta; ac, si celeriter malum serpit, non aliud magis
proficit. Purgato ulcere, quod in summa cute esse
proposui (B), satis ad sanitatem eadem lenia medicamenta proficient.

5 Chironeum autem ulcus appellatur, quod et magnum est et habet oras duras, callosas, tumentes.
Exit sanies non multa sed tenuis. Odor malus neque
in ulcere neque in eius umore est; nulla inflammatio,
dolor modicus est; nihil serpit, ideoque nullum
periculum affert, sed non facile sanescit. Interdum
tenuis cicatrix inducitur, deinde iterum rumpitur
ulcusque renovatur. Fit maxime in pedibus et
cruribus. Super id imponi debet, quod et lene
aliquid et vehemens et reprimens habeat. Quale
eius rei causa fit ex his: squamae aeris, plumbi
eloti combusti, singulorum P. ✳ IIII; cadmiae,
cerae, singulorum P. ✳ VIII; rosae quantum satis
est ad ceram simul cum eis molliendam.

6 Fiunt etiam ex frigore ulcera hiberna, maxime in
pueris, et praecipue pedibus digitisque eorum,
nonnunquam etiam in manibus. Rubor cum inflammatione mediocri est; interdum pusulae oriuntur, deinde exulceratio: dolor autem modicus.

a V. 22. 7.    b V. 24. 4.    c Vol. I. 494.
d V. 22. 2.    e V. 19. 9.
f A chronic ulcer which was so called in reference to the
story of the centaur Cheiron who received a wound which
would not heal and therefore gave up his immortality.

putrid flesh.[a] When the inflammation is relieved
and the ulcer cleaned, soothing ointment should be
applied.[b] But in the former kind,[c] quinces, boiled
in wine and pounded, may prove beneficial, as also
a plaster, either that of Heras[d] or the tetrapharmacum,[e] with a fifth part of frankincense added, or
black ivy boiled in dry wine; and if the disease is
spreading rapidly there is nothing better. When
the ulceration has been cleaned, the same soothing
remedies which I prescribed above for the superficial variety are sufficient to induce healing.

Again, the ulcer called chironean[f] is large and
has hard, callous, swollen margins. A sanies
exudes, which is not copious, but thin. There
is no bad odour, either in the ulcer or in its
discharge; no inflammation; pain is moderate; it
does not spread, so it brings no danger, but it does
not heal readily. At times a thin scab is produced,
then in turn it is broken down and the ulceration is
renewed. It occurs chiefly on the feet and legs.
On it should be applied something which is at once
soothing, and active and repressant, such as the
following: copper scales, washed lead calcined, 16
grms. each, cadmia and wax, 32 grms. each, along
with enough rose-oil to give the wax together with
the other materials a soft consistence.

Ulcers are also produced in winter by the cold,[g]
mostly in children, and particularly on their feet and
toes, sometimes also on the hands. There is redness with moderate inflammation; sometimes pustules arise followed by ulceration; the pain is

[g] Chilblain, *ulcus hibernum*, Greek χίμετλον. Chilblains
were also called *perniones* (Pliny, *N.H.* 23. 3. 37, § 74).

Prurigo maior est : nonnunquam umor exit, sed non
multus, qui referre vel pus vel saniem videtur.—
In primis multa calida aqua fovendum est, in qua
rapa decocta, aut si ea non sunt, aliquae verbenae ex
B reprimentibus. Si nondum adapertum ulcus, aes,
quam maxime calidum quis pati potest, admovendum
est. Si iam exulceratio est, imponi debet alumen
aequa portione cum ture contritum vino adiecto,
aut malicorium in aqua coctum deinde contritum.
Si summa detracta pellicula est, hic quoque melius
lenia medicamenta proficiunt.
7    Struma quoque est tumor, in quo subter concreta
quaedam ex pure et sanguine quasi glandulae oriuntur ; quae vel praecipue fatigare medicos solent,
quoniam et febres movent nec unquam facile mature-
scunt ; et sive ferro sive medicamentis curantur,
plerumque iterum iuxta cicatrices ipsas resurgunt
multoque post medicamenta saepius ; quibus id
quoque adcedit, quod longo spatio detinent. Nascuntur maxime in cervice, sed etiam in alis et inguinibus . . .[1] lateribus : in mammis quoque feminarum se reperisse [chirurgicus] Meges auctor est.
B Propter haec et album veratrum recte datur, atque
etiam saepius, donec ea digerantur, et medicamenta
imponuntur, quae umorem vel educant vel dissipent,
quorum supra (*cap.* xviii, 1–7 A, 13 *seqq.*) mentio
facta est. Adurentibus quoque quidam utuntur,

[1] *Some words have fallen out ; Marx suggests* subinde *in
which is translated.*

[a] Celsus is here describing swellings of the lymphatic
glands of the neck, axilla and groins often tuberculous
(scrofulous) in origin and leading to the formation of a cold
abscess. Cf. II. 1. 19 and V. 18. 5–31. The word struma

moderate. The itching is greater; at times humour exudes, but not much; it seems to resemble either pus or sanies. In the first place, the ulcers are to be fomented freely with a hot decoction of turnips, or, if these are not to be had, some kind of repressant vervain. If there is not yet an open ulcer, copper scales as hot as can be borne are to be applied. If there is already an ulceration, then apply equal parts of alum and frankincense pounded together with the addition of wine, or pomegranate-rind boiled in water and then pounded. If the skin has become detached, in that case also soothing medicaments do good.

Struma,[a] again, is a swelling, in which there occur underneath certain concretions of pus and blood like little glands; they are specially embarrassing to medical men, for they set up fever and yet do not quickly come to a head; and whether they are treated by incision or by medicaments, they are generally prone to recur in the neighbourhood of their scars, and this happens much more often after the application of medicaments; and in addition to all this, they are of long duration. These swellings arise particularly in the neck, but also in the armpits and groins and in the flanks. [The surgeon] Meges stated that he had met with them also in the breasts of women.

For these white hellebore is an appropriate remedy, and this must be taken frequently until they are dispersed; and also the medicaments which have been mentioned above are applied in order to draw out or disperse the humour. Some also use caustics[b]

formerly used to describe the condition by English writers is now generally applied especially to goitre.     [b] V. 9.

CELSUS

quae exedunt crustaque eum locum astringant;
tunc vero ut ulcus curant. Quaecunque autem ratio
curandi est, corpus puro ulcere exercendum atque
alendum est, donec ad cicatricem perveniat. Quae
cum medici doceant, quorundam rusticorum experimento cognitum, quem struma male habet, si
[eum] anguem edit, liberari.

8 Furunculus vero est tuberculum acutum cum
inflammatione et dolore, maximeque ubi iam in
pus vertit. Qui ubi adapertus est, et exit pus,
apparet pars carnis in pus versa, pars corrupta
subalbida, subrubra, quem ventriculum quidam
furunculi nominant. In eo nullum periculum est,
etiam ut nulla curatio adhibeatur: maturescit enim
per se atque erumpit: sed dolor efficit, ut potior
medicina sit, quae maturius liberet.—Proprium eius
medicamentum galbanum est: sed alia quoque quae
supra (*cap.* xviii) comprehensa sunt. Si cetera
desunt, imponi debet primum non pingue emplastrum,
ut id reprimat; deinde, si non repressit, quodlibet
puri movendo accommodatum; si ne id quidem est,
vel resina vel fermentum. Expresso pure nulla
ultra curatio necessaria est.

9 Phyma vero nominatur tuberculum furunculo
simile, sed rotundius et planius, saepe etiam maius.
Nam furunculus ovi dimidii magnitudinem raro
explet, nunquam excedit: phyma etiam latius
patere consuevit, sed inflammatio dolorque sub eo
minores sunt. Ubi divisum est, pus eodem modo
apparet; ventriculus, ut in furunculo, non invenitur,

---

*a* V. 18. 21.

which eat away, and by forming a scab harden the
place; after which they dress it like an ulceration.
Whatever the mode of treatment, however, after
the ulcer has cleaned, the patient is to have
exercise and nourishment until the scar is formed.
Although these are the doctrines of the physicians;
it has been found out by the experience of some
country folk, that anyone with a bad struma may be
freed from it by eating a snake.

The boil, again, is a pointed swelling attended by
inflammation and pain, and especially so when it
is being converted into pus. When it has opened and
the pus gone out, it is seen that part of the flesh has
been turned into pus, part into a greyish-reddish core
which some call the sac of the boil. There is no
danger in it, even although no treatment is adopted;
for it ripens of itself, and bursts; but the pain
renders treatment preferable in order to afford
earlier relief. The special medicine for this is
galbanum;[a] but there are others also which have
been mentioned above. If none of these are avail-
able a plaster that is not greasy should first be
applied to disperse it; next, if this is not effective,
something adapted to promote suppuration; if even
that is not to be had, either raisin wine or yeast.
When the pus has been squeezed out, no further
treatment is needed.

A phyma is a swelling which resembles a boil,
but is rounder and flatter, often also larger. For
a boil rarely reaches the size of half an egg, and
never exceeds it; a phyma commonly extends even
over a wider area, but the pain and the inflammation in it are less. When it has been opened, pus
appears in the same way; no core is found as in a

verum omnis corrupta caro in pus vertitur. Id
autem in pueris et saepius nascitur et facilius tollitur :
in iuvenibus rarius oritur et difficilius curatur. Ubi
aetas induravit, ne nascitur quidem. Quibus vero
medicamentis discuteretur, supra (18, 16–20) propositum est.

10      Phygetron autem est tumor non altus, latus, in
quo quiddam pusulae simile est. Dolor distentioque
vehemens est, et maior quam pro magnitudine
tumoris, interdum etiam febricula. Idque tarde
maturescit neque magnopere in pus convertitur.
Fit maxime aut in vertice aut in alis aut inguinibus.
Panum a similitudine figurae nostri vocant. Atque
id ipsum quo medicamento tolleretur, supra (18, 19)
demonstravi.

11      Sed cum omnes hi nihil nisi minuti abscessus sint,
generale nomen trahit latius vitium ad suppurationem
spectans ; idque fere fit aut post febres aut post
dolores partis alicuius maximeque eos, qui ventrem
infestarunt. Saepiusque oculis expositum est, siquidem latius aliquid intumescit ad similitudinem
eius, quod phyma vocari proposui (§ 9), rubetque
cum calore et paulo post etiam cum duritia, magisque † innocenter † [1] indolescit et sitim vigiliamque
exprimit : interdum tamen nihil horum in cute
deprehendi potest, maximeque ubi altius pus movetur,
sed cum siti vigiliaque sentiuntur intus aliquae

---

[1] *This word must be corrupt. One MS. reads* inde venter.
*Targa suggests* id nocenter, *Marx conjectures* increscendo *for*
innocenter *and this is translated.*

---

<sup>a</sup> V. 18. 16, 20, 23.        <sup>b</sup> V. 28. 15.

boil, in fact all the corrupted flesh is turned into pus. Now in children this occurs more often and is more readily relieved; in young adults it is more rare and more difficult to treat. Where age has hardened the body, the disease does not even occur. By what medicaments it should be dispersed has been stated above.[a]

Phygetron, again, is a wide swelling, not much raised up, in which there is a certain resemblance to a pustule.[b] The pain and tension is severe, and more than would be expected from the size of the swelling; at times there is also feverishness. The ripening takes place slowly, and not much pus is formed. It occurs particularly on the top of the head, or in the armpits or groins. Our people call it panus, from its spindle-shape. And I have pointed out above by what medicament this should be relieved.[c]

But although all these diseases are really only minute abscesses, that name implies in general a more extensive lesion, tending to suppuration; and it occurs usually either after fevers or after pains in some part, and particularly after those which have attacked the abdomen. And generally it is visible, since there is some rather widespread swelling, like that which I have previously described as called phyma, and it grows red and hot and shortly afterwards hard as well, and becomes more painful as it increases and occasions both thirst and insomnia: sometimes, however, there may be none of these signs to note in the skin, and especially when pus is forming more deeply; but along with the thirst and insomnia some stabbing pains are felt internally.

[c] V. 18. 19.

B punctiones. Et quod desubito durius non est,
melius[1] est et quamvis non rubet, coloris tamen
aliter mutati est. Quae signa iam pure oriente
nascuntur: tumor ruborque multo ante incipiunt.
Sed si locus mollis est, avertendus is materiae aditus
est per cataplasmata, quae simul et reprimunt et
refrigerant; qualia et alias (II. 33, 2; V. 18, 21) et
paulo ante in erysipelate (V. 26, 33) proposui:
si iam durior est, ad ea veniendum est, quae digerant
et resolvant; qualis est ficus arida contusa, aut
faex mixta cum cerato, quod ex adipe suilla coactum
sit, aut cucumeris radix, cui ex farina duae partes
C adiectae sint ante ex mulso decoctae. Licet etiam
miscere aequis portionibus Hammoniacum, galbanum,
propolim, viscum, pondusque adicere myrrae dimidio minus quam in prioribus singulis erit. Atque
emplastra quoque et malagmata idem efficiunt,
quae supra (18, 7–20; 19, 9–17) explicui. Quod per
haec discussum non est, necesse est maturescat;
idque quo celerius fiat, imponenda est farina hordeacia ex aqua cocta . . .[2] recte miscetur. Eadem
autem haec in minoribus quoque abscessibus, quorum
nomina proprietatesque supra (§ 1–10) reddidi, recte
fiunt; eademque omnium curatio, tantum modo
distat.
D    Crudum est autem, in quo magis quasi . . .[3]
venarum motus est, et gravitas et ardor et distentio
et dolor et rubor et durities et, si maior abscessus est,
horror aut etiam febricula permanet; penitusque

---

[1] *Reading* melius *with one MS. Marx retains* mollius.
[2] *Constantius inserts :* cui et olerum aliquid.
[3] *Marx inserts* ferventium *and this is translated.*

---

[a] II. 33. 2; V. 18. 21–26. 33.
[b] V. 18. 7–20—19. 9–17.

And ⟨it is more favourable⟩ when it does not
become harder on a sudden, and although it does
not redden, nevertheless changes somewhat in
colour. Such are the signs which arise when pus
is already forming; the swelling and redness begin
long before. But if the place is soft, the gathering
of the diseased matter is to be diverted by poultices
which are at the same time repressant and cooling;
such as I have mentioned elsewhere, and just above
under erysipelas: [a] if it has become already hard,
recourse must be had to poultices for dispersing and
resolving; such as a dried and crushed fig, or wine-
lees mixed with cerate, made up with hog's lard, or
cucumber-root to which has been added twice the
quantity of flour, previously boiled in honey wine.
Again, we may mix equal part by weight of ammoniacum, galbanum, propolis, mistletoe-juice, and
of myrrh half as much by weight as of the other
ingredients. And the plasters and emollients which
I have described above [b] have the same effect. A
swelling which has not been dispersed by such
measures must needs mature; that it may do so
more quickly, barley-meal should be put on boiled
in water ⟨with which also some herb⟩ should be
mixed. The same applications are appropriate also
for the smaller abscesses, the names and peculiarities
of which I have referred to above; treatment is the
same for all, only differing in degree. [c]

Now a swelling is immature when the blood-
vessels throb more as if they were bubbling and
there is weight and heat and tension and pain and
redness and hardening and, if the abscess is larger,
shivering or even persistent feverishness; and a

[c] V. 28. 1–10.

condita suppuratio est, si pro his, quae alibi cutis
ostendit, punctiones sunt. Ubi ista se remiserunt,
iamque is locus prurit et aut sublividus aut subalbidus est, matura suppuratio est; eaque ubi vel per
ipsa medicamenta vel etiam ferro aperta est, pus
E debet emitti. Tum si qua in alis vel inguinibus sunt,
sine linamento nutrienda sunt. In ceteris quoque
partibus, si una plaga exigua est, si mediocris suppuratio fuit, si non alte penetravit, si febris non est,
si valet corpus, aeque linamenta supervacua sunt.
In reliquis, parce tamen, nec nisi . . .[1] plaga est,
imponi debent. Commode vero vel super linamenta
vel sine his imponitur lentricula ex melle aut malicorium ex vino coctum; quae et per se et mixta
F idonea sunt. Si qua circa duriora sunt, ad ea
mollienda vel malva contrita vel faeni·Graeci linive
semen ex passo coctum superdandum est. Quicquid
deinde impositum est, non astringi sed modice
deligari debet. Illo neminem decipi decet, ut in
hoc genere cerato utatur. Cetera quae pertinent
ad purgandum ulcus, ad implendum, ad cicatricem
inducendam, conveniuntque, in vulneribus (26. 27)
exposita sunt.

12   Nonnunquam autem et ex eiusmodi abscessibus
et ex aliis ulcerum generibus fistulae oriuntur.
Id nomen est ulceri alto, angusto, calloso. Fit in
omni fere parte corporis, habetque quaedam in
singulis locis propria. Prius de communibus dicam.
Genera igitur plura fistularum sunt, siquidem aliae
breves sunt, aliae altius penetrant; aliae rectae

----

[1] *Constantius inserts* magna.

----

[a] V. 26, 27.

suppuration is completely concealed, if, instead of
the signs presented by the skin in other cases,
there are stabbing pains. When these signs subside,
and the place begins to itch, and is either bluish or
greyish, the suppuration has matured; and when it
has been opened by means of these medicaments or
even by the knife, the pus must be let out. Then if
there are any abscesses in the armpits or groins,
they must be dressed without inserting lint. In
other parts also, if there is one small opening, if there
has been moderate suppuration, if it has not penetrated deeply, if there is no fever, if the patient is
strong, lint is equally superfluous. In other cases
lint should be applied, but sparingly, and only if the
opening is ⟨large⟩. It is beneficial, whether lint is
used or not, to apply lentil meal with honey, or
pomegranate rind boiled in wine; these are suitable alone or mixed together. If the parts are
hard, they should be softened by applying either
pounded mallow or fenugreek or flax seed boiled
in raisin wine. Whatever dressing is afterwards
applied should not be tight but bandaged on lightly.
No one should be misled into applying a cerate in
this sort of case. All the other directions for
cleaning the ulceration, forming flesh, and inducing
a scar have been described in treating of wounds.[a]

Sometimes, again, fistulae arise, both from abscesses
of this kind and from other sorts of ulceration. That
is the name for a deep, narrow, hardened ulcer. A
fistula occurs in almost any part of the body, but in
each place it has some peculiarities. I shall speak
first of its general characteristics. There are
many kinds of fistulae, then, and whilst some are
short, others penetrate deeper; some run straight

intus feruntur, aliae multoque plures transversae;
aliae simplices sunt, aliae duplices triplitesve ab uno
ore intus orsae quae fiunt; aut etiam in plures sinus
dividuntur; aliae rectae, aliae flexae et tortuosae
B sunt. Aliae intra carnem desinunt, aliae ad ossa
aut cartilaginem penetrant aut, ubi neutrum horum
subest, ad interiora perveniunt; aliae deinde facile,
aliae cum difficultate curantur; atque etiam quaedam insanabiles reperiuntur.—Expedita curatio in
fistula simplici recenti intra carnem, adiuvatque ipsum
corpus, si iuvenile, si firmum est: inimica contraria
his sunt; itemque si fistula os vel cartilaginem vel
nervum vel musculos laesit; si articulum occupavit;
si vel ad vessicam vel ad pulmonem vel ad vulvam vel
ad grandes venas arteriasve vel ad inania, ut guttur,
C stomachum, thoracem, penetravit. Ad intestina
quoque eam tendere semper periculosum, saepe
pestiferum est. Quibus multum mali accedit, si
corpus vel aegrum vel senile vel mali habitus est.
Ante omnia autem demitti specillum in fistulam
convenit, ut quo tendat at quam alte perveniat,
scire possimus, simul etiam protinus umida an siccior
sit; quod extracto specillo patet. Si vero os in
vicino est, id quoque disci potest, iam necne eo
fistula pervenerit; . . .[1] penetravit, quatenus nocu-
D erit. Nam si molle est, quod ultimo specillo
contingitur, intra carnem adhuc vitium est: si
magis id renititur, ad os ventum est. Ibi deinde si
labitur specillum, nondum caries est: si non labitur,
sed aequali innititur, caries quidem, verum adhuc

---

[1] *Marx inserts* et si eo.

inwards, others, and by far the most numerous,
crosswise; some are simple, others beginning by one
opening form two or three branches inside or even
divide into several passages; some go straight, others
are curved and tortuous. Some end in the flesh,
others penetrate to bone or to cartilage, or, when
neither of these is underneath, reach to the inner
parts; some, therefore, are treated easily, others
with difficulty; and some are even found to be incurable. The treatment is speedy when the fistula
is simple, recent and only involving the flesh, and
the body itself helps, when it is youthful and sound:
contrary conditions are inimical; also if the fistula has
damaged bone or cartilage or sinew or muscles; if
it has involved a joint; or if it has penetrated either
to the bladder or lung or womb or to large veins or
arteries or to hollow regions, such as the throat,
gullet or thorax. When too the fistula goes towards
the intestines it is always dangerous, often deadly.
When the body is either sick or aged or in bad
condition, the case is much worse. First of all,
however, it is proper to pass a probe into the fistula,
that we may learn both its direction and depth, and
at the same time whether it is moist or rather dry.
This is known when the probe is withdrawn. But if
there is bone in the neighbourhood, we can also
learn whether the fistula has reached and penetrated
the bone or not, and how far the damage has gone.
For if what is touched by the end of the probe is
soft, the disease is still limited to the flesh; if it
meets with more resistance, the fistula has reached
bone. But when the probe slides smoothly, there
is not yet decay; if it does not so slide, but meets
with an even surface, there is some decay although

levis est: si inaequale quoque et asperum subest,
E vehementius os exessum est. At cartilago ubi
subsit, ipsa sedes docet perventumque esse ad eam
ex renisu patet. Et ex his quidem colliguntur
fistularum sedes, spatia, noxae: simplices vero eae
sint, an in plures partes diducantur, cognosci potest
ex modo puris; cuius si plus fertur quam quod
simplici spatio convenit, plures sinus esse manifestum
est; cumque fere iuxta sint caro et nervos et aliqua
nervosa, quales fere tunicae membranaeque sunt,
genus quoque puris docebit, num plures sinus intus
F diversa corporis genera perroserint. Siquidem in
carne pus leve, album, copiosius fertur; at ex nervoso
loco coloris quidem eiusdem, sed tenuius et minus;
ex nervo pingue et oleo non dissimile. Denique
etiam corporis inclinatio docet, num in plures partes
fistulae penetrarint, quia saepe cum quis aliter
decubuit aliterve membrum conlocavit, pus ferri quod
iam desierat iterum incipit; testaturque non solum
alium sinum esse ex quo descendat, sed etiam in
G aliam corporis partem eum tendere. Sed si et in
carne et recens et simplex est, ac neque rugosa
neque cava sede neque in articulo, sed in eo membro,
quod per se inmobile non nisi cum toto corpore
movetur, satis proficiet emplastrum, quod recentibus
vulneribus inponitur, dum habeat vel sale vel alumen
vel squamam aeris vel aeruginem vel ex metallicis

still slight; if what underlies is uneven also and rough, the bone has become more seriously eaten away. But the position of the fistula shows where there is underlying cartilage, and resistance to the probe shows when this has been reached. And from these signs we may gather the situation, extent and harmfulness of fistulae; whether too they are simple, or have several branches, can be estimated from the amount of pus; for if there is more than one opening will account for, it is clear that there are several branches; and since generally flesh and sinew and sinewy tissue such as sheaths and membranes are near the fistula, the character of the pus also will show whether the several branches have eaten into other parts of the body. For pus derived from flesh is smooth, white and fairly plentiful; from sinewy structures it is of the same colour but thinner and less in quantity; from sinews it is fatty and not unlike oil. Further also, the bending of the body indicates whether the fistulae have penetrated in several directions, because often when a patient has changed his recumbent posture, or held a limb in a different position, pus which had previously ceased, begins to discharge again; and it then becomes evident, not only that there is another branch from which pus is being discharged, but also that it is tending into another part of the body. But if the fistula is in the flesh, and is recent and simple, and is not tortuous or in a cavity or joint, but in a part which remains still unless moved with the body generally, a sufficiently effective application is a plaster such as is applied to recent wounds, so long as it is composed of either salt or of alum or of copper scales or of verdigris or some other metallic

aliquid; exque eo collyrium fieri debet altera parte
tenuius, altera parte paulo plenius; idque ea parte,
qua tenuius est, antecedente demitti oportet in
H fistulam, donec purus sanguis se ostendat. Quae in
omnibus collyris fistularum perpetua sint. Idem
deinde emplastrum in linteolo superinponendum,
supraque inicienda spongia est in acetum ante
demissa; solvique quinto die satis est. Genusque
victus adhibendum est, quo carnem ali docui (V. 14.
26, 30). Ac si longius a praecordis fistula est, ex
intervallo ieiunum radiculas esse, deinde vomere
necessarium est. Vetustate callosa fit fistula.
Callus autem neminem fallit, quia durus est et aut
I albus aut pallidus. Sed tum validioribus medicamentis opus est; quale est, quod habet: papaveris
lacrimae P. ✳ I; cummis P. ✳ III =; cadmiae P. ✳
IIII; atramenti sutori P. ✳ VIII; ex quibus aqua
coactis collyrium fit. Aut in quo sunt: gallae
P. ✳ =—; aeruginis, sandaracae, aluminis Aegypti,
singulorum P. ꝫ I; atramenti sutori conbusti
P. ꝫ II. Aut quod constat ex chalcitide et saxo
calcis, quibus auripigmenti dimidio minus quam
in singulis prioribus est adicitur; eaque melle cocto
K excipiuntur. Expeditissimum autem est ex prae-
cepto Megetis aeruginis rasae P. ✳ II conterere,
deinde Hammoniaci thymiamatis P. ꝫ I aceto
liquare, eoque infuso aeruginem cogere; idque ex
primis medicamentis est. Sed ut haec maximi

---

*a* A tent or *collyrium* (Low Latin *tenta*, Greek κολλύριον)
was material made up with a glutinous paste which was rolled
and formed into sticks shaped like vermicelli (*collyra*). These
were used to dilate a fistula, or the uterus (τῶν μητρῶν
κολλούρια. Hippocrates, *Diseases of Women*, I. 51); or else
pieces were broken off the stick and dissolved for use (*e.g.*

substances; and from this a tent[a] should be made, thinner at one end, a little thicker at the other. This should be passed into the fistula with the pointed end forwards, and be kept until pure blood shows itself. Such are the general rules for the use of all tents for fistulae. Next, the same plaster spread on lint is put over the place, and over that is applied a sponge dipped in vinegar; it is sufficient to change the dressing on the fifth day. The class of food to be used is that which I have prescribed for making flesh.[b] And if the fistula is at some distance from the praecordia, the patient should eat radishes at intervals on an empty stomach, and then vomit. A fistula of long standing becomes callous. Now no one can mistake callus, for it is hard and either white or pallid. But there is then need for stronger medicines: such as that which has of poppy tears 4 grms., gum 12·66 grms., cadmia 16 grms., blacking 32 grms., worked up with water to form a tent. Or else there is the composition containing galls 1 grm., verdigris, sandarach, Egyptian alum, 1·16 grm. each, roasted blacking 2·32 grms. Or that which is composed of copper ore and limestone, with half as much orpiment as of each of the other two; and these are taken up in boiled honey. But the quickest remedy is that prescribed by Meges; rub up verdigris scrapings 8 grms., then dissolve ammoniacum for incense 1·16 grm. in vinegar, and work the verdigris into this infusion; and this is one of the best remedies. But whilst the above remedies are

as eye salves, VI. 6). As lately as thirty or forty years ago such sticks were still prepared and pieces broken off and used in this way.

[b] V. 14. 26, 30.

effectus sunt, sic, cui ista non adsunt, facile tamen
est callum quibuslibet adurentibus medicamentis
erodere: satisque est vel papyrum intortum vel
aliquid ex penicillo in modum collyri adstrictum
eo inlini. Scilla quoque cocta et mixta cum calce
L callum exest. Si quando vero longior sed transversa
fistula est, demisso specillo contra principium huius
incidi commodissimum est, et collyrium utrinque
demitti. At si duplicem esse fistulam aut multiplicem existimamus, sic tamen ut brevis intraque
carnem sit, collyrio uti non debemus, quod unam
partem curet, reliquas omittat; sed eadem medicamenta arida in calamum scriptorium coicienda
sunt, isque ori fistulae aptandus, inspirandumque, ut
M ea medicamenta intus conpellantur: aut eadem ex
vino liquanda, vel, si sordidior fistula est, ex mulso,
si callosior, ex aceto sunt idque intus infundendum.
Quicquid inditum est, superponenda sunt, quae
refrigerent et reprimant: nam fere quae circa
fistulam sunt, habent aliquid inflammationis. Neque
alienum est, ubi qui solverit, antequam rursus alia
medicamenta coiciat, per oricularium clysterem fistulam eluere; si plus puris fertur, vino; si callus
durior est, aceto; si iam purgatur, mulso vel aqua,
in qua ervum coctum sit, sic ut huic quoque mellis
N paulum adiciatur. Fere vero fit, ut ea tunica,
quae inter foramen et integram carnem est, victa
medicamentis tota exeat, infraque ulcus purum sit;
quod ubi contigit, imponenda glutinantia sunt,
praecipueque spongia melle cocto inlita. Neque

the most efficacious, when they are not at hand it is easy to eat away the callus with any of the caustic medicaments; it is enough to smear one of them on rolled papyrus, or upon a pledget of wool twisted into the shape of a tent. Squills boiled and mixed with quicklime also eat away callus. If, however, the fistula is longer but runs crosswise, it is best to insert a probe and to cut down upon its end; then a tent is passed into each opening. But if we deem the fistula to be double or multiple, yet only short and confined to flesh, we should not make use of a tent, because it treats one part and omits the rest; but the same medicaments, dry, are put into a writing-quill, and that having been placed against the orifice of the fistula is to be blown through, in order that these medicaments may be forced in; or the same materials dissolved in wine, or, if the fistula is more foul, in honey wine, or, if more callous, in vinegar, are to be poured in. Whatever is introduced, refrigerants and repressants must be put on over the wound; for generally the parts surrounding the fistula are somewhat inflamed. It is not inappropriate, when changing the dressings and again before inserting fresh medicaments, to wash out the fistula, using an ear syringe; with wine if there is much pus; with vinegar if there is hard callus; if it is already clean, with honey wine or a decoction of vetch, to which also a little honey should be added. Thus it generally happens that that covering which is between the opening and the sound flesh is destroyed by the medicaments and comes quite away, and underneath is a clean ulceration; when this has occurred, agglutinants are applied, especially a sponge steeped in boiled honey. I am

157

ignoro multis placuisse linamentum in modum collyri
compositum tinctum melle demitti; sed celerius id
glutinat quam impletur. Neque verendum est,
ne purum corpus puro corpori iunctum non coeat:
adiectis quoque medicamentis ad id efficacibus
. . .[1] cum saepe exulceratio digitorum, nisi magna
cura prospeximus, sanescendo in unum eos iungat.

13    Est etiam ulceris genus, quod a favi similitudine
κηρίον a Graecis nominatur, idque duas species habet.
Alterum est subalbidum, furunculo simile, sed maius
et cum dolore maiore. Quod ubi maturescit, habet
foramina, per quae fertur umor glutinosus et pu-
rulentus; neque tamen ad iustam maturitatem
pervenit. Si divisum est, multo plus intus corrupti
quam in furunculo apparet altiusque descendit.
B Raro fit nisi in scapulis. Alterum . . .[2] est minus
super corpus eminens, durum, latum, subviride,
subpallidum, magis exulceratum: siquidem ad singulorum pilorum radices foramina sunt, per quae
fertur umor glutinosus, subpallidus, crassitudinem
mellis aut visci referens, interdum olei. Si inciditur,
viridis intus caro apparet. Dolor autem et inflammatio ingens est, adeo ut acutam quoque febrem
movere consuerint.—Super id, quod minus crebris
foraminibus exasperatum est, recte inponitur et
ficus arida et lini semen in mulso coctum et emplastra
ac malagmata materiam educentia, aut quae pro-
C prie huc pertinentia supra (*cap.* XII) posui. Super
alterum et eadem medicamenta, et farina ex mulso
cocta, sic ut ei dimidium resinae terebenthinae

---

[1] *Some words have fallen out; Marx supplies* saepe non
opus esse videmus *after* efficacibus *and this is translated.*
[2] *Marx adds:* alterum <fit in capite tantum>.

---

    [a] A follicular abscess among hair.     [b] V. 12.

not unaware that many favour the insertion of lint formed into a tent and dipped in honey; but this agglutinates more quickly than flesh is formed. There need be no fear that clean flesh in contact with clean flesh will fail to unite: we see that there is often no need to add medicaments as well to effect this, since often when there is ulceration of the fingers, unless we have taken careful precautions, they become joined together whilst healing.

There is besides a class of ulceration which the Greeks call κηρίον[a] from its resemblance to honey-comb, and of this there are two kinds. One is greyish, like a boil, but larger and more painful. As it is maturing, holes appear through which is discharged a glutinous and purulent humour; yet it does not properly mature. If it is cut into, there appears much more corruption than in a boil, and it penetrates deeper. It is rare except in the scapular region. The other kind is found only in the head; it projects less above the surface, is hard, broad, greenish or greyish-green in colour, more ulcerated; there are holes at the root of each hair, through which is discharged a glutinous greenish-white humour, in consistency like honey or mistletoe-juice, or at times like olive-oil. If it is cut into, the flesh within appears green. The pain also and inflammation are so severe that they generally cause acute fever. On a case which is only irritated by a few openings, suitable applications are a dry fig and linseed boiled in honey wine or plasters or emollients which draw out diseased matter, or the medicaments noted above for such purposes.[b] For the other form of this, the same medicaments are good, also flour boiled in honey wine mixed with half its quantity of turpentine-resin;

misceatur; et ficus in mulso decocta, cui paulum
hysopi contriti sit adiectum; et uvae taminiae pars
quarta fico adiecta. Quod si parum in utrolibet
genere medicamenta proficiunt, totum ulcus usque ad
sanam carnem excidi oportebit. Ulcere ablato super
plagam medicamenta danda sunt, primum quae pus
citent, deinde quae purgent, tum quae impleant.

14 Sunt vero quaedam verrucis similia, quorum
diversa nomina ut vitia sunt. Acrochordona vocant,
ubi sub cute coit aliquid durius, et interdum paulo
asperius, coloris eiusdem, infra tenue, ad cutem
latius; idque modicum est, quia raro fabae magnitudinem excedit. Vix unum tantum eodem tempore
nascitur, sed fere plura, maximeque in pueris;
eaque nonnumquam subito desinunt, nonnumquam
mediocrem inflammationem excitant; sub qua etiam
B in pus convertuntur. At thymion nominatur, quod
super corpus quasi verrucula eminet, ad cutem tenue,
supra latius, subdurum et in summo perasperum.
Idque summum colorem floris thymi repraesentat,
unde ei nomen est, ibique facile finditur et cruentatur;
nonnumquam aliquantum sanguinis fundit, fereque
circa magnitudinem fabae Aegyptiae est, raro maius,
interdum perexiguum. Modo unum autem, modo
plura nascuntur, vel in palmis vel inferioribus pedum
partibus. Pessima tamen in obscenis sunt maxi-
C meque ibi sanguinem fundunt. Myrmecia autem
vocantur humiliora thymio durioraque, quae radices
altius exigunt maioremque dolorem movent: infra
lata, super autem tenuia, minus sanguinis mittunt;

---

ᵃ Vol. I. 94, note.          ᵇ V. **28**. 2 C, note.

ᶜ μυρμήκιον, an anthill (cf. Paulus Aegineta, IV. 15), was the
name given to this sort of wart because the irritation from it
resembled that caused by ants (*formicatio*).

also a fig boiled in honey wine, to which a little pounded hyssop may be added; also black bryony berries, added to a fig, one part to three. If in either case medicaments are of little service, the whole ulceration ought to be cut away down to the sound flesh. When the ulceration is removed, medicaments are put on the wound, first to promote suppuration, next to clean it, and then to make flesh.

There are also certain wart-like ulcerations, different in name and in their ill-effects. They call one acrochordon,[a] when some material which is rather hard and at times somewhat rough, collects under the skin: its colour is that of the skin; it is thin underneath, broadening nearer the skin; of moderate size, as it is seldom larger than a bean. It is rare to find one alone, but generally there are several, and they are mostly found in children; and sometimes they go suddenly, sometimes they cause slight inflammation, and under this they even turn into pus. But that which is named thymion[b] projects above the surface like a little wart, narrow near the skin, wider above, hardish and at the top very rough. The top in colour is like flowers of thyme, whence its name, and there it is readily split and made to bleed; at times the bleeding is considerable; it is generally about the size of an Egyptian bean, rarely larger, sometimes quite small. Sometimes one is alone, generally several grow together, either on the palms or soles of the feet. The worst, however, are situated upon the genitals, and there they bleed the most. But those called myrmecia[c] are less prominent and harder than the thymion, their roots are more deeply fixed and they are more painful: they are broad underneath but thin above, they bleed less,

magnitudine vix umquam lupini modum excedunt.
Nascuntur ea quoque aut in palmis, aut inferioribus
pedum partibus. Clavus autem nonnumquam quidem alibi, sed in pedibus tamen maxime nascitur,
praecipue ex contuso, quamvis[*] interdum aliter;
dolorem, etiamsi non alias, tamen ingredienti movet.

D Ex his acrochordon et thymium saepe etiam per se
finiuntur, et quo minora sunt, eo magis. Myrmecia
et clavi sine curatione vix umquam desinunt. Acrochordon, si excissa est, nullam radiculam relinquit,
ideoque ne renascitur quidem. Thymio clavoque
excissis, subter rotunda radicula nascitur, quae penitus descendit ad carnem, eaque relicta idem rursus
exigit. Myrmecia latissimis radicibus inhaerent,
ideoque ne excidi quidem sine exulceratione magna
possunt. Clavum subinde radere commodissimum
est: nam sine ulla vi sic mollescit; ac si sanguinis
E quoque aliquid emissum est, saepe emoritur. Tollitur etiam, si quis eum circumpurgat, deinde
inponit resinam, cui miscuit pulveris paulum,
quem ex lapide molari contrito fecit. Cetera vero
genera medicamentis adurenda sunt; aliisque id,
quod ex faece vini; myrmecis id, quod ex alumine et
sandaraca est, aptissimum. Sed ea, quae circa sunt,
foliis contegi debent, ne ipsa quoque exulcerentur;
deinde postea lenticula imponi. Tollit thymium
etiam ficus in aqua cocta.

15 At pusulae maxime vernis temporibus oriuntur.
Earum plura genera sunt. Nam modo circa totum
corpus partemve aspritudo quaedam fit, similis iis
pusulis, quae ex urtica vel sudore nascuntur: exanthemata[*] Graeci vocant; eaque modo rubent,

---

[a] A corn, callosity.      [b] V. 28. 2 C.
[c] ἐξάνθημα = efflorescence, blossom; cf. vol. I. p. 150;
Hipp. IV. 182 (Aph. VI. 9).

and they scarcely ever exceed the size of a lupin. These also grow either on the palms or soles of the feet. The clavus,[a] again, though occasionally found elsewhere, occurs mostly on the feet, and especially after contusions, although sometimes from other causes; it causes pain when walking, though not at other times.

Of these the acrochordon and thymion often end of themselves, and the more so the smaller they are. The myrmecia and corns scarcely ever subside without treatment. The acrochordon, if cut off, leaves no trace of a root behind, and so does not sprout again. When the thymion and clavus have been cut off, a small rounded root is formed underneath, which penetrates right down into the flesh, and if this is left behind it sprouts up again. The myrmecia are held by very broad roots, and so cannot be excised without causing a large wound. A corn is best scraped down from time to time; for thus, without any violence, it softens, and if also a little blood is let out, it often dies away. It is also removed if we clean the part round it and then put on resin mixed with a little powdered millstone. All the other varieties are to be burnt away by medicaments: for some the ash of wine-lees is best; for myrmecia the application made of alum and sandarach. But the skin all round should be covered with leaves that it also may not become ulcerated; afterwards lentil meal is put on. Even a fig in boiled water removes a thymium.[b]

Pustules arise chiefly in the spring; there are many kinds. For at times a sort of roughness comes all over the body, or a part of it, resembling the pustules which are set up by nettles or by sweating; exanthemata[c] the Greeks call them. At times

B modo colorem cutis non excedunt. Nonnumquam
plures similes varis oriuntur, nonnumquam maiores
pusulae lividae aut pallidae aut nigrae, aut aliter
naturali colore mutato; subestque his umor. Ubi
eae ruptae sunt, infra quasi exulcerata caro apparet:
phlyctaenae Graece nominantur. Fiunt vel ex
frigore vel ex igne vel ex medicamentis. Phlyzacion autem paulo durior pusula est, subalbida,
acuta, ex qua ipsa quod exprimitur umidum est.
At ex pusulis vero nonnumquam etiam ulcuscula fiunt
aut aridiora aut umidiora; et modo tantum cum
prurigine, modo etiam cum inflammatione aut
dolore; exitque aut pus aut sanies aut utrumque; maximeque id evenit in aetate puerili, raro in
medio corpore, saepe in eminentibus partibus.
C Pessima pusula est, quae epinyctis vocatur: ea
colore vel sublivida vel nigra vel alba esse consuevit.
Circa hanc autem vehemens inflammatio est; et
cum adaperta est, reperitur intus exulceratio muc-
cosa, colore umori suo similis. Dolor ex ea supra
magnitudinem eius est: neque enim ea faba maior
est. Atque haec quoque oritur in eminentibus
partibus et fere noctu; unde nomen quoque a Graecis
D ei inpositum est.—In omnium vero pusularum curatione primum est multum ambulare atque exerceri;
si quid ista prohibet, gestari. Secundum est cibum
minuere, abstinere ab omnibus acribus et extenuantibus: eademque nutrices facere oportet, si lactens
puer ita adfectus est. Praeter haec is, qui iam
robustus est, si pusulae minutae sunt, desudare in
balneo debet, simulque super eas nitrum inspergere

---

<sup>a</sup> φλύκταιναι = bubbles or blisters.
<sup>b</sup> ἐπινυκτίς, night pustule, *e.g.* from a bugbite.

they are red, at times no redder than the colour of
the skin; sometimes a number occur resembling
pimples, sometimes the pustules are larger, livid or
pallid or black or otherwise changed from the natural
colour; and there is humour underneath them. When
these have burst the flesh below looks as if it were
ulcerated; in Greek these are called phlyctaenae.[a]
They are produced either by cold or by heat or by
medicaments. A phlyzacion is a somewhat harder
pustule, whitish and pointed, from which moisture is
squeezed out. But after pustules at times small
ulcerations arise, either dry or moist, sometimes
attended only by itching, sometimes also by inflammation and pain; the discharge is either pus or
sanies or both; this generally occurs in children,
seldom on the trunk, often on the extremities.
The worst kind of pustule is that called epinyctis;[b] its colour is usually livid or black or white.
And there is severe inflammation round it; and when
laid open a mucous ulceration is found within, of a
colour like its own humour. It gives greater pain
than its size would suggest; for it is no larger than
a bean. And this too grows on the extremities, and
generally by night, whence also the name applied
to it by the Greeks. Now in all kinds of pustules,
the treatment first is much walking and exercise;
and if anything prevents these, then rockings.
Next food must be diminished, all things acrid and
thinning avoided; and the same treatment should
be applied to nursing women, if the sucking baby is
so affected. Moreover, the patient who is robust,
if the pustules are small, ought to go to the bath
and sweat, and at the same time to dust the pustules
with soda and to mix wine with oil and anoint

oleoque vinum miscere et sic ungui; tum descendere
in solium. Si nihil sic proficitur, aut si maius
pusularum genus occupavit, imponenda lenticula est,
detractaque summa pellicula ad medicamenta lenia
E transeundum est. Epinyctis post lenticulam recte
herba quoque sanguinali vel viridi coriandro curatur.
Ulcera ex pusulis facta tollit spuma argenti cum
semine feni Graeci mixta, sic ut his invicem rosa
atque intubi sucus adiciatur, donec mellis crassitudo
ei fiat. Proprie ad eas pusulas, quae infantes male
habent, lapidis, quem pyriten vocant, P. ℈ VIII cum
quinquaginta amaris nucibus miscetur, adiciunturque
olei cyathi tres. Sed prius ungui ex cerussa pusulae
debent, tum hoc inlini.

16    Scabies vero durior: cutis rubicunda, ex qua
pusulae oriuntur, quaedam umidiores, quaedam
sicciores. Exit ex quibusdam sanies, fitque ex his
continuata exulceratio pruriens; serpitque in quibusdam cito. Atque in aliis quidem ex toto desinit,
in aliis vero certo tempore anni revertitur. Quo
asperior est quoque prurit magis, eo difficilius
tollitur: itaque eam, quae talis est, agrian [id est
B feram] Graeci appellant.—In hoc quoque victus ratio
eadem quae supra (15 D) necessaria est: medicamentum autem ad incipientem hanc idoneum est,
quod fit ex spodi, croci, aeruginis, singulorum P. ℈ I;
piperis albi, omphaci, singulorum P. ✳ I; cadmiae
P. ℈ VIII. At ubi iam exulceratio est, id, quod fit

---

    ᵃ Scabies, originally a roughening or hardening of the skin.
See note c.
    ᵇ The name ψώρα ἄγρια (ψώρα = scab), or λέπρα, was applied
to many skin diseases, including leprosy (Lev. XXI. 20, septua-

166

himself, after which he goes down into the hot
bath. If this does no good, or if the pustules are
of the larger kind, lentil meal should be applied,
and after the upper skin has been detached, we
must pass on to soothing medicaments. The
epinyctis, after lentil meal application, is appropriately treated by means of polygonum or green
coriander. Ulcerations caused by the pustules are
relieved by litharge mixed with fenugreek seeds,
rose-oil and endive juice being added in turn until
the mixture becomes of the consistency of honey.
For the pustules which affect infants apply : pyrite
stone 9·3 grms., mixed with fifty bitter almonds, and
125 c.cm. of oil added. But first the pustules should
be anointed with white-lead, then smeared with the
above.

But scabies[a] is harder: the skin is ruddy, from
which the pustules grow up, some moist, some dry.
From some of these sanies escapes; and from
them comes a persistent itching ulceration, which in
some cases rapidly spreads. And whilst in some per-
sons it vanishes completely, in others it returns at a
definite time of the year. The rougher the skin,
and the more the itching, the more difficult is its
relief. Hence the Greeks call such scabies, agria[b]
[that is, savage]. In this case also the same regimen
as that given above is necessary ;[c] at the beginning
a suitable application is that composed of sublimed
zinc oxide, saffron, verdigris 1·16 grms. each; white
pepper and omphacium 4 grms.; zinc oxide ore 9·3
grms. But when ulceration already exists that com-

gint). The term scabies is now restricted to the pustules set
up by the itch insect (sarcoptes scabiei).
  [c] V. 28. 15 D.

ex sulpuris P. ꝶ- I; cerae P. ꝶ- IIII; picis liquidae
hemina; olei sextaris duobus; quae simul incoc-
C untur, dum crassitudo mellis sit. Est etiam quod ad
Protarchum auctorem refertur. Habet farinae lupi-
norum S.I.; nitri cyathos IIIIS.; picis liquidae heminam; resinae umidae selibram; aceti cyathos tres.
Crocum quoque, Lycium, aerugo, murra, cinis
aequis portionibus recte miscentur, et ex passo
cocuntur; idque omnem pituitam ubique sustinet.
Ac si nihil aliud est, amurca ad tertiam partem
decocta vel sulpur pici liquidae mixtum, sicut in
pecoribus proposui, hominibus quoque scabie laborantibus opitulantur.

17      Inpetiginis vero species sunt quattuor. Minime
mala est, quae similitudinem scabie repraesentat:
nam et rubet et durior est et exulcerata est et
roditur. Distat autem ab ea, quod magis exulcerata
est et varis similis pusulas habet; videnturque esse in
ea quasi bullulae quaedam, ex quibus interposito tempore squamulae resolvuntur; certioribusque hoc tem-
B poribus revertitur. Alterum genus peius est, simile
papulae fere, sed asperius rubicundiusque; figuras
varias habet; squamulae ex summa cute discedunt;
rosio maior est; celerius et latius procedit certioribusque etiamnum quam prior temporibus et fit et desinit:
rubrica cognominatur. Tertia etiannum deterior est:
nam et crassior est et durior et magis tumet; in
summa cute finditur et vehementius roditur. Ipsa

---

<sup>a</sup> V. **18**. 8.

<sup>b</sup> *Celsi Agriculturae Fragmenta* Marx, p. 11 (Frag. XXXIV.).

<sup>c</sup> *Impetigo*. The present meaning of impetigo is ill defined :
the word is probably derived from the sudden onset (impetus) of
some forms of skin disease. Celsus here appears to be describing a form of eczema or lichen: on skin diseases see also V.
**26**. 20 B, C, D.

posed of sulphur 1·16 grm., wax 4·65 grms., liquid
pitch 250 c.cm., oil one litre; these are heated
together until they are of the consistency of honey.
There is also the composition ascribed to Protarchus.[a]  It consists of half a litre of lupin meal,
190 c.cm. of soda, 250 c.cm. of liquid pitch, liquid
resin 168 grms., and 125 c.cm. of vinegar.  Also
a suitable mixture is saffron, lycium, verdigris,
myrrh, and charcoal in equal proportions boiled in
raisin wine; this checks everywhere all discharge
of phlegm.  And when there is nothing else at
hand, lees of olive-oil boiled down to one-third, or
sulphur mixed with liquid pitch, as I have suggested
for cattle[b] is also of service for men suffering from
scabies.

Impetigo,[c] again, has four species.  The least bad
is that which presents a resemblance to scabies; for
there is redness and some hardness and ulceration
and erosion.  But it is distinguished from scabies
because there is more ulceration and there are
pustules like pimples, and in it is seen an appearance
as of small bubbles from which after a time little
scales are detached; and this recurs at fixed seasons.
The second kind is worse, almost like a pimple, but
rougher and redder; it has various shapes; small scales
are detached from the skin surface; there is more
erosion; it spreads more rapidly and widely, and both
comes and goes at fixed seasons even more markedly
than the previous sort; it is called *rubrica*.[d]  The
third kind is worse still: for it is thicker, harder
and there is more swelling; there are cracks in the
skin and more active erosion.  This form also is scaly,

[d] The colour of red earth or ochre (*rubrica*), was like that
of the diseased area.

quoque squamosa sed nigra; proceditque et late nec
tarde; et minus errat in temporibus, quibus aut
oritur aut desinit neque ex toto tollitur: nigrae
C cognomen est.   Quartum genus est, quod curationem
omnino non recipit, distans colore: nam subalbidum
est et recenti cicatrici simile; squamulasque habet
pallidas, quasdam subalbidas, quasdam lenticulae
similes, quibus demptis nonnumquam profluit sanguis.
Alioqui vero umor eius albidus est, cutis dura atque
fissa est; proceditque latius.   Haec vero omnia
genera maxime oriuntur in pedibus et manibus;
atque ungues quoque infestant.   Medicamentum
non aliud valentius est quam quod ad scabiem quoque
pertinere sub auctore Protarcho retuli (28, 16 C).
Serapion autem nitri P. ℈ II, sulpuris P. ℈ IIII
excipiebat resina copiosa, eaque utebatur.

18    Papularum vero duo genera sunt.   Alterum est in
quo per minimas pusulas cutis exasperatur et rubet
leviterque roditur: medium habet pauxillo levius,
tarde serpit.   Idque vitium maxime rotundum
incipit, eademque ratione in orbem procedit.   Altera
autem est, quam agrian [id est feram] Graeci appellant; in qua similiter quidem sed magis cutis
exasperatur exulceraturque, ac vehementius et
roditur et rubet et interdum etiam pilos remittit.
B Minus rotunda est, difficilius sanescit: nisi sublata
est, in inpetiginem vertitur.   Sed levis papula etiam,
si ieiuna saliva cotidie defricatur, sanescit: maior
commodissime murali herba tollitur, si sub ea de-
trita est.   Ut vero ad composita medicamenta
veniamus, idem illud Protarchi (28, 17 C) tanto
valentius in his est, quanto minus in his viti est.

---

*a* The description here given by Celsus is approximately
that of lichen circumscriptus and lichen anulatus.

but the scales are black. It spreads widely and not slowly. It varies less in the times at which it increases or subsides, and is never quite got rid of: its name is black impetigo. The fourth kind, which is quite incurable, differs in colour, for it is whitish and like a recent scar, and has small pallid or whitish scales; some are like lentils, and when these are removed there is sometimes bleeding. Otherwise its humour is white, the skin hard and chapped; it spreads widely. Now all these kinds occur generally on the hands and feet; they also attack the nails. There is no more efficacious remedy than that which I have mentioned above as prescribed by Protarchus for scabies. But Serapion used soda 2·32 grms., and sulphur 4·64 grms., taken up with plenty of resin.

Of papules again there are two kinds.[a] There is one in which the skin is roughened by very small pustules, and is reddened and slightly eroded; in the middle it is a little smoother; it spreads slowly. This disease generally has a round shape at its beginning, and in the same fashion it spreads in a circle. But the other variety is that which the Greeks call agria [that is, savage]; and in this there is a similar but greater roughness of the skin with ulceration, more severe erosion, and redness; sometimes it even loosens the hair. It is less round in shape, heals with more difficulty, and unless it is got rid of, turns into an impetigo. But in fact a slight papule heals if it is rubbed daily with spittle before eating; a more severe one is got rid of best by an application of pounded pellitory. But turning to compound medicaments, that same one of Protarchus is efficacious in these cases, when the disorder is less severe. An alterna-

Alterum ad idem Myronis: nitri rubri, turis, singulorum P. ✳ I; cantharidum purgatarum P. ✳ II;
sulpuris ignem non experti tantundem; resinae
terebenthinae liquidae P. ✳ XX; farinae loli S.
III; gitti cyathos IIIS.; picis crudae S.I.

19    Vitiligo quoque quamvis per se nullum periculum
adfert, tamen et foeda est et ex malo corporis
habitu fit. Eius tres species sunt. Alphos vocatur,
ubi color albus est, fere subasper, et non continuus,
ut quaedam quasi guttae dispersae esse videantur.
Interdum etiam latius et cum quibusdam intermis-
B sionibus serpit. Melas colore ab hoc differt, quia
niger est et umbrae similis: cetera eadem sunt.
Leuce habet quiddam simile alpho, sed magis albida
est, et altius descendit, in eaque albi pili sunt et
lanugini similes. Omnia haec serpunt, sed in aliis
celerius, in aliis tardius. Alphos et melas in quibusdam variis temporibus et oriuntur et desinunt:
leuce quem occupavit, non facile dimittit. Priora
curationem non difficillimam recipiunt, ultimum vix
umquam sanescit; ac si quid ei vitio demptum est,
C tamen non ex toto sanus color redditur. Utrum
autem aliquod horum sanabile sit, an non sit, experimento facile colligitur. Incidi enim cutis debet
aut acu pungi: si sanguis exit, quod fere fit in duobus
prioribus, remedio locus est; si umor albidus, sanari
non potest; itaque ab hoc quidem abstinendum est.
Super id vero, quod curationem recipit, inponenda
lenticula mixta cum sulpure et ture, sic ut ea contrita

---

<sup>a</sup> Under the name *vitiligo* Celsus describes varieties of
psoriasis. *Alphos,* named from its dull white colour which
resembled that of leprosy, was probably psoriasis guttata.
The different colour of *melas* was perhaps only due to dirt.
*Leuce,* the bright white form, regarded as practically incur-

tive for the same affection is the composition of
Myron containing red soda and frankincense, 4 grms.
each, purified cantharides 8 grms., sulphur unheated,
the same amount, and turpentine resin 80 grms.,
darnel meal a litre and a half, cumin 145 c.cm.,
and half a litre of raw pitch.

Vitiligo *a* also, though not dangerous in itself, is
still ugly and is due to a bad habit of body. There
are three species. It is called alphos when it is white
in colour, generally rather rough, and not continuous,
so that it looks as if drops of some sort had been
sprinkled about. Sometimes also it spreads still
more widely with certain gaps. That called melas
differs from it in being of a black colour and like a
shadow; otherwise it is similar. Leuce is somewhat
like alphos, but is whiter and extends deeper; there
are hairs on it, white, and like down. All these spread,
but more quickly in some people than in others.
The alphos and melas come and go at various
seasons; the leuce, once established, is not easily
got rid of. The two former are not difficult to treat,
the latter is scarcely ever cured, for even if the
discoloration is mitigated, the colour of health does
not return altogether. But whether any one of
these is curable or not is easily learnt by this test.
The skin should be cut into or pricked with a needle:
if blood escapes, which it usually does in the first
two species, there is place for a remedy; if a whitish
humour, cure is impossible, and then we should
even refrain from treating it. But to the species
which admits of treatment we should apply lentil
meal, mixed with sulphur and frankincense, pounded

able, may have been only a more severe and intractable form
of a disease which still often resists all remedies.

ex aceto sint. Aliud ad idem, quod ad Irenaeum auctorem refertur: alcyonium, nitrum, cuminum, fici folia arida paribus portionibus contunduntur D adiecto aceto. His in sole vitiligo perunguitur, deinde non ita multo post, ne nimis erodatur, eluitur. Proprie quidam Myrone auctore eos, quos alphos vocari dixi, hoc medicamento perungunt: sulpuris P. ✳=—; aluminis scissilis P. ✳=; nitri P. ✳==; murti aridae contritae acetabulum miscent; deinde in balneo super vitiliginem inspergunt farinam ex faba, tum haec inducunt. Ii vero, quos melanas vocari dixi, curantur, cum simul contrita sunt alcyoneum, tus, hordeum, faba; eaque sine oleo in balineo ante sudorem insperguntur; tum genus id vitiliginis defricatur.

up together in vinegar. Another application for the same purpose, ascribed to Irenaeus, is composed of coral, soda, cumin and dried fig-leaves, in equal quantities, pounded up with vinegar added. The vitiligo is smeared with this in the sun, then it is soon washed off, lest it corrode too much. Some find it useful to anoint the species which I have said is called alphos with the following prescription ascribed to Myron:[a] they mix sulphur 1 grm., split alum 0·66 grm., soda 1·33 grms. with a cupful of dried myrtle leaves; then at the bath they dust bean-meal over the vitiligo and afterwards apply the above remedy. That which I said was termed melas is treated by pounding up together coral, frankincense, barley and bean-meal; and these are sprinkled on, using no oil in the bath before the patient sweats; then this kind of vitiligo is rubbed off.

[a] V. **28.** 18 B.

# BOOK VI

# LIBER VI

**1.** Dixi de iis vitiis, quae per totum corpus orientia medicamentorum auxilia desiderant (V. 26, 27, 28):[a] nunc ad ea veniam, quae non nisi in singulis partibus incidere consuerunt, orsus a capite.

In hoc igitur capillis fluentibus maxime quidem saepe radendo succurritur. Adicit autem vim quandam ad continendum ladanum cum oleo mixtum. Nunc de iis capillis loquor, qui post morbum fere fluunt: nam quominus caput quibusdam aetate nudetur, succurri nullo modo potest.

**2.** Porrigo[b] autem est, ubi inter pilos quaedam quasi squamulae surgunt haeque a cute resolvuntur: et interdum madent, multo saepius siccae sunt. Idque evenit modo sine ulcere, modo exulcerato loco, huic quoque modo malo odore, modo nullo accedente. Fereque id in capillo fit, rarius in barba, aliquando etiam in supercilio. Ac neque sine aliquo vitio corporis nascitur neque ex toto inutile est: nam bene integro capite non exit.—Ubi aliquod in eo vitium est, non incommodum est summam cutem

---

[a] V. 26. 27. 28.

[b] *Porrigo* means scurf or dandruff, and the name was given to conditions, such as seborrhoea or eczema capitis, where there was excessive detachment of such scales from the scalp. The word, according to Pliny, *N.H.* XX. 9. 29. = furfur, bran, and the corresponding Greek name for the condition,

178

# BOOK VI

**1.** I HAVE spoken of those lesions which affect the whole body and require the aid of medicaments [a]; now I come to those which customarily occur only in particular parts, beginning with the head.

In the head, then, when the hair falls out, the principal remedy is frequent shaving. Ladanum mixed with oil, however, is some help in preserving it. I am now referring to the falling out of hair after illness; for no kind of remedy can be given to stop the head of some people from becoming bald through age.

**2.** But the condition is called porrigo,[b] when between the hairs something like small scales rise up and become detached from the scalp: and at times they are moist, much more often dry. Sometimes this happens without ulceration, sometimes there is a localized ulceration, and from this comes sometimes a foul odour, sometimes none. This generally occurs on the scalp, more seldom on the beard, occasionally even on the eyebrow. It does not arise unless there is some general bodily lesion, so that it is not entirely without its use; for it does not exude from a thoroughly sound head. When there is present some lesion in the head, it is not disadvantageous for the surface of the scalp to become here

πιτυρίασις, had the same derivation (πίτυρα, bran), and is still used.

potius subinde corrumpi quam id quod nocet in aliam
2 partem magis necessariam verti. Commodius est
ergo subinde pectendo repurgare quam id ex toto
prohibere. Si tamen ea res nimium offendit, quod
umore sequente fieri potest, magisque si is etiam
mali odoris est, caput saepe radendum est, dein id
super adiuvandum aliquis ex leviter reprimentibus,
quale est nitrum cum aceto, vel ladanum cum
murteo et vino, vel myrobalanum cum vino. Si
parum per haec proficitur, vehementioribus uti licet
cum eo ut sciamus utique in recenti vitio id inutile
esse.

3. Est etiam ulcus, quod a fici similitudine sycosis
a Graecis nominatur : caro excrescit. Et id quidem
generale est : sub eo vero duae species sunt : alterum
ulcus durum et rotundum est, alterum umidum et
inaequale. Ex duro exiguum quiddam et gluti-
2 nosum exit, ex umido † sumplus [1] et mali odoris. Fit
utrumque in is partibus, quae pilis conteguntur :
sed id quidem, quod callosum et rotundum est,
maxime in barba, id vero, quod umidum, praecipue
in capillo.—Super utrumque oportet inponere elaterium aut lini semen contritum et aqua coactum aut
ficum in aqua decoctam aut emplastrum tetrapharmacum ex aceto subactum ; terra quoque
Eretria ex aceto liquata recte inlinitur.

4. Arearum quoque duo genera sunt. Commune

[1] *The text here is corrupt ; Marx conjectures* copiosum pus
*and this is translated.*

---

[a] σύκωσις was so named by Heraclides of Tarentum because the diseased area resembled the interior of a ripe fig.
When the disease occurred on the beard it was known as chin
disease, *mentagra*. It was said by Pliny (*N.H.* XXVI. 1. 2, 3)
to have been recently imported from Asia and to be
contagious.

and there corrupted, rather than for the harmful material to be diverted thence to another part of more importance. Hence it is more beneficial from time to time to clear the scalp by combing, than to repress the disorder altogether. But if this condition is too troublesome, which may happen when a discharge of humour has set in, and especially if this is malodorous, the head is to be shaved often, after which one of the mild repressants is applied, such as soda in vinegar, or ladanum in myrtle oil and wine, or bennut oil with wine. If there is little benefit from these measures it is permissible to use stronger ones, whilst bearing in mind that, at any rate when the disease is of recent origin, this is not a good thing.

3. There is also an ulceration, called sycosis [a] by the Greeks from its resemblance to a fig : a sprouting up of flesh occurs. That is the general description : but there are two subordinate species; in one the ulceration is indurated and circular, in the other moist and irregular in outline. From the hard species there is a somewhat scanty and glutinous discharge; from the moist the discharge is abundant and malodorous. Both occur in those parts which are covered by hair; but the callous and circular ulceration mostly on the beard, the moist form, on the other hand, chiefly on the scalp. In both it is good to apply elaterium, or pounded linseed worked up in water, or a fig boiled in water, or the plaster tetrapharmacum [b] moistened with vinegar; also Eretrian earth dissolved in vinegar is suitable for smearing on.

4. Bald spots [c] also are of two kinds. In both,

[b] See V. 19. 9.
[c] To these the term "areae Celsi" has often been applied in medical works in reference to this description.

# CELSUS

utrique est, quod emortua summa pellicula pili
primum extenuantur, deinde excidunt; ac si ictus
is locus est, sanguis exit liquidus et mali odoris.
Increscitque utrumque in aliis celeriter, in aliis
tarde; peius est id quod densam cutem et sub-
2 pinguem et ex toto glabram fecit. Sed ea, quae
alopecia nominatur, sub qualibet figura dilatatur.
Est et in capillo et in barba. Id vero, quod a similitudine ophis appellatur, incipit ab occipitio; duorum
digitorum latitudinem non excedit; ad aures
duobus capitibus serpit, quibusdam etiam ad frontem,
donec se duo capita in priore parte committant.
Illud vitium in qualibet aetate est, hoc fere in
infantibus.—Illud vix umquam sine curatione, hoc
3 per se saepe finitur. Quidam haec genera arearum
scalpello exasperant: quidam inlinunt adurentia ex
oleo, maximeque chartam conbustam: quidam
resinam terebenthinam cum thapsia inducunt. Sed
nihil melius est quam novacula cottidie radere, quia,
cum paulatim summa pellicula excisa est, adaperi-
untur pilorum radiculae; neque ante oportet
desistere, quam frequentem pilum nasci appareurit.
Id autem, quod subinde raditur, inlini atramento
scriptorio satis est.

5. Paene ineptiae sunt curare varos et lenticulas
et ephelidas, sed eripi tamen feminis cura cultus,
sui non potest. Ex his autem, quas supra posui,
vari lenticulaeque vulgo notae sunt; quamvis
rarior ea species est, quam semion Graeci vocant,

---

*a* ἀλωπεκία = mange in a fox (ἀλώπηξ).
*b* From its resemblance to the track of a serpent (ὄφις).
Sabouraud described the occurrence of this disease in 19 Paris
school children (*Monatschrift. f. prakt. Dermatol.* 1898, **27.**
439, 3).
182

owing to the dying of the surface pellicle, hairs are first rendered thin, and then they fall out; and when the place is cut into, the blood which flows is thin and malodorous. Both kinds spread, in some quickly, in others slowly; the worse kind is that in which the skin has become thick, somewhat fatty, and quite smooth. But that which is named alopecia [a] spreads without defined configuration. It occurs in the hairy scalp or in the beard. That again which is called from its shape ophis,[b] commences at the back of the head, and without exceeding two fingers in breadth, creeps forward to the ears with two heads, in some even to the forehead, until the two heads join one another in front. The former affection occurs at any age, the latter generally in young children. The former scarcely ever terminates, except under treatment, the latter often by itself. Some scarify these bald patches with a scalpel; some smear on caustics mixed with oil, and especially burnt papyrus; some apply turpentine-resin with fennel. But there is nothing better than to shave the part daily with a razor, because as the surface skin is gradually removed, the hair roots become exposed; and the treatment should continue until a number of hairs are seen to be growing up. Following upon the shaving it is sufficient to smear on Indian ink.

**5.** To treat pimples and spots and freckles is almost a waste of time, yet women cannot be torn away from caring for their looks. But of these just mentioned, pimples and spots are commonly known, although that species of spot is more rare which is called by the Greeks semion,[c] since it is

<hr>

[c] σημεῖον, a birth mark, naevus.

# CELSUS

cum sit ea lenticula rubicundior et inaequalior.
Ephelis vero a plerisque ignoratur, quae nihil est
nisi asperitas quaedam et durities mali coloris.
2 Cetera non nisi in facie, lenticula etiam in alia parte
nonnumquam nasci solet; de qua per se scribere
alio loco visum operae pretium non est.—Sed vari
commodissime tolluntur inposita resina, cui non
minus quam ipsa est aluminis scissilis, et paulum
mellis adiectum est. Lenticulam tollunt galbanum
et nitrum, cum pares portiones habent contritaque
ex aceto sunt, donec ad mellis crassitudinem venerint.
His corpus inlinendum et interpositis pluribus horis
[mane] eluendum est oleoque leviter unguendum.
3 Ephelidem tollit resina, cui tertia pars salis fossilis
et paulum mellis adiectum est. Ad omnia ista vero
atque etiam ad colorandas cicatrices potest ea compositio, quae ad Tryphonem patrem auctorem
refertur. In ea pares portiones sunt myrobalani
magmatis, cretae Cimoliae subcaeruleae, nucum
amararum, farinae hordei atque ervi, struthi albi,
sertulae Campanae seminis. Quae omnia contrita
melle quam amarissimo coguntur, inlitumque id
vespere mane eluitur.

6. Sed haec quidem mediocria sunt. Ingentibus
vero et variis casibus oculi nostri patent; qui cum
magnam partem ad vitae simul et usum et dulce-
dinem conferant, summa cura tuendi sunt. Protinus
autem orta lippitudine quaedam notae sunt, ex
quibus quid eventurum sit colligere possumus.

---

*a* Celsus uses *lippitudo* to translate the ὀφθαλμία of Hippocrates = running or blear eyes (ὀφθαλμοὶ λημῶντες); *pituita*
for λήμη, rheum; *aspritudo* for τράχωμα, which was used to
denote chronic conjunctivitis, ophthalmia and trachoma, the

rather red and irregular. Freckles are, in fact,
ignored by most; they are nothing more than a
roughened and indurated discoloration. Whilst
the others occur only on the face, a spot sometimes
also appears on other parts of the body; of that by
itself I do not think it worth while to write elsewhere.
But pimples are best removed by the application of
resin to which not less than the same amount of
split alum and a little honey has been added. A spot
is removed by equal quantities of galbanum and
soda pounded in vinegar to the consistency of honey.
With this the part is to be smeared, and after the
lapse of several hours, [the next morning,] it is washed
off, and the place anointed lightly with oil. Freckles
are removed by resin to which a third part of rock-
salt and a little honey has been added. For all the
above and also for colouring scars that composition
is useful which is said to have been invented by
Trypho the father. In this are equal parts of the
dregs of bennut oil, bluish Cimolian chalk, bitter
almonds, barley and vetch meal, along with white
soapwort and mellilot seeds. These are all rubbed
up together with very bitter honey, smeared on at
night and washed away in the morning.

**6.** Now the foregoing are subjects of minor importance. But there are grave and varied mishaps
to which our eyes are exposed; and as these have
so large a part both in the service and the amenity
of life, they are to be looked after with the
greatest care. Now directly ophthalmia[a] sets in,
there are certain signs by which it is possible to
foretell the course of the disease. For if lacrima-

eye diseases general among eastern races. For the whole
chapter cf. Hippocrates (*Prorrhetica* II. 18) Littré IX. 44.

Nam si simul et lacrima et tumor et crassa pituita
coeperint, si ea pituita lacrimae mixta est, si ea
lacrima calida non est, pituita vero alba et mollis,
tumor non durus, longae valetudinis metus non est.

B At si lacrima multa et calida, pituitae paulum,
tumor modicus est, idque in uno oculo est, longum
id, sed sine periculo futurum est. Idque lippitudinis
genus minime cum dolore est, sed vix ante vicensi-
mum diem tollitur, nonnumquam per duos menses
durat. Quandoque finitur, pituita alba et mollis
incipit esse, lacrimaeque miscetur. At si simul ea
utrumque oculum invaserunt, potest esse brevior,
sed periculum ulcerum est. Pituita autem sicca et
arida dolorem quidem movet, sed maturius desinit,

C nisi quid exulceravit. Tumor magnus si sine dolore
est et siccus, sine ullo periculo est: si siccus quidem,
sed cum dolore est, fere exulcerat, et nonnumquam
ex eo casu fit, ut palpebra cum oculo glutinetur.
Eiusdem exulcerationis timor in palpebris pupillisve
est, ubi super magnum dolorem lacrimae salsae
calidaeque eunt, aut etiam, si tumore [in] finito diu

D lacrima cum pituita profluit. Peius etiamnum est,
ubi pituita pallida aut livida est, lacrima calida et
multa profluit, caput calet, a temporibus ad oculos
dolor pervenit, nocturna vigilia urget, siquidem sub
his oculus plerumque rumpitur, votumque est, ut
tantum exulceretur. Intus ruptum oculum febricula
iuvat. Si foras iam ruptus procedit, sine auxilio est.

tion and swelling of the eyelids and a thick rheum
appear all at once : if that rheum is mixed with tears,
if the tears are not hot, but the rheum is white
and bland, and the swelling not hard, there is then
no apprehension of a prolonged illness. But if
lacrimation is profuse and hot, rheum scanty, swelling moderate, and that in one eye only, the case
will be a prolonged one, but without danger. And
that kind of ophthalmia is the least painful, but is
seldom relieved before the twentieth day, and at
times lasts two months. As it subsides, the rheum
begins to be white and bland, mixed with tears.
But if both eyes are attacked simultaneously, the
duration may possibly be shorter, but there is danger
of ulceration. Now rheum, when it is dry and sticky,
gives rise to some pain, but subsides sooner unless
ulceration is set up. If there is great swelling
without pain and dryness, there is no danger; if
there is dryness, accompanied by pain, there is
generally ulceration, and at times the result is that
the eyelid sticks to the eyeball. There is danger of
similar ulceration in the eyelids or in the pupils when,
in addition to great pain, the tears are salt and hot;
or if, even after the swelling has subsided, there
continues for some time a flow of tears mixed with
rheum. The case is worse still when the rheum is
pallid or livid, the tears hot and profuse, the head
hot, and pain shoots from the temples to the eyes,
causing wakefulness at night; in these circumstances
generally the eyeball ruptures, and we must pray
that there may be ulceration only. When the
eyeball has ruptured inwards a touch of fever is
beneficial. If the eyeball protrudes after rupturing
outwards, there is no remedy. If something white

Si de nigro aliquid albidum factum est, diu manet :
at si asperum et crassum est, etiam post curationem
E vestigium aliquod relinquit.—Curari vero oculos
sanguinis detractione, medicamento, balneo, vino
vetustissimus auctor Hippócrates memoriae pro-
didit : sed eorum tempora et causas parum explicuit,
in quibus medicinae summa est. Neque minus in
abstinentia et alvi ductione saepe auxilii est. Hos
igitur interdum inflammatio occupat, ubi cum
tumore in his dolor est, sequiturque pituitae cursus
nonnumquam copiosior vel acrior, nonnumquam
utraque parte moderatior. In eiusmodi casu prima
F omnium sunt quies et abstinentia. Ergo primo die
loco obscuro cubare debet, sic ut a sermone quoque
abstineat ; nullum cibum adsumere, si fieri potest,
ne aquam quidem ; si[n] minus, certe quam minimum eius. Quod si graves dolores sunt, commodius
secundo die ; si tamen res urget, etiam primo sanguis
mittendus est, utique, si in fronte venae tument, si
firmo corpore materia superest. Si vero minor
impetus, minus acrem curationem requirit ; alvum,
G sed non nisi secundo tertiove die, duci oportet. At
modica inflammatio neutrum ex his auxilium desiderat, satisque est uti quiete et abstinentia.
Neque tamen lippientibus longum ieiunium necessarium est, ne pituita tenuior atque acrior fiat : sed
secundo die dari debet id, quod levissimum videri

188

has developed from the dark part of the eye, it
persists for a long while; but if it is rough and
thick, some vestige remains even after treatment.
According to Hippocrates, the oldest authority, the
treatment of the eyes includes bloodletting, medicaments, the bath and wine; but he gave little explan-
ation of the proper times and reasons for these
remedies, things of the highest importance in the art
of medicine. There is no less help, often, in abstinence and clysters. Now at times inflammation
seizes the eyes, and there is pain in them together
with swelling, and there follows a flow of rheum,
sometimes rather profuse or acrid, sometimes in both
respects rather moderate. In such a case, rest in
bed and abstinence are the chief remedies. From
the first day, therefore, the patient should lie in
bed in a dark room, and at the same time he should
refrain even from talking; take no food at all, and
if feasible not even water, or at any rate the least
possible amount. If the pains are severe, it is
better that he should be bled on the second day, but
when urgent this may be done even on the first day, at
any rate if the veins on the forehead are swollen, and
if there is superfluity of matter in a robust patient.
But if the attack is less violent, it requires less
drastic treatment : the bowel should be clystered,
but only on the second or third day. But moderate
inflammation requires neither blood-letting nor
clystering, it is sufficient for the patient to stay in
bed and fast. A prolonged abstinence, however,
is not necessary in patients with ophthalmia, for it
may render the rheum thinner, and more acrid;
hence some of the lightest kind of food should be
given on the second day, such as seems likely to

189

potest ex iis, quae pituitam faciunt crassiorem;
qualia sunt ova sorbilia: si minor vis urget, pulticula
quoque aut panis ex lacte. Insequentibusque diebus
quantum inflammationi detrahetur, tantum adici
cibis poterit, sed generis eiusdem; utique ut nihil
salsum, nihil acre, nihil ex iis, quae extenuant,
H sumatur, nihil potui praeter aquam. Et victus
quidem ratio talis maxime necessaria est. Protinus
autem primo die croci P. ✳ I, et farinae candidae
quantum tenuissimae P. ✳ II, excipere oportet ovi
albo, donec mellis crassitudinem habeat, idque in
linteolum inlinere, et fronti adglutinare, ut conpressis
venis pituitae impetum cohibeat. Si crocum non
est, tus idem facit. Linteolo an lana excipiatur, nihil
I interest. Superinungui vero oculi debent, sic ut
croci quantum tribus digitis conprehendi potest,
sumatur; murrae ad fabae, papaveris lacrimae ad
lenticulae magnitudinem; eaque cum passo conterantur, et specillo super oculum inducantur.
Aliud ad idem: murrae P. ✳ —; mandragorae
suci P. ✳ I; papaveris lacrimae P. ✳ II; foliorum
rosae, cicutae seminis, singulorum P. ✳ III; acaciae
K P. ✳ IIII; cummis P. ✳ VIII. Et haec quidem
interdiu: nocte vero, quo commodior quies veniat,
non alienum est superinponere candidi panis inte-
riorem partem ex vino subactam: nam et pituitam
reprimit, et, si quid lacrimae processit, absorbet, et
oculum glutinari non patitur. Si grave id et durum
propter magnum oculorum dolorem videtur, ovi et

---

ᵃ Cf. V. 1, p. 4 which includes *acacia* and *cummis* among
medicaments which suppress haemorrhage. *Acacia* must mean

render the rheum thicker; for instance, raw eggs; in a less severe case, porridge also or bread soaked in milk. On the following days, according as the inflammation subsides, additional food may be taken, but of the same class; certainly nothing salted, or acrid, or likely to make the rheum thinner should be consumed, and nothing but water drunk. Such a dietetic regimen is exceedingly necessary. But from the first day, saffron 4 grms. and the finest wheat flour 8 grms. should be made up with white of egg to the consistency of honey, then spread on lint and stuck on the forehead, in order that by compressing the veins the flow of rheum may be checked. If saffron is not at hand, frankincense has the same effect. Whether it is spread on linen, or on wool, makes no difference. There should be smeared over the eyeball, of saffron as much as can be taken up in three fingers, of myrrh in amount the size of a bean, of poppy-tears the size of a lentil: these are pounded up in raisin wine, and applied on a probe to the eyeball. Another composition having the same efficacy is made up of: myrrh 0·33 grms., mandragora juice 4 grms.; poppy-tears 8 grms.; rose-leaves and hemlock seeds 12 grms. each; acacia *a* 16 grms.; gum 32 grms. These applications are made by day; at night, in order better to assure sleep, it is not inappropriate to apply above the eye, the crumb of white bread soaked in wine; for this at once represses rheum, and absorbs any flow of tears, and prevents the eye from becoming glued up. If this application, owing to the great pain in the eye, seems oppressive and hard,

the gum prepared from the acacia shrub and *cummis* some other gum—probably mecca balsam.

album et vitellus in vas defundendum est, adiciendumque eo mulsi paulum, idque digito permiscendum. Ubi facta unitas est, demitti debet lana mollis bene carpta, quae id excipiat, superque
L oculos inponi. Ea res et levis est et refrigerando pituitam coercet, et non exarescit, et glutinari oculum non patitur. Farina quoque hordeacea cocta, et cum malo Cotoneo cocto mixta commode inponitur; neque a ratione abhorret etiam penicillo potissimum uti expresso, si levior impetus est, ex aqua, si maior, ex posca. Priora fascia deliganda sunt, ne per somnum cadant: at hoc superinponi satis est, quia et reponi ab ipso commode potest, et,
M cum inaruit, iterum madefaciendum est. Si tantum mali est, ut somnum diu prohibeat, eorum aliquod dandum est, quae anodyna Graeci appellant; satisque puero quod ervi, viro quod fabae magnitudinem impleat. In ipsum vero oculum primo die, nisi modica inflammatio est, nihil recte coicitur: saepe enim potius concitatur eo pituita quam minuitur. A secundo die gravi quoque lippitudini per indita medicamenta recte succurritur, ubi vel iam sanguis missus vel alvus ducta est, aut neutrum necessarium esse manifestum est.

2    Multa autem multorumque auctorum collyria ad id apta sunt, novisque etiam nunc mixturis temperari possunt, cum lenia medicamenta et modice reprimentia facile et varie misceantur. Ego nobilissima exequar.

---

a V. 25. 1–3.
b For the meaning of *collyrium* see p. 154, note *a*.

eggs, both the white and the yolk, are poured into a vessel, a little honey-wine added, and the mixture stirred with the finger. When thoroughly mixed, soft well-combed wool is soaked in it and the wool then applied over the eyes. This is both a light application and one which by cooling checks rheum, yet does not quite dry it up, and so the eye is not allowed to become glued up. Boiled barley-meal, mixed with boiled quinces, is also a suitable application; nor is it inconsistent with the treatment, even to put on a pad of wool wrung as hard as possible out of water, if the attack is a lighter one, or out of vinegar and water, if it is more severe. The former applications are to be bandaged on, so that they do not fall off during sleep; the latter it suffices to lay on because it can be changed readily by the patient himself, and when it becomes dry, it must be wetted again. If the affection is so severe as to prevent sleep, for a time one of the remedies which the Greeks call anodyna [a] should be administered, an amount the size of a vetch to a child, that of a bean to a man. For the eyeball itself there is no appropriate application on the first day, unless the inflammation is only moderate, for by such the flow of rheum is often stimulated rather than lessened. From the second day, even when the disease is severe, the direct application of medicaments is proper, when blood has been let or clystering applied, or after it has become evident that neither is needed.

Now for this disease there are many salves [b] devised by many inventors, and these can be blended even now in novel mixtures, for mild medicaments and moderate repressants may be readily and variously mingled. I will mention the most famous.

3   Est igitur Philonis, quod habet cerussae elotae, spodii, cummis, singulorum P. ✳ I; papaveris lacrimae conbustae P. ✳ II. Illud scire oportet, hic quoque omnia medicamenta singula primum per se teri, deinde mixta iterum adiecta paulatim vel aqua vel alio umore: cummi cum quasdam alias facultates habeat, hoc maxime praestare, ut, ubi collyria facta inaruerunt, glutinata sint neque frientur.

4   Dionysi vero collyrium est: papaveris lacrimae combustae, donec tenerescat, P. ✳ I =; turis combusti, cummis, singulorum P. ✳ S; spodii P. ✳ IIII.

5   Cleonis nobile admodum: papaveris lacrimae frictae P. ✳ I; croci P. ✳ =; cummis P. ✳ I; quibus cum teruntur adicitur rosae sucus. Aliud eiusdem valentius: squamae aeris, quod stomoma appellant, P. ✳ I; croci P. ✳ II; spodii P. ✳ IIII; plumbi eloti et combusti P. ✳ VI; cummis tantun-

B dem. Attalium quoque ad idem est, maxime ubi multa pituita profluit: castorei P. ✳ —; aloes P. ✳ =; croci P. ✳ I; murrae P. ✳ II; Lyci P. ✳ III; cadmiae curatae P. ✳ VIII; stibis tantundem, acaciae suci P. ✳ XII. Quod cum cummis quid hoc non habet, liquidum in puxidicula servatur. Theodotus vero huic compositioni adiecit papaveris lacrimae combustae P. ✳ —; aeris combusti et eloti P. ✳ II; nucleos palmularum combustos P. ✳ X; cummis P. ✳ XII.

6   At ipsius Theodoti, quod a quibusdam acharistum nominatur, eiusmodi est: castorei, nardi Indici, singulorum P. ✳ I; Lyci P. ✳ =; papaveris lacrimae tantundem; murrae P. ✳ II; croci, cerussae

---

   *a* Hardened in the fire.
   *b* "Ungrateful": relieving so quickly that the patient felt no gratitude for his cure (Galen, XII. 749).

There is then the salve of Philo, which contains : washed cerussa, spode and gum 4 grms. each ; poppy-tears toasted 8 grms. It is important to know that each of these ingredients should be pounded separately, then mixed together, gradually adding water, or some other fluid. Gum, amongst other properties, has this particular advantage, that when salves made of it have become dry, they stick together and do not break up.

The salve of Dionysius consists of : poppy-tears toasted until they soften 4·66 grms., toasted frankincense and gum 2 grms. each, and zinc oxide 16 grms.

The salve of Cleon is quite famous : poppy-tears toasted 4 grms., saffron 0·66 grms., gum 4 grms., to which after being pounded is added rose juice. The same man prescribed another more active salve : scales of the copper which is called stomoma [a] 4 grms. ; saffron 8 grms. ; zinc oxide 16 grms. ; lead washed and roasted 24 grms. ; with a like quantity of gum. There is also for the same complaint the salve of Attalus especially when the rheum is profuse : castoreum 0·33 grms. ; lign-aloes 0·66 grms. ; saffron 4 grms. ; myrrh 8 grms. ; lycium 12 grms. ; prepared zinc oxide 32 grms. ; a like quantity of antimony sulphide and acacia juice 48 grms. And when no gum is added it is preserved liquid in a small receptacle. Theodotus added to the above mixture : poppy-tears toasted 0·33 grms. ; copper scales roasted and washed 8 grms. ; toasted date kernels 40 grms. ; gum 48 grms.

The salve of Theodotus himself, which by some is called achariston,[b] is composed of : castoreum and Indian nard 4 grms. each ; lycium 0·66 grm. ; an equal amount of poppy-tears ; myrrh 8 grms. ; saffron,

elotae, aloes, singulorum P. ✳ III; cadmiae bo-
truitidis elotae, aeris conbusti, singulorum P.
✳ VIII; cummis P. ✳ XVIII; acaciae suci P. ✳ XX;
stibis tantundem; quibus aqua pluvia[ti]lis adicitur.

7    Praeter haec ex frequentissimis collyriis est id,
quod quidam cycnon, quidam a cinereo colore
tephron appellant: amuli, tracantae, acaciae suci,
cummis, singulorum P. ✳ I; papaveris lacrimae
P. ✳ II; cerussae elotae P. ✳ IIII; spumae elotae
P. ✳ VIII, quae aeque ex aqua pluvia[ti]li conteruntur.

8    Euelpides autem, qui aetate nostra maximus
fuit ocularius medicus, utebatur eo, quod ipse con-
posuerat: trygodes nominabat: castorei P. ✳ = =;
Lyci, nardi, papaveris lacrimae, singulorum P. ✳ I;
croci, murrae, aloes, singulorum P. ✳ IIII; aeris
combusti P. ✳ VIIII; cadmiae et stibis, singulorum
P. ✳ XII; acaciae suci P. ✳ XXXVI; cummis
tantundem.

B    Quo gravior vero quaeque inflammatio est, eo
magis leniri medicamentum debet adiecto vel albo
ovi vel muliebri lacte. At si neque medicus neque
medicamentum praesto est, saepius utrumlibet
horum in oculos penicillo ad id ipsum facto infusum
id malum lenit. Ubi vero aliquis relevatus est,
iamque cursus pituitae constitit, reliquias fortasse
leniores futuras discutiunt balneum et vinum.

C    Igitur lavari debet leviter ante oleo perfricatus
diutiusque in cruribus et feminibus, multaque calida
aqua fovere oculos; deinde per caput prius calida,

---

ª The κυκνάριον κολλύριον was stamped with the likeness of
a swan; it is mentioned also by Galen, Alexander of Tralles and
Aetius. It was also known as the ashen (τέφριον) salve, from
its colour due to the litharge (black oxide of lead and silver)
which it contained.

washed white lead and lign-aloes 12 grms. of each; cluster-shaped oxide of zinc, washed and roasted copper scales 32 grms. each; gum 72 grms.; acacia juice 80 grms.; the same amount of antimony sulphide, to which is added rain-water.

Besides the above, among the most commonly used salves is that which some call cycnon,[a] others from its ashen colour tephron, which contains: starch, tragacanth, acacia juice, gum 4 grms. each; poppy-tears 8 grms.; washed cerussa 16 grms.; washed litharge 32 grms. These ingredients likewise are compounded with rain-water.

Euelpides, the most famous oculist of our time, used a salve of his own composition called trygodes [b]: castoreum 1·33 grms.; lycium, nard and poppy-tears 4 grms. each; saffron, myrrh and lign-aloes 16 grms. each; roasted copper scales 36 grms.; oxide of zinc and antimony sulphide 48 grms.; acacia juice 144 grms.; the same amount of gum.

The more severe the inflammation, the milder should the application be made, by adding to it white of egg or woman's milk. But if neither doctor nor medicine is at hand, either of the above, dropped into the eye with a little screw of lint prepared for the purpose, often relieves the trouble. But when the patient has been relieved and the discharge of rheum is already checked, any slight symptoms which remain may be got rid of by making use of the bath and of wine. Therefore when at the bath the patient should be first rubbed over gently with oil, especially over the legs and thighs, and he should bathe his eyes freely with hot water, next hot water should be poured over his head, followed

---

[b] So called from its resemblance to τρύξ (Latin *faex*) wine lees.

deinde egelida perfundi: a balineo cavere ne quo
frigore afflatuve laedatur; post haec cibo paulo
pleniore quam ex eorum dierum consuetudine uti
vitatis tamen omnibus pituitam extenuantibus.
Vinum bibere lene, subausterum, modice vetus,
neque effuse neque timide, ut neque cruditas ex eo
et tamen somnus fiat lenianturque intus latentia

D acria. Si quis in balineo sensit maiorem oculorum
perturbationem quam attulerat, quod incidere iis
solet, qui manente adhuc pituitae cursu festinarunt,
quam primum discedere debet, nihil eo die vini
adsumere, cibi minus etiam quam pridie. Deinde
cum primum satis pituita substitit, iterum ad usum
balinei redire. Solet tamen evenire nonnumquam
sive tempestatium vitio sive corporis, ut pluribus
diebus neque dolor neque inflammatio et minime
pituitae cursus finiatur. Quod ubi incidit iamque
ipsa vetustate res matura est, ab his iisdem auxilium

E petendum est [id est balineo et vino]. Haec enim
ut in recentibus malis aliena sunt, quia concitare ea
possunt et accendere, sic in veteribus, quae nullis
aliis auxiliis cesserunt, admodum efficacia esse consuerunt, videlicet hic quoque ut alibi, cum secunda
vana fuerunt, contrariis adiuvantibus. Sed ante
tonderi ad cutem convenit, deinde in balineo aqua
calida quam plurima caput atque oculos fovere,

---

[a] i.e. the period of his illness.
[b] *Secunda remedia* were the ordinary remedies, those which
followed the rule laid down in the text-books of the time,
and were contrasted with *contraria remedia* (vol. I. p. 38).

by tepid water; after the bath he must take care that
he is not harmed by cold or draught: subsequently he
should use a diet rather fuller than had been customary for those days,[a] whilst avoiding everything which
may render the rheum thinner. He should drink
mild wine, not too dry, and moderately old, taking it
neither too freely nor too sparingly, so that, without
causing indigestion, it may nevertheless induce
sleep, and mollify the internal latent acrid humour.
If at the bath the patient feels the trouble in the eyes
becoming worse than before he entered, which often
happens to those who have hurried on to this course
of treatment whilst there is still a discharge of rheum,
he ought immediately to leave the bath, take no
wine that day, and less food even than on the previous
day. Afterwards, as soon as the flow of rheum has
subsided sufficiently, he may return again to the use
of the bath. Nevertheless, from the fault of the
weather, or of the patient's constitution, it often
happens that for many days neither the pain nor inflammation is checked, and least of all the discharge
of rheum. When this occurs and the affection is
now established by reason of its long standing,
recourse must be had to these same remedies
[that is, the bath and wine.] For whilst they are
unsuitable early in the complaints because they can
then irritate and stir up inflammation, yet in inveterate cases which have not yielded to other
remedies, they are quite effectual, that is to say, in
this as in other instances, when ordinary remedies [b]
have proved useless, contrary ones are beneficial.
But beforehand the patient should be shaved down
to the scalp, then in the bath he should foment both
his head and eyes with plenty of hot water, next

tum utrumque penicillo detergere, et ungere caput
irino unguento; continereque in lectulo se, donec
omnis calor, qui conceptus est, finiatur desinatque
F sudor, qui necessario in capite collectus est. Tum
ad idem cibi vinique genus veniendum, sic ut potiones
meracae sint; obtegendumque caput et quiescendum.
Saepe enim post haec gravis somnus, saepe sudor,
saepe alvi deiectio pituitae cursum finit. Si levatum
malum est, quod aliquanto saepius fit, per plures dies
idem fieri oportet, donec ex toto sanitas restituatur.
Si diebus iisdem alvus nihil reddit, ducenda est, quo
G magis superiores partes leventur. Nonnumquam
autem ingens inflammatio tanto impetu erumpit, ut
oculos sua sede propellat: proptosin id, quoniam
oculi procidunt, Graeci appellant. His utique, si
vires patiuntur, sanguinem mitti; si id fieri non
potest, alvum duci, longioremque inediam indici
necessarium est. Opus autem lenissimis medicamentis est, ideoque Cleonis collyrio quidam, quod ex
duobus ante (5 *init.*) positum est, utuntur: sed op-
tumum est Nilei, neque de ullo magis inter omnes
auctores convenit.
9 Id habet nardi Indici, papaveris lacrimae, singulorum P. ✳ —; cummis P. ✳ I; croci P. ✳ II;
foliorum rosae recentium P. ✳ IIII; quae vel aqua
pluvia[ti]li, vel vino leni, subaustero coguntur.
Neque alienum est malicorium vel sertulam Cam-
panam ex vino coquere, deinde conterere; aut
murram nigram cum rosae foliis miscere; aut

---

*a* πρόπτωσις is not found in any extant works of earlier
authors as a description of the eye condition to which the
name is still applied, though this passage of Celsus shows that
it was so used in Greek writers on medicine.
*b* VI. 6. 5 A.

clean both with a little roll of lint, and anoint the
head with iris ointment: and he should keep to
his bed until all the heat so produced has ended, and
the sweat which of necessity has collected in the
head has passed off. He is then to take food and
wine of the same sort as above, drinking the wine
undiluted; and he must rest with the head wrapped
up. For often after these measures a sound sleep,
or a sweat, or a clearance of the bowel, terminates
the discharge of rheum. If, as more often happens,
the malady is in some measure relieved, the same
regimen is pursued for a number of days until recovery is completed. If, meanwhile, the bowels do
not act, clysters are given to relieve the upper parts
of the body. But occasionally a violent inflammation breaks out with so much force as to push
forwards the eyes out of their place: the Greeks
call this proptosis,[a] because the eyes drop forwards.
In these cases especially, if the strength allows of
it, blood is to be let; if that is impracticable, then
a clyster and prolonged abstinence should be prescribed. The blandest medicaments are required;
hence some use that salve of Cleon's[b] which has
been noted above, as consisting of two ingredients,
poppy-tears and gum, but the best is the salve of
Nileus,[c] and this point is agreed on by all authorities.

This salve consists of Indian nard and poppy-tears
0·33 grm. each.; gum 4 grms.; saffron 8 grms.; fresh
rose leaves 16 grms., which are mixed up in rain-
water or in a rather mild wine. And it is not out of
place to boil pomegranate rind or melilot in wine and
then pound it; or to mix black myrrh with rose leaves,

[c] Mentioned also by Galen, *De Comp. Med.*, *sec. loc.* IV.
XII. 765.

hyoscyami folia cum ovi vitello cocti aut farinam
cum acaciae suco vel passo aut mulso; quibus si
folia quoque papaveris adiciuntur, aliquanto valen-
B tiora sunt.   Horum aliquo praeparato penicillo fovere
oculos oportet ex aqua calida expresso, in qua ante
vel murti vel rosae folia decocta sint; deinde ex
illis aliquid inponi.   Praeter haec ab occipitio incisa
cute cucurbitula adhibenda est.   Quod si per haec
restitutus oculus in sedem suam non est eodemque
modo prolapsus permanet, scire oportet lumen esse
amissum; deinde futurum ut aut indurescat is aut
in pus vertatur.   Si suppuratio se ostendit ab eo
angulo, qui tempori propior est, incidi oculus debet,
ut effuso pure et inflammatio ac dolor finiatur, et
intus tunicae residant, quo minus foeda postea facies
C sit.   Utendum deinde vel his collyriis est ex lacte
aut ovo, vel croco [1] . . . vel cui album ovi misceatur.
At si induruit et sic emortuus est, ne in pus ver-
teretur, quatenus foede prominebit, excidendum
erit, sic ut'hamo summa tunica adprehendatur, infra
id scalpellus incidat; tum eadem medicamenta erunt
coicienda, donec omnis dolor finiatur.   Iisdem medicamentis in eo quoque oculo utendum est, qui prius
procidit, dein per plura loca fissus est.

10   Solent etiam carbunculi ex inflammatione nasci,
nonnumquam in ipsis oculis, nonnumquam in palpebris, et in his ipsis modo ab interiore modo ab
exteriore.—In hoc casu alvus ducenda est, cibus

---

[1] *Marx adds by conjecture the words* vel per se *after* croco, *and
this is translated.*

or hyoscyamus leaves with the yolk of a boiled egg, or flour with acacia juice and raisin wine or honeyed wine; if poppy-tears too be added to these, they are rendered somewhat more active. Having prepared one of the above, the eyes should be swabbed with a small screw of lint, wrung out in a hot decoction of myrtle or rose leaves and then one of the salves placed in them. Furthermore, after incising the skin of the occiput, a cup is to be applied there. But if the eye is not restored into position by the above remedies, but remains pushed forward as before, it should be recognised that its sight is lost; and that the eyeball will harden or will be converted into pus. If suppuration shows itself in the corner nearest the temple, the eyeball should be cut into, in order that by letting out the pus, both inflammation and pain may be ended, and the coats of the eyeball may recede, so that the patient's looks afterwards may be less disfigured. There should then be applied either one of the above salves with milk or egg, or saffron, either by itself or mixed with white of egg. But if the eyeball has grown hard and is dead, but not converted into pus, so much of it is to be cut out as projects in an ugly fashion; for this purpose the sclerotic coat is seized with a hook, and the scalpel cuts under it; then the same medicaments are to be inserted until all pain has stopped. Use is to be made of the same medicaments for an eye which has first prolapsed, and then has split open in several places.

It is also customary for inflammation to give rise to carbuncles, sometimes upon the actual eyeballs, sometimes upon the eyelids, either on the inner or on the outer surface of these. When this occurs, the

minuendus, lac potui dandum, ut acria quae laeserunt
leniantur. Quod ad cataplasmata et medicamenta
pertinet, is utendum, quae adversum inflammationem
proposita sunt (6, 1 E—8 B. 26. 27). Atque hic
quoque Nilei collyrium optimum est: si tamen
carbunculus in exteriore palpebrae parte est, ad
cataplasmata aptissimum est lini semen ex mulso
coctum; aut si id non est, tritici farina eodem modo
cocta.

11 Pusulae quoque ex inflammatione interdum
oriuntur. Quod si inter initia protinus incidit,
magis etiam servanda sunt, quae de sanguine et
quiete supra proposui (1 EF, 8 F): sin serius quam
ut sanguis mitti possit, alvus tamen ducenda est;
si id quoque aliqua res inhibet, utique victus ratio
servanda est. Medicamentis autem huc quoque
lenibus opus est, quale Nilei, quale Cleonis est.

12 Id quoque, quod Philalethus vocatur, huc aptum
est: murrae, papaveris lacrimae, singulorum P. ✳ I;
plumbi eloti, terrae Samiae, quae aster vocatur,
tracanti, singulorum P. ✳ IIII; stibis cocti, amuli,
singulorum P. ✳ VI; spodi eloti, cerussae elotae,
singulorum P. ✳ VIII. Quae aqua pluvia[ti]li excipiuntur. Usus collyrii vel ex ovo vel ex lacte est.

13 Ex pusulis ulcera interdum fiunt; ea recentia aeque
lenibus medicamentis nutrienda sunt, et iisdem fere,
quae supra in pusulis posui (V. 28, 15 E).—Fit quoque
proprie ad haec quod dia libanu vocatur. Habet
aeris combusti et eloti, papaveris lacrimae frictae,

---

*a* V. 6. 8 G, 9 A.  　　　　　 *b* VI. 6. 2.
*c* Potter's clay from Samos ; it was stamped with a star.
*d* V. 28. 15 E.
*e* διὰ λιβάνου so called because it contained frankincense.

patient should be clystered, the food diminished, and milk given as drink, in order to mollify the acrid matter which is doing harm. As regards poultices and medicaments, what has been prescribed for inflammation must be used. And here again the salve of Nileus *a* is best : but when the carbuncle is on the outer surface of the eyelid, the most suitable poultice is one of linseed boiled in honeyed wine, or, if that is not at hand, flour boiled in the same.

Pustules are also an occasional consequence of inflammation. If this happens early during the first stage, the blood-letting and rest prescribed above should be even more strictly enforced; if later than the stage when blood-letting is possible, the bowels, nevertheless, should be clystered; and if anything should prevent this also, at any rate the regimen as to diet should be followed. For this condition also soothing medicaments are necessary, such as those of Nileus and Cleon.

Also the salve *b* named after Philalethus is suitable, consisting of : myrrh and poppy-tears 4 grms. each ; washed lead, Samian earth called aster,*c* and tragacanth 16 grms. each ; boiled antimony sulphide and starch 24 grms. each ; washed oxide of zinc and washed cerussa 32 grms. each. These are made up with rain-water. The salve is used either with white of egg or milk.

From pustules ulcerations sometimes arise. These when recent are likewise to be treated by mild applications, generally by the same as I have prescribed above for pustules.*d* That which is called ' dia libanu ' *e* is specially prepared for the above condition. It is composed of roasted and washed copper, and parched poppy-tears 4 grms.

singulorum P. ✻ I; spodi eloti, turis, stibis combusti
et eloti, murrae, cummis, singulorum P. ✻ II.

14 Evenit etiam, ut oculi vel ambo vel singuli minores
fiant quam esse naturaliter debeant; idque et acer
pituitae cursus in lippitudine efficit et continuati
fletus et ictus parum bene curati.—In his quoque
iisdem lenibus medicamentis ex muliebri lacte
utendum est; cibis vero is, qui maxime corpus alere
et inplere consuerunt; vitandaque omni modo causa,
quae lacrimas excitet, curaque domesticorum;
quorum etiam, si quid tale incidit, [eius] notitiae
subtrahendum. Atque acria quoque medicamenta et
acres cibi non alio magis nomine his nocent, quam
quod lacrimas movent.

15 Genus quoque viti est, quom inter pilos palpe-
brarum peduculi nascuntur: pthiriasin Graeci
nominant. Quod cum ex malo corporis habitu fiat,
raro non ultra procedit. Sed fere tempore interposito pituitae cursus acerrimus sequitur, exulcera-
tisque vehementer oculis aciem quoque ipsam
corrumpit.—His alvus ducenda est, caput ad cutem
tondendum, diuque cotidie ieiunis perfricandum; his
ambulationibus aliisque exercitationibus diligenter
utendum; gargarizandum ex mulso, in quo nepeta
B et pinguis ficus decocta sit; saepe in balineo multa
aqua calida fovendum caput; vitandi acres cibi,
lacte vinoque pingui utendum, bibendumque libera-
lius quam edendum est. Medicamenta vero intus
quidem lenia danda sunt, ne quid acrioris pituitae

---

ᵃ *i.e.* any worry likely to cause tears.

each; washed zinc oxide, frankincense, roasted
and washed, antimony sulphide, myrrh, and gum
8 grms. each.

It happens too that the eyeballs, either both or
one, become smaller than naturally they ought to
be. An acrid discharge of rheum in the course of
ophthalmia causes this, also continuous weeping, and
an injury improperly treated. In these cases the
same mild applications mixed with woman's milk
should also be used, and for food, that which is most
nourishing and body-building. In every way any
cause which may excite tears must be avoided, and
anxiety about home affairs also, knowledge of which,
if anything of that sort has arisen,[a] must be kept
from the patient. And acrid medicaments and sour
food do harm in these cases, chiefly because of the
tears which they excite.

There is also a kind of disorder in which lice are
born between the eyelashes; the Greeks call it
phthiriasis. Since this comes from a bad state of
health it seldom fails to get worse; but usually in
time a very acrid discharge of rheum follows, and
if the eyeballs become severely ulcerated, it even
destroys their vision. In these cases the bowel
should be clystered, the head shaved to the scalp,
and rubbed for a good while daily whilst the patient
fasts; walking and other exercises should be dili-
gently practised; he should gargle honey wine in
which mint and ripe figs have been boiled; at the
bath the head should often be freely fomented with
hot water, acrid food avoided, milk and sweet
wine should be taken, with more drink than food.
Medicaments administered internally should be
bland lest they stimulate the acridity of the rheum;

concitent, super ipsos vero peduculos alia, quae
necare eos, et prohibere, ne similes nascantur,
possint. Ad id ipsum spumae nitri P. ✳ —; sandaracae P. ✳ —; uvae taminiae P. ✳ I simul
teruntur, adiciturque vetus oleum pari portione
atque acetum, donec mellis ei crassitudo sit.

16    Hactenus oculorum morbi[1] lenibus medicamentis
nutriuntur. Genera deinde alia sunt, quae diversam
curationem desiderant, fereque ex inflammationibus
nata, sed finitis quoque his manentia. Atque in
primis in quibusdam perseverat tenuis pituitae
cursus; quibus alvus ab inferiore parte evocanda
est, demendum aliquid ex cibo. Neque alienum est
inlini frontem compositione Andriae, quae habet
cummis P. ✳ I; cerussae, stibis, singulorum P. ✳ II;
B  spumae argenti coctae et elotae P. ✳ IIII. Sed ea
spuma ex aqua pluvia[ti]li coquitur, et arida haec
medicamenta ex suco murti conteruntur. His inlita
fronte cataplasma quoque superiniciendum est ex
farina, quae frigida aqua coacta sit, cuique aut
acaciae sucus aut cupressus adiecta sit. Cucurbitula
quoque inciso vertice recte adcommodatur aut ex
temporibus sanguis emittitur. Inungui vero eo
C  debet, quod habet: squamae aeris, papaveris lacrimae, singulorum P. ✳ I; cervini cornus conbusti et
eloti, plumbi eloti, cummis, singulorum P. ✳ IIII;
turis P. ✳ XII. Hoc collyrium, quia cornu habet,
dia tu ceratos nominatur. Quotienscumque non

---

[1] *Marx conjectures that the words* reperiuntur qui *have
fallen out after* morbi; *V. d. Linden supplies* qui.

---

[a] διὰ τοῦ κέρατος: boiled stag's horn yielded a glutinous
mucus and is mentioned by Galen as a bland application;

other medicaments too are put upon the lice themselves in order to kill them and prevent any more
from being born. For this purpose soda-scum
0·33 grm., sandarach 0·33 grm. and black bryony
berries 4 grms. are pounded up together, with equal
proportions of old oil and vinegar, until of the
consistency of honey.

The preceding diseases of the eyes are treated
with bland applications. Next come other classes
which require a different treatment, and they usually
originate from inflammation, but also persist after
the inflammation has subsided. And first in some
cases there is a thin discharge of rheum which persists; in these the bowel is to be clystered, and the
amount of food somewhat reduced. And it is not
inappropriate to smear the forehead with the composition of Andrias; this consists of gum 4 grms.,
cerussa and antimony sulphide 8 grms. each, litharge
heated and washed 16 grms. But the litharge must
be boiled in rain-water, and the dry ingredients
pounded up in myrtle juice. When the forehead
has been smeared with this, a poultice is put on of
flour made into a paste with cold water, to which is
added acacia juice or cypress oil. It is also useful
to apply a cup to the top of the head after making
an incision, or blood may be let from the temples.
The following ointment should be used : copper
scales and poppy-tears 4 grms. each; stag's horn
calcined and washed, washed lead, and gum, 16 grms.
each; frankincense, 48 grms. This salve, because it
contains horn, is called dia tu keratos.[a] Whenever

it is to be distinguished from *cornu cervinum ustum*, incinerated
stag's horn yielding calcium oxide, quicklime, which was used
for cleaning wounds, V. 5. 2.

adicio, quod genus umoris adiciendum sit, aquam intellegi volo.

17 Ad idem Euelpidis, quod memigmenon nominabat. In eo papaveris lacrimae et albi piperis singulae unciae sunt; cummis libra P.; aeris combusti P. ✳ I S. Inter has autem curationes post intermissiones aliqua prosunt balineum et vinum. Cumque omnibus lippientibus vitandi cibi qui extenuant, tum praecipue, quibus tenuis umor diu fertur. Quod si iam fastidium est eorum, quae pituitam crassiorem reddunt (sicut in hoc genere materiae maxime promptum est), confugiendum est ad ea, quae, quia ventrem, corpus quoque adstringunt.

18 At ulcera, si cum inflammatione finita . . .[1] non sunt, aut supercrescentia aut sordida aut cava aut certe vetera esse consuerunt. Ex his supercrescentia collyrio, quod memigmenon vocatur, optime reprimuntur: sordida purgantur et eodem et eo,

19 quod zmilion nominatur. Habet aeruginis P. ✳ IIII; cummis tantundem; Hammoniaci, mini Sinopici, singulorum P. ✳ XVI; quae quidam ex aqua, quidam, quo vehementiora sint, ex aceto terunt.

20 Id quoque Euelpidis, quod pyrron[a] appellabat, huc utile est: croci P. ✳ I; papaveris lacrimae, cummis, singulorum P. ✳ II; aeris combusti et eloti, murrae, singulorum P. ✳ IIII; piperis albi P. ✳ VI. Sed ante leni, tum hoc inunguendum est.

---

[1] *Marx inserts* sanata *after* finita, *and this is translated.*

---

[a] μεμιγμένον κολλύριον—mixed salve.
[b] Zmilion (σμιλίον, the little scalpel) was sharp as a knife in its effect.

I do not name the kind of fluid to be added, I would
have water to be understood.

For the same purpose there is the salve of Euelpides, which he called memigmenon,ᵃ containing
poppy-tears and white peppercorns 28 grms. each;
gum 336 grms.; roasted copper 6 grms.  However,
in the course of the treatment, after a subsidence of
the disease, the bath and wine are of some service.
In all cases of ophthalmia food that makes thin
should be avoided, but especially in those who have
had for long a discharge of thin humour.  But if
food which renders the rheum thicker comes to be
disliked, which very readily happens with this kind
of diet, recourse should be had to those foods which,
in bracing up the bowels, do the same to the body
in general.

Again, ulcerations which do not heal after inflammation has ended, tend to become fungous or
foul or excavated, or at any rate chronic.   Such as are
fungous are best repressed by the salve called
memigmenon; those which are foul are cleaned
both by the same and by that called zmilion.ᵇ  This
contains : verdigris 16 grms.; gum the same; ammoniacum and Sinopic minium 64 grms.; some pound
up these with water, others with vinegar, in order
to make it more active.

The salve of Euelpides also which he called pyrronᶜ
is of use for this : saffron 4 grms.; poppy-tears
and gum 8 grms.; roasted and washed copper and
myrrh 16 grms. each; white pepper 24 grms.  But
the eyes are first smeared with a mild ointment, then
with the above.

ᶜ From its red (πυρρός) colour : it contained red oxide of
copper.

21    Id quoque eiusdem, quod sphaerion nominabat,
eodem valet: lapidis haematitis eloti P. ✻ I =;
piperis grana sex; cadmiae elotae, murrae, papaveris
lacrimae, singulorum P. ✻ II; croci P. ✻ IIII;
cummis P. ✻ VIII. Quae cum vino Aminaeo
conterantur.

22    Liquidum autem medicamentum ad idem con-
ponebat, in quo erant haec: aeruginis P. ✻ =;
misy conbusti, atramenti sutori, cinnamomi, singulorum P. ✻ I; croci, nardi, papaveris lacrimae,
singulorum P. ✻ I =; murrae P. ✻ II; aeris combusti P. ✻ III; cineris ex odoribus P. ✻ IIII;
piperis grana XV. Haec ex vino austero teruntur,
deinde cum passi tribus heminis decocuntur, donec
corpus unum sit; idque medicamentum vetustate
efficacius fit.

23    Cava vero ulcera commodissime implent ex iis,
quae supra posita sunt, sphaerion et id, quod
Philalethus vocatur. Idem sphaerion vetustis ulceribus et vix ad cicatrices venientibus optime succurrit.

24    Est etiam collyrium, quod, cum ad plura valeat,
plurimum tamen proficere in ulceribus videtur.
Refertur ad Hermonem auctorem. Habet piperis
longi P. ✻ I =; albi P. ✻ —; cinnamomi, costi,
singulorum P. ✻ I; atramenti sutori, nardi, casiae,
castorei, singulorum P. ✻ II; gallae P. ✻ V; murrae,
croci, turis, Lyci, cerussae, singulorum P. ✻ VIII;
papaveris lacrimae P. ✻ XII; aloes, aeris combusti,
cadmiae, singulorum P. ✻ XVI; acaciae, stibis,
cummis, singulorum P. ✻ XXV.

25    Factae vero ex ulceribus cicatrices duobus vitiis
periclitantur, ne aut cavae aut crassae sint. Si

---

ᵃ From its shape which was that of a ball (σφαῖρα): see
also V. **6**, 23, 25, 26, 28.

That salve of his which he named sphaerion [a] has the same effect : washed haematite stone 4·66 grms.; 6 peppercorns ; washed zinc oxide, myrrh and poppy-tears 8 grms.; saffron 16 grms.; gum 32 grms.; these are pounded up in Aminean wine.

For the same purpose he prepared a liquid salve, containing verdigris 0·66 grm.; roasted antimony sulphide, shoemakers-blacking, and cinnamon 4 grms. each ; saffron, nard and poppy-tears 4·66 grms. each ; myrrh 8 grms.; roast copper 12 grms.; ash of aromatic herbs 16 grms.; 15 peppercorns. These are pounded up in dry wine, then boiled in 750 c.cm., of raisin wine until of uniform consistency. This is rendered more efficacious by age.

Excavated ulcerations, too, are most readily replenished with flesh by the compositions mentioned above, sphaerion, and that called Philalethus.[b] Sphaerion is the best remedy for old-standing ulcerations, and those that are difficult to heal.

There is also a salve, which whilst efficacious in many ways seems to be specially so in the case of ulcerations. It is said to have been invented by Hermon. It contains : long pepper 4·66 grms.; white pepper 0·33 grm.; cinnamon and costmary 4 grms. each ; shoemaker's blacking, nard, casia and castoreum 8 grms. each ; gall 20 grms.; myrrh, saffron, frankincense, lycium and cerussa, 32 grms. each ; poppy-tears 48 grms.; lign-aloes, roasted copper and oxide of zinc 64 grms. each ; acacia, antimony sulphide and gum 100 grms. each.

Scars resulting from ulcerations are liable to two defects, they are either depressed or thick. If

[b] VI. 6. 12.

cavae sunt, potest eas implere id, quod sphaerion
vocari dixi, vel id, quod Asclepios nominatur.   Habet
papaveris lacrimae P. ✳ II; sagapeni, opopanacis,
singulorum P. ✳ III; aeruginis P. ✳ IIII; cummis
P. ✳ VIII;   piperis   P. ✳ XII;   cadmiae elotae,
B cerussae, singulorum P. ✳ XVI.   At si crassae
cicatrices sunt, extenuat vel zmilion vel Canopite
collyrium, quod habet: cinnamomi, acaciae, singulorum P. ✳ I; cadmiae elotae, croci, murrae papaveris lacrimae, cummis, singulorum P. ✳ II; piperis
albi, turis singulorum P. ✳ III;   aeris combusti
C P. ✳ VIII.   Vel Euelpidis pyxinum, quod ex his
constat: salis fossilis P. ✳ IIII;   Hammoniaci
thymiamatis P. ✳ VIII;  papaveris lacrimae P.
✳ XII; cerussae P. ✳ XV; piperis albi, croci Siculi,
singulorum   P. ✳ XXXII;   cummis   P. ✳ XIII;
cadmiae elotae P$_t$ ✳ VIIII.   Maxime tamen tollere
cicatricem videtur id, quod habet: cummis P. ✳ =;
aeruginis P. ✳ I; croci magmatis P. ✳ IIII.

26     Est etiam genus inflammationis, in qua, si cui
tument ac distenduntur cum dolore oculi, sanguinem
ex fronte emitti necessarium est, multaque aqua
calida caput atque oculos fovere; gargarizare ex
lenticula vel fici cremore; inungui acribus medicamentis, quae supra (16 *seqq.*, 21 *seqq.*) conprehensa
sunt, maximeque eo, quod sphaerion nominatur,
quod lapidem haematitem habet.   Atque alia
quoque utilia sunt, quae ad extenuandam aspritudinem fiunt, de qua protinus dicam.

27     Haec autem inflammationem oculorum fere sequi-

---

*a* A salve named after the town of Canopus in Egypt.

*b* *Collyrium pyxinum*, a salve kept in a box-wood case;
such receptacles, specially labelled, have been unearthed from
*apothecae* or drug shops excavated in Pompei and elsewhere.

depressed, new flesh may be grown by applying that salve called sphaerion, or that named Asclepios, which contains : poppy-tears 8 grms.; sagapenum and all-heal 12 grms. each; verdigris 16 grms.; gum 32 grms.; pepper 48 grms.; washed oxide of zinc and cerussa 64 grms. each. But thick scars are thinned either by the smilion, or by the salve of Canopus *a* which contains : cinnamon and acacia 4 grms. each; washed oxide of zinc, saffron, myrrh, poppy-tears and gum 8 grms. each; white pepper and frankincense 12 grms. each; roasted copper 32 grms. Or the pyxinum *b* of Euelpides, which consists of : rock-salt 16 grms.; ammoniacum used for incense, 32 grms.; poppy-tears 48 grms.; cerussa 60 grms.; white pepper and Sicilian saffron 128 grms. each; gum 52 grms.; washed zinc oxide 36 grms. However, the best for elevating a scar seems to be : gum 0·66 grm.; verdigris 4 grms.; dregs of saffron 16 grms.

There is also a class of inflammation in which, if the eyes swell and become tense with pain, it is necessary to let blood from the forehead, and to foment the head and eyes freely with hot water; also to gargle, using a decoction of lentils, or the cream of figs; to apply as an ointment acrid medicaments, such as have been noted above, especially that named sphaerion, and that containing haematite stone. There are also other salves of use for softening trachoma *c* of which I am just going to speak.

Now this condition generally follows inflammation

*c* For trachoma see p. 184 note *a*; the disease continues unaltered to this day among eastern races; in Egypt especially it is general among the populace in various degrees of severity.

tur, interdum maior, interdum levior. Nonnumquam
etiam ex aspritudine lippitudo fit, ipsam deinde aspritudinem auget, fitque ea alias brevis, in aliis longa et
quae vix umquam finiatur.—In hoc genere valetudinis quidam crassas durasque palpebras et ficulneo
folio et asperato specillo et interdum scalpello era-
dunt, versasque cotidie medicamentis suffricant;
quae neque nisi in magna vetustaque aspritudine
neque saepe facienda sunt: nam melius eodem
ratione victus et idoneis medicamentis pervenitur.

B Ergo exercitationibus utemur et balneo frequentiore,
multaque . . .[1] oculorum aqua calida fovebimus;
cibos autem sumemus acres et extenuantis, medicamentum id, quod Caesarianum vocatur. Habet
atramenti sutori P. $\ast$ I —; misy P. $\ast$ I =; piperis
albi P. $\ast$ = =; papaveris lacrimae, cummis, singulorum P. $\ast$ II; cadmiae elotae P. $\ast$ IIII; stibis
P. $\ast$ VI; satisque constat hoc collyrium adversus
omne genus oculorum valetudinis idoneum esse,
exceptis is, quae lenibus nutriuntur.

28     Id quoque, quod Hieracis nominatur, ad aspritudinem potest. Habet murrae P. $\ast$ I; Hammoniaci
thymiamatis P. $\ast$ II; aeruginis rasae P. $\ast$ IIII.
Ad idem idoneum est etiam id, quod Canopitae est et,
quod zmilion vocatur, et id, quod pyxinum et id,
quod sphaerion. Si conposita medicamenta non
adsunt, felle caprino vel quam optimo melle satis
commode aspritudo curatur.

29     Est etiam genus aridae lippitudinis : xeropthalmian[a]
Graeci appellant. Neque tument neque fluunt oculi,

---

[1] *Marx proposed to insert* oras *as translated.*

---

[a] *i.e.* chronic conjunctivitis.

of the eyes; sometimes it is more serious, sometimes less so. Often too, as the result of trachoma, inflammation _a_ is set up, which in its turn increases the trachoma, and sometimes lasts a short time, sometimes long, and then it is scarcely ever terminated. In this class of affection, some scrape the thick and indurated eyelids with a fig-leaf and a rasp and sometimes with a scalpel, and every day rub medicaments into the under surface of the eyelid; such things should only be done when there is marked and inveterate hardness, and not often; for the same result is better attained by dieting and proper medicaments. Therefore we shall make use of exercise and frequent baths, and foment the eye-lids freely with hot water, and the food we give will be acrid and attenuating, and the medicine the salve called caesarianum. This contains: shoemaker's blacking 1·33 grms.; antimony sulphide 1·66 grms.; white pepper 1·33 grms.; poppy-tears and gum 8 grms. each; washed oxide of zinc 16 grms.; antimony sulphide 24 grms. And this preparation will do for all kinds of eye-inflammations, except such as are relieved by bland remedies.

That called after Hierax is also efficacious for trachoma. It contains: myrrh 4 grms.; ammoniacum used for incense 8 grms.; copper filings 16 grms. For the same purpose there are also those called respectively Canopite, smilion, pyxinum, and sphaerion. But when none of these made up medicaments is at hand, then goat's bile or honey of the best is suitable enough for the treatment of trachoma.

There is a kind of dry inflammation of the eyes called by the Greeks xerophthalmia. The eyes neither swell nor run, but are none the less red

sed rubent tamen et cum dolore quodam gravescunt
et noctu praegravi pituita inhaerescunt; quantoque
minor generis huius impetus, tanto finis minus
expeditus est. — In hoc vitio multum ambulare,
multum exerceri, lavari saepe,[1] . . . ibique desudare,
multaque frictione uti necessarium est. Cibi neque
ii qui implent, neque nimium acres apti sunt, sed
inter hos medi. Mane, ubi concoxisse manifestum
est, non est alienum ex sinapi gargarizare, tum
deinde caput atque os diutius defricare.

30     Collyrium vero aptissimum est, quod rinion vocatur.
Habet murrae P. ✱ =; papaveris lacrimae, acaciae
suci, piperis, cummis, singulorum P. ✱ I; lapidis
haematitis, lapidis Phrygii, Lucii, lapidis scissilis,
singulorum P. ✱ II; aeris combusti P. ✱ IIII.
Ac pyxinum quoque eodem accommodatum est.

31     Si vero scabri oculi sunt, quod maxime in angulis
esse consuevit, potest prodesse rinion, id quod supra
positum est; potest militare: id, quod habet
aeruginis rasae, piperis longi, papaveris lacrimae,
singulorum P. ✱ II; piperis albi, cummis, singulorum P. ✱ IIII; cadmiae elotae, cerussae, singulorum P. ✱ XVI. Nullum tamen melius est quam
Euelpidis, quod basilicon nominabat. Habet papaveris lacrimae, cerussae, lapidis Assii, singulorum
P. ✱ II; cummis P. ✱ III; piperis albi P. ✱ IIII;
B croci P. ✱ VI; psorici P. ✱ XIII. Nulla autem per
se materia est, quae psoricum nominetur, sed
chalcitidis aliquid et cadmiae dimidio plus ex aceto

---

[1] *Marx would add after* saepe: in balineo sedere, *and this
is translated.*

---

[a] Cf. Paulus Aegineta, **3.** 22. ῥινάριον.    [b] Split alum, cf. V. 2.
[c] Inflammation of the eyelid (Blepharitis marginalis or
angularis).

and heavy and painful, and at night the lids get stuck together by very troublesome rheum; the less violent the onset of this kind of trouble is, the less readily it is terminated. In this lesion there is need for much walking, much exercise, frequent bathing, sitting in the bath and sweating, and much rubbing. The food should not be too flesh-making, neither is acrid food suitable, but a mean between the two. In the morning, when it is plain that all food has been digested, it is not inappropriate to gargle with mustard, then next to rub the head and face for a considerable time.

Again, a most suitable salve is that called rhinion.[a] It contains : myrrh 0·66 grm.; poppy-tears, acacia juice, pepper and gum 4 grms. each; haematite stone, Phrygian and Lycian stone, and split stone,[b] 8 grms. each; roasted copper 16 grms. The salve pyxinum is also fitting for this same purpose.

When the eyes are scabrous,[c] which mostly occurs at their angles, the rhinion salve noted above may do good; that one may also serve which contains : copper filings, long pepper and poppy-tears 8 grms. each; white pepper and gum 16 grms. each; washed oxide of zinc and cerussa 64 grms. each. Nothing, however, is better than that named by Euelpides basilicon. It contains : poppy-tears cerussa and Assos stone, 8 grms. each; gum 12 grms.; white pepper 16 grms.; saffron 24 grms.; psoricum [d] 42 grms. Now there is no drug called psoricum, but some copper ore and a little more than half as much oxide of zinc are pounded up together in vinegar,

---

[d] Psoricum (ψωρικὸν φάρμακον) was a remedy for itch, ψώρα. The composition was noted by Dioscorides and Pliny; oxides of copper and zinc were the active ingredients.

simul conteruntur, idque in vas fictile additum et
contectum ficulneis foliis sub terra reponitur, sub-
latumque post dies viginti rursus teritur, et sic †
appellatur.[1] Verum in basilico quoque collyrio
convenit ad omnes affectus oculorum id esse idoneum,
C qui non lenibus medicamentis curantur. Ubi non
sunt autem medicamenta composita, scabros angulos
levant et mel et vinum; succurritque et his et
aridae lippitudini, si quis panem ex vino subactum
super oculum inponit. Nam cum fere sit umor
aliquis, qui modo ipsum oculum, modo angulos aut
palpebras exasperat, sic et, si quid prodit umoris,
extrahitur, et, si quid iuxta est, repellitur.

32    Caligare vero oculi nonnumquam ex lippitudine,
nonnumquam etiam sine hac propter senectutem
inbecillitatemve aliam consuerunt. Si ex reliquis
lippitudinis id vitium est, adiuvat collyrium, quod
Asclepios nominatur, adiuvat id, quod ex croci
magmate fit.

33    Proprie etiam ad id componitur, quod dia crocu
vocant. Habet piperis P. ✳ I; croci Cilici, papaveris
lacrimae, cerussae, singulorum P. ✳ II; psorici,
cummis, singulorum P. ✳ IIII.

34    At si ex senectute aliave inbecillitate id est, recte
inungui potest et melle quam optumo et cypro et
oleo vetere. Commodissimum tamen est balsami
partem unam et olei veteris aut cypri partes duas,
mellis quam acerrimi partes tres miscere. Utilia
huc quoque medicamenta sunt, quaeque ad caliginem

---

[1] *Marx suggests* adhibeatur *for the MSS.* appellatur. *One
MS. inserts* psoricum *after* appellatur.

and this is placed in an earthenware jar and covered over with fig-leaves and is buried underground; after twenty days it is taken up, and again pounded, when it is given this name. It is generally agreed that the salve basilicum is suitable for all affections of the eyes which are not treated by bland medicaments. But when such compositions are not at hand, honey and wine relieve the scabrous angles of the eyes; in this and in dry ophthalmia relief is afforded by soaking bread in wine, and applying it over the eyes. For since there is generally some humour which is irritating either the eyeball itself, or its angles, or the eyelids, by this application any humour on the surface is drawn out and any near at hand driven back.

Again the eyes tend at times to become dim from ophthalmia, but also apart from that, on account of old age, or other weakness. If the disorder is owing to the remnants of an ophthalmia, the salve called Asclepios is of service and that which is composed of saffron dregs.

Also there is a special preparation for this purpose called dia crocu.[a] It contains pepper 4 grms.; cilician saffron, poppy-tears and cerussa 8 grms. each; psoricum and gum 16 grms. each.

But if the eyes are dim from old age or other weakness, it is good to anoint with best honey, cyprus oil, and old olive oil. The most suitable unguent, however, is made of balsam one part, and old olive or cyprus oil two parts, and three parts of the sharpest honey. Here too those applications are suitable which were noted just above

---

[a] διὰ κρόκου, containing saffron from Corycus (now Khorgos) in Cilicia.

proxime (32, 33) quaeque ad extenuandas cicatrices
B supra (25 B) comprehensa sunt. Cuicumque vero
oculi caligabunt, huic opus erit multa ambulatione
atque exercitatione, frequenti balneo, ubi totum
quidem corpus perfricandum est, praecipue tamen
caput, et quidem irino, donec insudet velandumque
postea nec detegendum antequam sudor et calor
domi conquierint. Tum cibis utendum acribus et
extenuantibus, interpositisque aliquibus diebus ex
sinapi gargarizandum.

35 Suffusio quoque, quam Graeci hypochysin nominant, interdum oculi potentiae, qua cernit, se opponit.
Quod si inveteravit, manu curandum est. Inter
initia nonnumquam certis observationibus dis-
cutietur. Sanguinem ex fronte vel naribus mittere,
in temporibus venas adurere, gargarizando pituitam
evocare, subfumigare, oculos acribus medicamentis
inunguere expedit. Victus optimus est, qui pituitam
extenuat.

36 Ac ne resolutio quidem oculorum, quam paralysin
Graeci nominant, alio victus modo vel aliis medicamentis curanda est. Exposuisse tantum genus vitii
satis est. Igitur interdum evenit, modo in altero
oculo, modo in utroque, aut ex ictu aliquo aut ex
morbo comitiali, aut ex distentione nervorum, qua
vehementer ipse oculus concussus est, ut is neque
quoquam intendi possit, neque omnino consistat,
sed huc illucve sine ratione moveatur; ideoque ne
conspectum quidem rerum praestat.

---

ᵃ See VI. 6. 25 B.
ᵇ Suffusio (ὑπόχυσις) is a collection of humour behind the
pupil. The name *cataracta* (καταρράκτης) was first used by
Constantinus about 1070 in a translation from the Arabic.
See also VII. 7. 13.

for dim vision and previously for thinning [a] scars.
If anyone finds his eyes becoming dim he must
walk and exercise a great deal; also bathe frequently, and in the bath he is to be rubbed all
over, especially, however, on his head, with iris
unguent, until he sweats; and he should then be
wrapped up, and not uncover, until after reaching
home the sweating and heat have passed off. Then
he should take acrid foods which will make him thin
and some days afterwards gargle with mustard.

Cataract [b] also, which the Greeks call hypochysis,
sometimes interferes with the vision of the eye.
When it has become long established it is to be treated
surgically. In its earliest stages it may be dispersed
occasionally by certain measures : it is useful to
let blood from the forehead or nostrils, to cauterize
the temporal blood vessels, to bring out phlegm
by gargling, to inhale smoke, to anoint the eyes
with acrid medicaments. That regimen is best which
makes phlegm thin.

Again, even the relaxation of the eyes which the
Greeks call paralysis [c] is not to be treated by any
different regimen or by any different medicaments.
It is sufficient to explain just the kind of lesion it is.
It happens then sometimes in the case of one eye,
sometimes of both, from some blow, or from epilepsy,
or from a spasm, by which the eyeball itself is
violently shaken, that it cannot be directed at any
object, or be held at all steady, but with no reason
it turns now this way, now that, and so does not
even afford a view of objects.

[c] *Paralysis* and *resolutio nervorum* are used alternatively.
The description is rather of a functional disorder than of a
muscular paralysis.

37 Non multum ab hoc malo distat id, quod mydriasin
Graeci vocant. Pupilla funditur et dilatatur, acies-
que eius hebetescit ac paene. . . .[1]— Difficillime
genus id inbecillitatis eliditur. In utraque parte
vero [id est et paralysi et mydriasi] pugnandum est
per eadem omnia, quae in caligine oculorum praecepta
sunt (32–34), paucis tantum mutatis, siquidem ad
caput irino interdum acetum, interdum nitrum
B adiciendum est, melle inungui satis est. Quidam
in posteriore vitio calidis aquis usi relevatique:
quidam sine ulla manifesta causa subito obcaecati
sunt. Ex quibus nonnulli cum aliquamdiu nihil
vidissent, repentina profusione alvi lumen rece-
perunt; quo minus alienum videtur et recenti re et
interposito tempore medicamentis quoque moliri
deiectiones, quae omnem noxiam materiam in
inferiora depellant.

38 Praeter haec inbecillitas oculorum est, ex qua
quidem interdiu satis, noctu nihil cernunt; quod in
feminam bene respondentibus menstruis non cadit.—
Sed sic laborantes inungui oportet sanie iocineris
maxime hirquini, si minus, caprini, ubi id assum
coquitur, excepta; atque edi quoque ipsum iecur
debet. Licet tamen etiam iisdem medicamentis
non inutiliter uti, quae vel cicatrices vel aspritudinem
extenuant: quidam contrito semini portulacae mel
adiciunt, eatenus ne id ex specillo destillet, eoque

---

[1] *A word has fallen out here, Marx supplied* deficit.

---

[a] Mydriasis (μυδρίασις). The reflex effect of more light
entering through the dilated pupil is to cause the eyelids to
close (μύειν).

[b] Celsus here describes a particular functional disorder
*caecitas crepuscularis,* inability to see at dusk, and at night;

The malady the Greeks call mydriasis [a] is not very different from the above. The pupil spreads out and is dilated, and its vision becomes dimmed and almost lost. This kind of weakness is most difficult to relieve. Both of these [paralysis and mydriasis] are to be countered by all the same prescriptions as mistiness of the eyes, but with a few alterations such as the addition sometimes of vinegar, sometimes of soda, to the iris unguent for the head; while honey is sufficient for the eye inunctions. In the case of mydriasis, some patients have been relieved by the use of hot water, some without any obvious cause have suddenly become blind. Some of these after seeing nothing for some time have suddenly regained vision following a profuse stool. Hence it seems not inappropriate, whether in a recent case or in one of some standing, by the use of medicaments to force stools in order to drive downwards all noxious matter.

There is besides a weakness of the eyes, owing to which people see well enough indeed in the daytime but not at all at night; [b] in women whose menstruation is regular this does not happen. But such sufferers should anoint their eyeballs with the stuff dripping from a liver whilst roasting, preferably of a he-goat, or failing that of a she-goat; and as well they should eat some of the liver itself. But, we may also use with advantage the same remedies which dry up scars and trachoma. Some add honey to pounded purslane seed until the mixture no longer drops from the end of a probe, and with it anoint the

cats and other animals have better vision than man in this respect. The term *nyctalopia* (night blindness) is meaningless and so has led to endless confusion.

inungunt. Exercitationibus, balneo, frictionibus, gargarizationibus isdem his quoque utendum est.

39 Et haec quidem in ipsis corporibus oriuntur. Extrinsecus vero interdum sic ictus oculum laedit, ut sanguis in eo suffundatur. — Nihil commodius est quam sanguine vel columbae vel palumbi vel hirundinis inunguere. Neque id sine causa fit, cum horum acies extrinsecus laesa interposito tempore in anticum statum redeat, celerrime hirundinis.

B Unde etiam fabulae locus factus est, per parentes id herba restitui, quod per se sanescit. Eorumque ergo sanguis nostros quoque oculos ab externo casu commodissime tuetur, hoc ordine, ut sit hirundinis optimus, deinde palumbi, minime efficax columbae et illi ipsi et nobis. Supra percussum vero oculum ad inflammationem leniendam non est alienum inponere

C etiam cataplasma. Sal Hammoniacus vel quilibet alius quam optimus teri debet, sic ut ei paulatim oleum adiciatur, donec crassitudo strigmenti fiat. Id deinde miscendum est cum hordeacia farina, quae ex mulso decocta sit. Facile autem recognitis omnibus, quae medici prodiderunt, apparere cuilibet potest, vix ullum ex iis, quae supra conprehensa sunt, oculi vitium esse, quod non simplicibus quoque et promptis remediis summoveri possit.

7. Hactenus in oculis ea . . .[1] reperiuntur, in quibus medicamenta plurimum possint : ideoque ad aures transeundum est, quarum usum proximum a

---

[1] *Marx would supply* morborum genera *after* ea.

---

[a] Chelidonium majus, the greater celandine, which blooms when the swallow ($\chi\epsilon\lambda\iota\delta\omega\nu$) is arriving on the swallow wind

eyeballs. The same exercises, baths, rubbings and gargles are also to be used for these patients.

All the foregoing disorders arise within the body; but a blow from without at times so injures the eye that it is suffused with blood. Nothing is then better than to anoint the eyeball with the blood of a pigeon, dove, or swallow. There is some reason for this, because the vision of these birds, when injured from without, returns after an interval to its original state, most speedily in the case of the swallow. This also has given rise to the fable that the old birds restore the vision by a herb,[a] when it really returns spontaneously. Hence the blood of these birds most properly protects our eyes too after an external injury, and in the following order: swallow's blood is best, next that of the pigeon, and the dove's is the least efficacious, both as regards the birds themselves and us. In order to relieve inflammation, it is not unfitting to apply a poultice over the injured eye. The best salt from Ammon, or some other salt, is pounded, and oil gradually added until it is of the consistency of strigil scrapings. Then this is mixed with barley-meal which has been boiled in honey wine. But it is easy, after looking through all that medical practitioners have written, for anyone to see that there is scarcely any one of the eye disorders among those included above which it may not be possible to clear up by simple and readily procured remedies.

**7.** So much, then, for those classes of eye disease, for which medicaments are most successful; and now we pass to the ears, the use of which comes next to eye-

(Theophrastus, *Enquiry into Plants*, VII. **15**. 1, Loeb translation, II. 136). Its juice yields a narcotic alkaloid.

luminibus natura nobis dedit. Sed in his aliquanto
maius periculum est: nam vitia oculorum intra
ipsos nocent, aurium inflammationes doloresque
interdum etiam ad dementiam mortemque praecipi-
tant. Quo magis inter initia protinus succurrendum
B est, ne maiori periculo locus sit.—Ergo ubi primum
dolorem aliquis sensit, abstinere et continere se debet;
postero die, si vehementius malum est, caput tondere,
idque irino unguento calido perunguere et operire.
At magnus cum febre vigiliaque dolor exigit, ut
sanguis quoque mittatur; si id aliquae causae pro-
hibent, alvus solvenda est. Cataplasmata quoque
calida subinde mutata proficiunt, sive feni Graeci
sive lini sive alia farina ex mulso decocta et recte
etiam subinde admoventur spongiae ex aqua calida
C expressae. Tum levato dolore ceratum circumdari
debet ex irino aut cyprino factum: in quibusdam
tamen melius quod ex rosa est proficit. Si vehemens
inflammatio somnum ex toto prohibet, adici cata-
plasmati debent papaveris cortices fricti atque contriti, sic ut ex his pars dimidia sit, eaque tum simul ex
passo mixto decoquatur. In aurem vero infundere
aliquod medicamentum oportet, quod semper ante
tepefieri convenit, commodissimeque per striglem
instillatur. Ubi auris repleta est, super lana mollis
D addenda est, quae umorem intus contineat. Et
haec quidem communia sunt medicamenta: verum
est et rosa et radicum harundinis sucus, et oleum, in
quo lumbrici cocti sunt, et umor ex amaris nucibus

---

[a] The truth of this statement, unique in ancient medical
literature, only came to be appreciated after the middle of
the 19th century.

[b] The strigil, commonly made of horn, had a groove like our
shoehorn, into which liquid medicaments were poured, and
from which fluid could be poured in drops.

sight as Nature's gift to us. But in the case of the
ears there is a somewhat greater danger; for whereas
lesions of the eyes keep the mischief to themselves,
inflammations and pains in the ears sometimes
even serve to drive the patient to madness and death.[a]
This makes it more desirable to apply treatment at
the very beginning, that there may be no opening
for the greater danger. As soon, therefore, as the
pain is first felt, the patient should fast and keep
quiet; the next day, if the pain is still severe, the
head should be shaved, and after it has been anointed
with hot iris unguent, covered up. But great pain
with fever and sleeplessness require also that blood
should be let; if anything prevents this, the bowels
are to be moved. Hot poultices also, frequently
changed, are of service, whether composed of fenugreek or linseed or other meal boiled in honey wine,
and sponges also wrung out of hot water, applied
at intervals, are appropriate. Then, when the pain
is relieved, iris or cyprus unguent should be spread
around the ears; in some cases, however, the rose
unguent is more advantageous. If severe inflammation entirely prevents sleep, there should be added to
the poultice half its quantity of toasted and pounded
poppy-head rind, and this should be boiled down
with the rest in diluted raisin wine. It is desirable
also to pour some medicament into the ear, and
this should always be made lukewarm beforehand;
and is best dropped in from a strigil.[b] When the
ear is full, soft wool is applied over it to keep in the
fluid. And these are the medicaments generally
used for this purpose: but also there is rose oil and
arundo-root juice and oil in which worms have been
boiled, and juice expressed from bitter almonds or

229

aut ex nucleo mali Persici expressus. Conposita vero ad inflammationem doloremque leniendum haec fere sunt: castorei, papaveris lacrimae pares portiones conteruntur; deinde adicitur his passum. Vel papaveris lacrimae, croci, murrae par modus sic teritur, ut invicem modo rosa modo passum instilletur.

E Vel id, quod amarum in Aegyptia faba est, conteritur rosa adiecta; quibus murrae quoque paulum a quibusdam miscetur vel papaveris lacrimae aut tus cum muliebri lacte vel amararum nucum cum rosa sucus. Vel castorei, murrae, papaveris lacrimae pares portiones cum passo. Vel croci P. * = —; murrae, aluminis scissilis, singulorum P. * =; quibus dum teruntur paulatim miscentur passi cyathi tres, mellis minus cyatho, idque ex primis medicamentis est.

F Vel papaveris lacrima[e] ex aceto. Licet etiam compositione uti Themisonis, quae habet castorei, opopanacis, papaveris lacrimae, singulorum P. * II; spumae Lyci P. * IIII. Quae contrita passo excipiuntur, donec cerati crassitudinem habeant, atque ita reponuntur. Ubi usus requiritur, rursus id medicamentum adiecto passo specillo teritur. Illud perpetuum est, quotienscumque crassius medicamentum est quam ut in aurem instillari possit, adiciendum eum esse umorem, ex quo id componi debet, donec satis liquidum sit.

2 Si vero pus quoque aures habent, recte Lycium per se infunditur, aut irinum unguentum aut porri sucus cum melle aut centauri sucus cum passo aut dulcis mali Punici sucus in ipsius cortice tepefactus, adiecta murrae exigua parte. Recte etiam miscentur

from peach-kernels. But the compositions for relieving inflammation and pain generally employed are : castoreum and poppy-tears in equal amounts, pounded together; then to these there is added raisin wine. Or poppy-tears, saffron and myrrh in equal quantities pounded, while rose oil and raisin wine are dropped in by turns. Or the bitter part of the Egyptian bean pounded up with rose oil added; with these some mix a little myrrh or poppy-tears, or frankincense in woman's milk, or the juice of bitter almonds with rose oil. Or castoreum, myrrh and poppy-tears, equal parts, with raisin wine. Or saffron 1 grm.; myrrh and shredded alum 0·66 grm. of each; whilst this is being pounded there is slowly added to it 125 c.cm. of raisin wine, of honey rather less than 40 c.cm., and this is one of the best remedies. Or poppy-tears in vinegar. Themison's compound may also be used; it contains : castoreum, opopanax and poppy-tears 8 grms. each, buckthorn scum 16 grms. These are pounded and made up in raisin wine, until they have the consistency of a wax salve and are so preserved. When required for use, this composition is again stirred with a probe whilst adding raisin wine. The rule is general, that when a composition has become too thick to be dropped into the ear, some of the fluid with which it was made up is added until it becomes sufficiently liquid.

If again the ears have pus in them as well, it is proper to pour in boxthorn juice by itself, or iris unguent or leek juice with honey or centaury juice with raisin wine or the juice of a sweet pomegranate warmed in its rind, to which a little myrrh is added. It is useful to mix together myrrh of the sort called

murrae, quam stacten cognominant, P. ✳ I; croci
tantundem; nuces amarae XXV; mellis sex cyathi;
quae contrita, cum utendum est, in cortice mali
Punici tepefiunt. Ea quoque medicamenta, quae
oris exulcerati causa componuntur, aeque ulcera
B aurium sanant. Quae si vetustiora sunt et multa
sanies fluit, apta compositio est, quae ad auctorem
Erasistratum refertur: piperis P. ✳ =; croci P. ✳
=; murrae, misy cocti, singulorum P. ✳ I; aeris
combusti P. ✳ II. Haec ex vino teruntur: deinde
ubi inaruerunt, adiciuntur passi heminae tres et
simul incocuntur. Cum utendum est, adicitur his
mel et vinum. Est etiam Ptolemaei chirurgi medicamentum, quod habet: lentisci P. ✳ =; gallae P.
C ✳ =; omphaci P. ✳ I; sucum Punici mali. Est
Menophili validum admodum, quod ex his constat:
piperis longi P. ✳ I; castorei P. ✳ II; murrae, croci,
papaveris lacrimae, nardi Suriaci, turis, malicori, ex
Aegyptia faba partis interioris, nucum amararum,
mellis quam optumi, singulorum P. ✳ IIII; quibus
cum teruntur adicitur acetum quam acerrimum,
donec crassitudo in his passi fit. Est Cratonis:
cinnamomi, casiae, singulorum P. ✳ =; Lyci, nardi,
murrae, singulorum P. ✳ I; aloes P. ✳ II; mellis
cyathi tres; vini sextarius; ex quibus Lycium cum
D vino decoquitur, deinde his alia miscentur. At si
multum puris malusque odor est, aeruginis rasae,
turis, singulorum P. ✳ II; mellis cyathi duo;
aceti quattuor simul incocuntur. Ubi utendum est,

---

⁎ VI. 11.

stacte 4 grms.; the same amount of saffron; 25 bitter almonds; of honey 250 c.cm.; these are pounded together, and when they are to be used, are warmed in a pomegranate rind. The medicaments which are compounded for ulcerations of the mouth are equally healing for ulcerations of the ear.[a] If the disease is of longer standing, and much matter is discharged, the composition said to have been invented by Erasistratus is suitable : pepper 0·66 grm.; saffron 0·66 grm.; myrrh and cooked antimony sulphide 4 grms. each; roasted copper 8 grms. These are pounded up in wine, and when the mixture has become dry, 750 c.cm. of raisin wine are added, and are boiled up with it. When it is to be used, wine and honey are added to these ingredients. There is also the medicament of the surgeon Ptolemaeus, which contains : mastich 0·66 grm., oak galls 0·66 grm., omphacium 4 grms.; and pomegranate juice. There is the very active remedy of Menophilus, which consists of : long pepper 4 grms.; castoreum 8 grms.; myrrh, saffron, poppy-tears, Syrian nard, frankincense, pomegranate rind, the embryo of an Egyptian bean, bitter almonds, and the best honey 16 grms. each. These are pounded together with the addition of very sour vinegar until of the consistency of raisin wine. The prescription of Craton is the following : cinnamon and casia 0·66 grm. each, boxthorn juice, nard and myrrh 4 grms. each, lign-aloes 8 grms., honey 125 c.cm., wine half a litre. The lycium is first boiled in the wine, and the rest added. But when there is much pus, and the odour bad, verdigris scrapings and frankincense 8 grms. each, honey 85 c.cm.; vinegar 170 c.cm. are boiled together. For use, it is mixed with sweet

dulce vinum miscetur. Aut aluminis scissilis, papaveris lacrimae, acaciae suci par pondus miscetur, hisque adicitur hyoscyami suci dimidio minor quam unius ex superioribus portio, eaque trita ex vino diluuntur. Per se quoque hyoscyami sucus satis proficit.

3 Commune vero auxilium adversus omnes aurium casus iamque usu conprobatum Asclepiades conposuit. In eo sunt cinnamomi, casiae, singulorum P. ✳ I; floris iunci rotundi, castorei, albi piperis, longi, amomi, myrobalani, singulorum P. ✳ II; turis masculi, nardi Syriaci, murrae pinguis, croci, spumae nitri, singulorum P. ✳ III. Quae separatim contrita, rursus mixta ex aceto conteruntur, atque ita condita, B ubi utendum est, aceto diluuntur. Eodem modo commune auxilium auribus laborantibus est Polyidi sphragis ex dulci vino liquata, quae conpositio priore libro (V. 20, 2) continetur. Quod si et sanies profluit et tumor est, non alienum est mixto vino per oricularium clysterem eluere, et tum infundere vinum austerum cum rosa mixtum, cui spodi paulum sit adiectum, aut Lucium cum lacte aut herbae sanguinalis sucum cum rosa aut mali Punici sucum cum exigua murrae parte.

4 Si sordida quoque ulcera sunt, melius mulso eluuntur, et tum aliquid ex iis, quae supra scripta sunt, quod mel habeat, infunditur. Si magis pus profluit, et caput utique tondendum est et multa calida aqua perfundendum, et gargarizandum, et usque ad lassitudinem ambulandum, et cibo modico utendum est. Si cruor quoque ex ulceribus apparuit, Lycium cum

---

ª V. 20. 2.

wine. Or equal weights of shredded alum, poppy-tears and acacia juice are mixed together, and to these is added of hyocyamus juice less than half the quantity of each one of the above; and these are pounded together and diluted with wine. Also hyocyamus juice is sufficiently beneficial by itself.

A general remedy for all ear cases, and one approved by experience, was composed by Asclepiades. This contains : cinnamon and casia 4 grms. each; flowers of round cyperus, castoreum, white pepper, long pepper, cardamomum and bennut, 8 grms. each; male frankincense, Syrian nard, fatty myrrh, saffron, soda-scum, 12 grms. each. These are pounded separately, then mixed with vinegar and again pounded, and so preserved; when for use they are diluted with vinegar. In the same way a general remedy for all ear disorders is the tablet of Polyidus, dissolved in sweet wine, the prescription for which is given in the last book.[a] But if there is both a discharge of matter and a swelling, it is not unfitting to wash out the ear with diluted wine through an ear syringe, and then pour in dry wine mixed with rose oil, to which a little oxide of zinc has been added, or boxthorn juice with milk, or polygonum juice with rose oil, or pomegranate juice with a very little myrrh.

If there is also foul ulceration, it is better to wash out with honey wine, and then pour in some one of the compositions described above which contain honey. If there is a great discharge of pus the head is to be shaved, and hot water poured freely over it, also the patient should gargle with the same, walk until tired, and take food sparingly. If there is bleeding from the ulcerations, boxthorn

235

lacte debet infundi, vel aqua, in qua rosa decocta sit,
suco aut herbae sanguinalis aut acaciae adiecto.
B Quod si super ulcera caro increvit, eaque mali odoris
saniem fundit, aqua tepida elui debet, tum infundi id,
quod ex ture et aerugine et aceto et melle fit, aut
mel cum aerugine incoctum. Squama quoque
aeris cum sandaraca contrita per fistulam recte
instillatur.

5 Ubi vero vermes orti sunt, si iuxta sunt, protrahendi
oriculario specillo sunt; si longius, medicamentis
enecandi, cavendumque ne postea nascantur. Ad
utrumque proficit album veratrum cum aceto
contritum. Elui quoque aurem oportet vino, in
quo marrubium decoctum sit. Emortui sub his
vermes in primam partem auris provocabuntur, unde
educi facillime possunt.

6 Sin foramen auris conpressum est, et intus crassa
sanies subest, mel quam optimum addendum est.
Si id parum proficit, mellis cyatho et dimidio aeruginis
rasae P. ✳ II adiciendum est incoquendumque, et eo
utendum. Iris quoque cum melle idem proficit.
Item galbani P. ✳ II, murrae et fellis taurini, singulorum P. ✳ = = , vini quantum satis est ad murram
diluendam.

7 Ubi vero gravius aliquis audire coepit, quod
maxime post longos capitis dolores evenire consuevit,
in primis aurem ipsam considerare oportet: apparebit
enim aut crusta, qualis super ulcera innascitur, aut

juice should be poured in mixed with milk, or with water in which rose leaves have been boiled, with polygonum juice or that of acacia added. If flesh has formed over the ulcerations and there is a malodorous discharge, the ear should be washed out with tepid water, then that composition poured in which contains frankincense, verdigris, vinegar and honey; or honey boiled with verdigris. Copper scales also pounded up with sandarach may be instilled through a tube with advantage.

When maggots have appeared, if they are near the surface, they must be extracted by an ear scoop; if further in they must be killed by medicaments, and afterwards care taken that they do not breed. White veratrum pounded up in vinegar serves for both these purposes. The ear should also be washed out with a decoction of horehound in wine. By this procedure dead maggots will be driven forwards into the outer part of the ear, whence they can be readily withdrawn.

But if the ear-passage has been narrowed and thick matter collects within, honey of the best ought to be introduced. If this does not help, there must be added to 65 c.cm. of honey 8 grms. of verdigris scrapings; they must be boiled together and so used. Iris root with honey has the same efficacy. So also has galbanum 8 grms., myrrh and ox bile 1·33 grms. each, and of wine a sufficient quantity to dissolve the myrrh.

When a man is becoming dull of hearing, which happens most often after prolonged headaches, in the first place, the ear itself should be inspected: for there will be found either a crust such as comes upon the surface of ulcerations, or concretions of wax.

sordium coitus. Si crusta est, infundendum est
oleum calidum, aut cum melle aerugo vel porri sucus,
aut cum mulso nitri paulum. Atque ubi crusta a
corpore iam recedit, eluenda auris aqua tepida est,
quo facilius ea per se diducta oriculario specillo
B protrahatur. Si sordes haeque molles sunt, eodem
specillo eximendae sunt: at si durae sunt, acetum
et cum eo nitri paulum coiciendum est; cumque
emollitae sunt, eodem modo elui aurem purgarique
oportet. Quod si capitis gravitas manet, attonden-
dum; idem leniter [1] . . . sed diu perfricandum est,
adiecto vel irino vel laureo oleo, sic ut utrilibet
paulum aceti misceatur; tum diu ambulandum, leniterque post unctionem aqua calida caput fovendum.
C Cibisque utendum ex inbecillissima et media materia,
magisque adsumendae dilutae potiones; nonnumquam gargarizandum est. Infundendum autem in
aurem castoreum cum aceto et laureo oleo et suco
radiculae corticis, aut cucumeris agrestis sucus ad-
ditis contritis rosae foliis. Inmaturae quoque uvae
sucus cum rosa instillatus adversus surditatem satis
proficit.

8     Aliud viti genus est, ubi aures intra se ipsas sonant;
atque hoc quoque fit, ne externum sonum accipiant.
Levissimum est, ubi id ex gravidine est; peius, ubi
ex morbis capitisve longis doloribus incidit; pessimum, ubi magnis morbis venientibus maximeque
comitiali praevenit.
B     Si ex gravidine est, purgare aurem oportet et

---

[1] *Marx supplies* castoreo *after* leniter.

---

*a* Vol. I. p. 370.

If a crust, hot oil is poured in, or verdigris mixed with honey or leek juice or a little soda in honey wine. And when the crust has been separated from the ulceration, the ear is irrigated with tepid water, to make it easier for the crusts now disengaged to be withdrawn by the ear scoop. If it be wax, and if it be soft, it can be extracted in the same way by the ear scoop; but if hard, vinegar containing a little soda is introduced; and when the wax has softened, the ear is washed out and cleared as above. When the heaviness of the head persists it should be shaved; the head rubbed over gently and for some time with castoreum to which either iris or laurel oil has been added with either of which a little vinegar has been mixed; then the patient must take a long walk, and after the rubbing his head is to be fomented gently with hot water. And the food should be of the lightest and of the middle class, and the drinks especially diluted; he should occasionally gargle. Further, the ear should be syringed with castoreum mixed with vinegar and laurel oil and the juice of young radish rind, or with cucumber juice, mixed with crushed rose leaves. The dropping in of the juice of unripe grapes mixed with rose oil is also fairly efficacious against deafness.

Another class of lesion is that in which the ears produce a ringing noise within themselves : and this also prevents them from perceiving sounds from without. This is least serious when due to cold in the head; worse when occasioned by diseases or prolonged pains of the head; worst of all when it precedes the onset of serious maladies, and especially epilepsy.

If it is due to a cold,[a] the ear should be cleaned

spiritum continere, donec inde umor aliquis exspumet.
Si ex morbo vel capitis dolore, quod ad exercita-
tionem, frictionem, perfusionem gargarizationemque
pertinet, eadem facienda sunt.  Cibis non utendum
nisi extenuantibus.  In aurem dandus radiculae
sucus cum rosa vel cum suco radicis ex cucumere
agresti; vel castoreum cum aceto et laureo oleo;
veratrum quoque ad id ex aceto conteritur, deinde
melle cocto excipitur, et inde collyrium factum in
aurem demittitur.

C   Si sine his coepit ideoque novo metu terret, in
aurem dari debet castoreum cum aceto vel irino
aut laureo oleo; aut huic mixtum castoreum cum
suco nucum amararum; aut murra et nitrum cum
rosa et aceto.  Plus tamen in hoc quoque proficit
victus ratio, eademque facienda sunt, quae supra (B)
conprehendi, cum maiore quoque diligentia; et
praeterea, donec is sonus finiatur, a vino abstinendum.

D Quod si simul et sonus est et inflammatio, laureum
oleum coniecisse abunde est, aut id, quod ex amaris
nucibus exprimitur, quibus quidam vel castoreum vel
murram miscent.

9   Solet etiam interdum in aurem aliquid incidere, ut
calculus aliquodve animal.  Si pulex intus est,
conpellendum eo lanae paulum est, quo ipse is subit
et simul extrahitur.  Si non est secutus aliudve
animal est, specillum lana involutum in resina quam
glutinosissima maximeque terebenthina demittendum, idque in aurem coiciendum ibique vertendum

---

<sup>a</sup> 8. B.

and the breath held until some humour froths out from it. If it arises from disease and pain in the head, the prescriptions as to exercise, rubbing, affusion and gargling should be carried out. Only foods that make thin are to be used. Into the ear radish juice should be dropped with oil of roses or with the juice of wild cucumber root; or castoreum with vinegar and laurel oil. Also veratrum is pounded up for this purpose in vinegar, then mixed with boiled honey, and a salve made of it and introduced into the ear.

If the noise begins without these reasons and so causes dread of some new danger, there should be inserted into the ear castoreum in vinegar or with either iris oil or laurel oil; or castoreum is mixed with this together with the juice of bitter almonds; or myrrh and soda with rose oil and vinegar. But in this case also, there is more benefit from regulation of the diet, and the same is to be done as was prescribed above,[a] with even greater care. And, besides, until the noise has ceased the patient must abstain from wine. But if there is at the same time both ringing and inflammation, laurel oil should be freely inserted, or the oil expressed from bitter almonds with which some mix myrrh or castoreum.

It happens also occasionally that something slips into the ear, such as a small stone, or some living thing. If a flea has got in, a little wool is introduced in which it becomes engaged and so is extracted. If it does not come out, or if it is some other creature, a probe is wrapped round with a little wool, soaked in very sticky resin, especially turpentine resin, which after being passed into the ear is there twisted

est: utique enim conprehendit [eximet]. Sin aliquid
exanime est, specillo oriculario protrahendum est aut
B hamulo retuso paulum recurvato. Si ista nihil proficiunt, potest eodem modo resina protrahi. Sternumenta quoque admota id commode elidunt, aut
oriculario clystere aqua vehementer intus conpulsa.
Tabula quoque conlocatur, media inhaerens, capitibus
utrimque pendentibus; superque eam homo deligatur
in id latus versus, cuius auris eo modo laborat, sic ut
extra tabulam emineat. Tum malleo caput tabulae,
quod a pedibus est, feritur; atque ita concussa aure
id quod inest excidit.

8. Nares vero exculceratas fovere oportet vapore
aquae calidae. Id et spongia expressa atque admota
fit et subiecto vase oris angusti calida aqua repleto.
Post id fomentum inlinenda ulcera sunt aut plumbi
recremento aut cerussa aut argenti spuma: cum
quolibet horum [1] . . . aliquod conteri[t,] eique, dum
teritur, in vicem vinum et oleum murteum adici[t],
donec [2] mellis crassitudinem fecerit. Sin autem ea
ulcera circa os sunt pluresque crustas et odorem
foedum habent, quod genus Graeci ozenam appellant,
B sciri quidem debet vix ei malo posse succurri. Nihilo
minus tamen haec temptari possunt, ut caput ad
cutem tondeatur adsidueque vehementer perfricetur,
multa calida aqua perfundatur, multa dein ambulatio

---

[1] *After* horum, *Marx would read:* malagma debet aliquod
conteri, *and this is translated.*
[2] *The text here is corrupt: Marx conjectures* donec ad mellis
crassitudinem venerit, *and this is translated.*

---

[a] Celsus is the first to use the word ozaena (Greek ὄζαινα,
bad-smelling breath, cf. Dioscorides IV. 140) of the ulcers,
which are one of the causes of this condition: Galen (*Med.*,

round; for that will certainly catch it. If it is some inanimate object, it is to be withdrawn by an ear scoop or by a small blunt hook slightly bent. If these are ineffectual it is possible to extract it by means of resin as above. Also if a sneezing fit is induced, this easily moves it away or a forcible injection of water through an ear syringe. Again, a plank may be arranged, having its middle supported and the ends unsupported. Upon this the patient is tied down, with the affected ear downwards, so that the ear projects beyond the end of the plank. Then the end of the plank at the patient's feet is struck with a mallet, and the ear being so jarred what is within drops out.

8. Now ulcerated nostrils should be fomented with steam from hot water; that is done either by applying a sponge after squeezing it out, or by holding the nose over a narrow-mouthed vessel filled with hot water. After this fomentation the ulcerations should be smeared with lead slag, white lead or litharge; with any of these a kind of poultice is compounded, and to this, while it is being pounded up, wine and myrtle oil are added alternately, until it becomes of the consistency of honey. But if these ulcerations involve bone, and have numerous crusts with a foul odour, which kind the Greeks call ozaena,[a] it ought to be understood that it is scarcely possible to afford relief in that disease. The following measures, none the less, can be tried: the head may be shaved to the scalp, rubbed frequently and vigorously, and sluiced with quantities of hot water; then the patient is to take a great deal of

19, XIV. 785) describes the relief of ὄζαινα by the removal of polypi.

sit, cibus modicus, neque acer neque valentissimus.
Tum in narem ipsam mel cum exiguo modo resinae
terebenthinae coiciatur (quod specillo quoque invo-
luto lana fit) adtrahaturque spiritu is sucus, donec
C in ore gustus eius sentiatur. Sub his enim crustae
resolvuntur, quae tum per sternumenta elidi debent.
Puris ulceribus vapor aquae calidae subiciendus est;
deinde adhibendum aut Lycium ex vino dilutum,
aut amurca aut omphacium aut mentae aut marrubii
sucus aut atramentum sutorium, quod concande-
factum, deinde contritum sit; aut interior scillae
pars contrita, sic ut horum cuilibet mel adiciatur.
D Cuius in ceteris admodum exigua pars esse debet;
in atramento sutorio tanta, ut ea mixtura liquida fiat;
cum scilla utique pars maior; involvendumque lana
specillum est, et in eo medicamento tinguendum,
eoque ulcera inplenda sunt. Rursusque linamentum
involutum et oblongum eodem medicamento inlinendum demittendumque in narem est et ab inferiore
parte leniter deligandum. Idque per hiemem et
ver bis die, per aestatem et autumnum ter die fieri
debet.

2   Interdum vero in naribus etiam carunculae quaedam similes muliebribus mammis nascuntur, eaeque
imis partibus, quae carnosissimae sunt, inhaerent.
Has curare oportet medicamentis adurentibus, sub
quibus ex toto consumuntur. Polypus vero est
caruncula, modo alba modo subrubra, quae narium
ossi inhaeret, ac modo ad labra tendens narem

exercise, and a moderate amount of food, neither sour nor very nutritious. Further, into the nostril itself may be inserted honey to which a very small quantity of turpentine resin has been added (this is done on a probe wrapped round with wool), and this juice is drawn inwards by the breath until it can be tasted in the mouth. For in this way the crusts are loosened, and they should then be blown out by sneezing. The ulcerations having been cleaned are steamed over hot water; then there should be applied either box-thorn juice diluted with wine or wine lees or ompha-cium or the juice of mint or horehound or blacking made glowing hot and then pounded, or the interior part of a squill crushed; provided that to any of these honey is added. The honey should be a very small part in all these mixtures, except with the blacking, when there should be just enough to make the mixture liquid, whilst with the squill certainly the honey should form the larger part; a probe should be wrapped round with wool, and dipped into this medicament, and with it the ulcers are filled. And further, a strip of linen is folded into a long roll, smeared with the same medicament, and inserted into the nostril, and is lightly bandaged on below. This should be done in winter and spring twice a day, in summer and autumn three times a day.

Again, inside the nostrils there are sometimes formed little lumps like women's nipples, and these are fixed by their deepest and most fleshy parts. These should be treated by caustics, under which they are completely eaten away. A polypus, in fact, is a lump of this sort, sometimes white, sometimes reddish, which is attached to the bone of the nose, and fills the nostril, being directed

implet, modo retro per id foramen, quo spiritus
a naribus ad fauces descendit, adeo increscit, uti
B post uvam conspici possit; strangulatque hominem,
maxime austro aut euro flante; fereque mollis est,
raro dura, eaque magis spiritum impedit et nares
dilatat; quae fere carcinodes est; itaque attingi
non debet. Illud aliud genus fere quidem ferro
curatur, interdum tamen inarescit, si addita in
narem per linamentum aut penicillum ea compositio
est, quae habet: mini Sinopici, chalcitidis, calcis,
sandaracae, singulorum P. ✳ I; atramenti sutori
P. ✳ II.

9. In dentium autem dolore, qui ipse quoque
maximis tormentis adnumerari potest, vinum ex toto
circumcidendum est. Cibo quoque primo abstinendum, deinde eo modico mollique utendum, ne man-
dentis dentes inritet; tum extrinsecus admovendus
per spongiam vapor aquae calidae, inponendumque
ceratum ex cyprino exve irino factum, lanaque id
conprehendendum, caputque velandum est. Quod
si gravior dolor est, utiliter et alvus ducitur, et calida
cataplasmata super maxillas inponuntur, et ore
umor calidus cum medicamentis aliquibus continetur,
2 saepiusque mutatur. Cuius rei causa et quinque-
folii radix in vino mixto coquitur, et hyoscyami radix
vel in posca vel in vino, sic ut paulum his salis adiciatur
et papaveris non nimium aridi cortices et mandragorae radix eodem modo. Sed in his tribus utique
vitandum est, ne, quod haustum erit, devoretur.
Ex populo quoque alba cortex radicis in hunc usum

---

<sup>a</sup> VII. 10.

sometimes towards the lips, sometimes backwards through that passage by which the breath goes from the nose to the throat. In this direction it may grow until it can be seen behind the uvula; it chokes the patient, especially when the south or east wind blows; generally it is soft, rarely hard, and the latter sort hinders breathing more and dilates the nose; it is then generally cancerous, and so should not be touched. But the other kind can generally be removed by the knife [a]; sometimes, however, it dries up, if the following composition is inserted into the nostril on lint or on a feather : minium from Sinope, copper ore, lime, and sandarach 4 grms. each, blacking 8 grms.

**9.** Now in the case of pain in the teeth, which by itself also can be counted among the greatest of torments, wine must be entirely cut off. At first the patient must fast, then take sparingly of soft food, so as not to irritate the teeth when masticating; then externally steam from hot water is to be applied by a sponge, and an ointment put on made from cyprus or iris oil, with a woollen bandage over it. and the head must be wrapped up. For more severe pain a clyster is useful, with a hot poultice upon the cheeks, and hot water containing certain medicaments held in the mouth and frequently changed. For this purpose cinquefoil root may be boiled in diluted wine, and hyoscyamus root either in vinegar and water, or in wine, with the addition of a little salt, also poppy-head skins not too dry and mandragora root in the same condition. But with these three remedies, the patient should carefully avoid swallowing the fluid in the mouth. The bark of white poplar roots boiled in diluted wine may be

in vino mixto recte coquitur, et in aceto cornus
cervini ramentum, et nepeta cum taeda pingui ac
ficu item pingui vel in mulso vel in aceto et melle ; ex
quibus cum ficus decocta est, is umor percolatur.
3 Specillum quoque lana involutum in calidum oleum
demittitur, eoque ipse dens fovetur. Quin etiam
quaedam quasi cataplasmata in dentem ipsum
inlinuntur ; ad quem usum ex malo Punico acido
arido malicorii pars interior cum pari portione et
gallae et pinei corticis conteritur, misceturque
his minium ; eaque contrita aqua pluvia[ti]li coguntur.
Aut panacis, papaveris lacrimae, peucedani, uvae
taminiae sine seminibus pares portiones conteruntur.
Aut galbani partes tres, papaveris lacrimae pars
quarta. Quicquid dentibus admotum est, nihilo
minus supra maxillas ceratum, quale supra (1) posui,
4 esse debet lana optentum. Quidam etiam murrae,
cardamomi, singulorum P. ✳ I ; croci, pyrethri,
ficorum, spartes, singulorum P. ✳ IIII ; sinapis
P. ✳ VIII contrita linteolo inlinunt, inponuntque in
umero partis eius, qua dens dolet : si is superior est,
a scapulis ; si inferior, a pectore ; idque dolorem
levat, et cum levavit, protinus summovendum est.
5 Si vero exesus est dens, festinare ad eximendum eum,
nisi res coegit, non est necesse : sed tum omnibus
fomentis, quae supra (3 *seq.*) posita sunt, adiciendae
quaedam valentiores conpositiones sunt quae dolorem
levant ; qualis Herae est. Habet autem papaveris
lacrimae P. ✳ I ; piperis P. ✳ II ; soreos P. ✳ X ;
quae contrita galbano excipiuntur, idque circum-

appropriately used for the same purpose, and stag's
horn shavings boiled in vinegar, and catmint together
with a torch rich in resin and a fig equally rich boiled
either in honey wine or in vinegar and honey. When
the fig has been boiled down with these, this fluid
is strained. Also a probe wrapped round with
wool is dipped in hot oil, and the tooth itself
fomented with this. Moreover, some applications,
like poultices, are smeared on the tooth itself, and
for this purpose the inside rind of an unripe dry
pomegranate is pounded up with equal parts of
oak-galls and pine bark, with which minium is
mixed; and these when pounded together are made
up with rain-water. Or equal quantities of all-heal,
poppy-tears, sulphur wort, and black bryony berries
without the seeds are pounded together. Or three
parts of galbanum to one of poppy juice. Whatever is applied to the teeth directly, none the less
the ointment mentioned above must also be put
on the jaws and covered over with wool. Some
rub up together myrrh and cardamoms, 4 grms.
each; saffron chamomile figs and broom 16 grms.
each; and mustard 32 grms.; spread it on lint and
apply to the shoulder on the side of the painful
tooth; over the shoulder-blade, if it is an upper
tooth; on the chest if a lower one; and this relieves the pain, and as soon as it has relieved it,
must be at once taken off. When a tooth decays,
there is no hurry to extract it, unless it cannot be
helped, but rather to the various applications described above, we must add more active compositions
for the relief of pain, such as that of Heras. This
has: poppy juice 4 grms.; pepper 8 grms.; sory
40 grms., pounded, taken up in galbanum, and

datur; aut Menemachi, maxime ad maxillares
dentes, in qua sunt croci P. ✳ =; cardamomi,
turis fuliginis, ficorum, spartes, pyrethri, singulorum
P. ✳ IIII; sinapis P. ✳ VIII. Quidam autem miscent pyrethri, piperis, elateri, spartes, singulorum
P. ✳ I; aluminis scissilis, papaveris lacrimae, uvae
taminiae, sulpuris ignem non experti, bituminis, lauri
6 bacarum, sinapis, singulorum P. ✳ II. Quod si
dolor eximi eum cogit, et piperis semen cortice
liberatum, et eodem modo baca hederae coniecta in
[id] foramen dentem findit, isque per testas excidet.
Et plani piscis, quam pastinacam nostri, trygona
Graeci vocant, aculeus torretur, deinde conteritur
resinaque excipitur, quae denti circumdata hunc
solvit. Et alumen scissile et . . .¹ in foramen con-
iectum dentem citat. Sed id tamen involutum in
lanula demitti commodius est, quia sic dente servato
7 dolorem levat. Haec medicis accepta sunt. Sed
agrestium experimento cognitum est, cum dens dolet,
herbam mentastrum cum suis radicibus evelli debere,
et in pelvem coici, supraque aquam infundi, collo-
carique iuxta sedentem hominem undique veste
contectum; tum in pelvem candentes silices demitti,
sic ut aqua tegantur; hominemque eum hiante ore
vaporem excipere, ut supra dictum est, undique
inclusum. Nam et sudor plurimus sequitur, et per
os continens pituita defluit, idque saepe longiorem,
semper annuam valetudinem bonam praestat.
**10.** Si vero tonsillae sine exulceratione per inflam-

¹ *Probably some word has fallen out here. One MS. has*
id in *for* et in, *V. d. Linden suggests* id *for* in.

---

*a* The sting ray (Pliny, *N.H.* IX. 155); the spine calcined
would produce calcium oxide, quick-lime.

applied round the tooth; or that of Menemachus,
especially for molar teeth, containing saffron 0·66 grm.,
cardamons, frankincense root, figs, broom and pellitory 16 grms. each; mustard 32 grms. Again, some
mix chamomile, pepper, elaterium and broom 4 grms.
each; shredded alum, poppy juice, black bryony
berries, crude sulphur, bitumen, laurel berries and
mustard 8 grms. each. But if pain compels its removal, a peppercorn without the tegument, or an ivy
berry without the tegument is inserted into the cavity
of the tooth, which it splits, and the tooth falls out in
bits. Also the tail spine of the flat fish which we call
pastinaca, and the Greeks trygon,[a] is roasted, pounded
and taken up in resin, and this, when applied around
the tooth, loosens it. Also shredded alum and . . .
put into the cavity loosens the tooth. However, it
is better to insert this wrapped up in a flake of
wool, for it thus relieves the pain whilst preserving
the tooth. These are the remedies recognized by
medical practitioners, but country people have
found out by experience that if a tooth aches, catmint should be pulled up with its roots, and put into
a pot, and water poured over it, and placed beside
the patient as he sits all covered by clothes; then
red-hot stones are thrown in so as to be covered by
the water; the patient inhales the steam with his
mouth open, whilst, as stated above, he is completely
covered over. For profuse sweating follows, and
also a steady stream of phlegm flows from the mouth,
and this ensures good health always for a year, and
often for longer.

10. Again, if the tonsils [b] owing to inflammation

[b] See III. 370, note *b*, where an operation for their removal
is described.

mationem intumuerunt, caput velandum est; extrinsecus is locus vapore calido fovendus; multa ambulatione utendum; caput in lecto sublime habendum; gargarizandumque reprimentibus. Radix quoque ea, quam dulcem appellant, contusa et in passo mulsove decocta idem praestat. Leniterque quibusdam medicamentis eas inlini non alienum est, 2 quae hoc modo fiunt: ex malo Punico dulci sucus exprimitur, et eius sextarius in leni igne coquitur, donec ei mellis crassitudo est; tum croci, murrae, aluminis scissilis, singulorum P. ✳ II per se conteruntur, paulatimque his adiciuntur vini lenis cyathi duo, mellis unus; deinde priori suco ista miscentur, et rursus leniter incocuntur. Aut eiusdem suci sextarius eodem modo coquitur, atque eadem ratione trita haec adiciuntur: nardi P. ✳ —; omphaci P. ✳ I; cinnamomi, murrae, casiae, singulorum P. ✳ —; eadem autem haec et auribus et naribus 3 purulentis adcommodata sunt. Cibus in hac quoque valetudine lenis esse debet, ne exasperet. Quod si tanta inflammatio est, ut spiritum impediat, in lecto conquiescendum, cibo abstinendum, neque adsumendum quicquam praeter aquam calidam est; alvus quoque ducenda est; gargarizandum ex fico et mulso; inlinendum mel cum omphacio; intrinsecus admovendus sed aliquanto diutius vapor calidus, donec ea suppurent et per se aperiantur. Si pure substante non rumpuntur hi tumores, incidendi 4 sunt; deinde ex mulso calido gargarizandum. At

---

[a] *Radix dulcis* (γλυκύρριζα), liquorice, yielded a peculiar sugar, an important alternative to honey in the days before the introduction of cane sugar.

[b] *i.e.* for a longer time than was necessary for the external treatment described in sect. 1.

[c] For the operation see VII. 12. 2. 3.

are swollen but not ulcerated, the head is to be kept
covered; externally the painful part should be
fomented by steam; the patient is to take walking
exercise freely; when in bed his head should be
raised; repressive gargles should be used. Also
that root which they call sweet,[a] crushed and boiled
in raisin wine or honey wine, has the same beneficial
effect. It is useful to anoint them gently with
certain medicaments prepared as follows : the juice
is squeezed out of sweet pomegranates, and of this
half a litre is boiled over a slow fire until of the consistency of honey; then saffron, myrrh, and shredded
alum 8 grms. each are pounded together, and to
this is added a little at a time 85 c.cm. of mild wine
and 42 c.cm. of honey; next these latter are mixed
with the pomegranate juice aforesaid, and all gently
boiled again. Or half a litre of the pomegranate
juice is boiled in the same way, and the following
after being pounded in like manner are added :
nard 0·33 grm.; omphacium 4 grms.; cinnamon,
myrrh and casia 0·33 grm. each; these same compositions are also appropriate both for purulent ears
and nostrils. Food too in this affection should be
bland that it may not irritate. If the inflammation
is so severe that breathing is hindered, the patient
should keep in bed, abstaining from food, and take
nothing else except hot water; the bowels should
be moved by a clyster, and the gargle of fig and honey
wine used; the tonsils are to be smeared with honey
and omphacium; internally steam is to be inhaled
somewhat longer[b] until the tonsils suppurate and
spontaneously open. If after pus has formed these
swellings do not burst, they are to be cut into;[c] then
the patient must gargle with warm honeyed wine.

253

# CELSUS

si modicus quidem tumor sed exulceratio est, furfurum cremori ad gargarizandum paulum mellis
adiciendum est; inlinendaque ulcera hoc medicamento: passi quam dulcissimi tres heminae ad
unam cocuntur; tum adicitur turis P. ✳ I; ali
P. ✳ I; croci, murrae, singulorum P. ✳ = ; leviterque
omnia rursus fervescunt. Ubi pura ulcera sunt,
eodem furfurum cremore vel lacte gargarizandum
est. Atque hic quoque cibis lenibus opus est, quibus
adici dulce vinum potest.

**11.** Ulcera autem oris si cum inflammatione sunt
et parum pura ac rubicunda sunt, optume iis medicamentis curantur, quae [supra (*cap.* X, 2) posita] ex
malis Punicis fiunt. Continendusque saepe ore
reprimens cremor est, cui paulum mellis sit adiectum:
utendum ambulationibus et non acri cibo. Simul
atque vero pura ulcera esse coeperunt, lenis umor,
interdum etiam quam optima aqua ore continenda est.
Prodestque adsumptum pirum mitius pleniorque
cibus cum acri aceto inspergique ulcera debent
alumine scissili, cui dimidio plus gallae inmaturae
2 sit adiectum. Si iam crustas habent, quales in
adustis esse consuerunt, abhibendae sunt hae conpositiones, quas Graeci antheras nominant: iunci
quadrati, murrae, sandaracae, aluminis pares portiones. Aut croci, murrae, singulorum P. ✳ I;
iridis, aluminis scissilis, sandaracae, singulorum P. ✳
IIII; iunci quadrati P. ✳ VIII. Aut gallae, murrae,
singulorum P. ✳ I; aluminis scissilis P. ✳ II; rosae
foliorum P. ✳ IIII. Quidam autem croci P. ✳ =;
aluminis scissilis, murrae, singulorum P. ✳ I; sanda-

---

*a* VI. 10. 2.
*b* For these medicaments from flower blossoms, cf. VI. **13**.
2, 4; **15**. 1; **18**. 2, and see Galen (XIII. 839).

254

But if with only moderate swelling there is ulceration
as well, the throat is to be gargled with bran gruel to
which a little honey should be added; and the ulcers
smeared with the following composition : 750 c.cm. of
the sweetest raisin wine are boiled down to one-third,
then are added : frankincense 4 grms.; garlic 4 grms;
saffron and myrrh 0·66 grm. each; and all are then
gently heated together. When the ulcers have
cleaned, the throat is gargled with bran gruel or
milk. And here also bland food is necessary, and
in addition sweet wine can be taken.

11. Now ulcerations of the mouth if accompanied
by inflammation, and if they are foul and reddish,
are best treated by the medicaments made from
pomegranates [mentioned above].[a] And, as a repressant, pearl barley gruel to which a little honey
has been added is to be often held in the mouth; the
patient must walk and not take acrid food. As soon
as the ulcerations begin to clean, a bland liquid, at
times even the purest water, is held in the mouth.
It is then beneficial to eat a pear of the softer sort,
and more food along with sharp vinegar; then the
ulcers should be dusted over with split alum, to
which about half as much again of unripe oak-galls
has been added. If the ulcers are already en-
crusted, as happens after cauterization, those compositions are to be applied which the Greeks call
antherae :[b] equal portions of galingale, myrrh, sandarach, and alum. Or saffron and myrrh 4 grms.
each; iris, split alum and sandarach 16 grms. each;
galingale 32 grms. Or oak-galls and myrrh 4 grms.
each; split alum 8 grms.; rose leaves 16 grms. But
some mix saffron 0·66 grm.; split alum and myrrh
4 grms. each; sandarach 8 grms.; galingale 16 grms.

racae P. ✳ II; iunci quadrati P. ✳ IIII miscent.
Priora arida insperguntur: hoc cum melle inlinitur,
neque ulceribus tantum sed etiam tonsillis.

3    Verum ea longe periculosissima sunt ulcera, quas
apthas Graeci appellant, sed in pueris: hos enim
saepe consumunt, in viris et mulieribus idem periculum non est.  Haec ulcera a gingivis incipiunt;
deinde palatum totumque os occupant; tum ad
uvam faucesque descendunt, quibus obsessis non
facile fit, ut puer convalescat.  Ac miserius etiam
est, si lactens adhuc infans est, quo minus imperari
4 remedium aliquod potest.  Sec inprimis nutrix
cogenda est exerceri et ambulationibus et iis operibus,
quae superiores partes movent; mittenda in balineum iubendaque ibi calida aqua mammas perfundere;
tum alenda cibis lenibus et iis, qui non facile corrum-
puntur: potione, si febricitat puer, aquae; si sine
febre est, vini diluti.  Ac si alvus nutricis substitit,
5 ducenda est.  Si pituita eius in os coit, vomere debet.
Tum ipsa ulcera perunguenda sunt melle, cui rhus,
quem Syriacum vocant, aut amarae nuces adiectae
sunt; vel mixtis inter se rosae foliis aridis, pineis
nucleis, menta,[1] coliculo, melle, vel eo medicamento,
quod ex moris fit, quorum sucus eodem modo quo
Punici mali ad mellis crassitudinem coquitur; eademque ratione ei crocum, murra, alumen, vinum, mel,
miscetur: neque quicquam dandum, a quo umor
6 evocari possit.  Si vero iam firmior puer est, gargari-

---

[1] *Daremberg suggests* mentae coliculo "young mint-stalks."

[a] I. 195 note; Appendix I, p. 591.

The first compositions are dried and then dusted on; the last one is smeared on with honey added, and used not only for ulcerations of the mouth, but also of the tonsils.

But by far the most dangerous are those ulcers which the Greeks call aphthae,[a] certainly in children; in them they often cause death, but there is not the same danger for men and women. These ulcers begin from the gums : next they invade the palate and the whole mouth; then they pass downwards to the uvula and throat, and if these are involved, it is not easy for the child to recover. But the disease is even worse in a suckling, for there is then less possibility of its conquest by any remedy. But it is most important that the nurse should be made to take exercise both by walking and by doing work which moves her arms; she should be sent to the bath, and ordered when there to have hot water poured over her breasts; moreover, she should have bland, easily digestible food; and for drink, if the infant is feverish, water; if free from fever, diluted wine. And if the nurse is constipated, her bowels are to be moved by a clyster. If there is clotted phlegm in her mouth, she must vomit. Then the child's ulcers are to be anointed with honey, to which is added sumach, which they call Syrian, or bitter almonds; or a mixture of dried rose leaves, pine-cone seeds, mint, young stalks, and honey, or that medicament which is made of mulberries, the juice of which is concentrated in the same way as pomegranate juice to the consistency of honey; similarly too there is mixed with it saffron, myrrh, alum, wine and honey; nothing should be given which can provoke spittle. If it is an older child he should

zare debet is fere, quae supra (*cap.* X, 3,4) conprehensa
sunt. Ac si lenia medicamenta in eo parum proficiunt, adhibenda sunt ea, quae adurendo crustas
ulceribus inducant. Quale est scissile alumen vel
chalcitis vel atramentum sutorium. Prodest etiam
fames et abstinentia quanta maxime inperari potest.
Cibus esse debet lenis: ad purganda tamen ulcera
interdum caseus ex melle recte datur.

**12.** Linguae quoque ulcera non aliis medicamentis
egent, quam quae prima parte superioris capitis
(11, 1. 2) exposita sunt. Sed quae in latere eius
nascuntur, diutissime durant; videndumque est,
num contra dens aliquis acutior sit, qui sanescere
saepe ulcus eo loco non sinit, ideoque levandus est.

**13.** Solent etiam interdum iuxta dentes in gingivis
tubercula quaedam oriri dolentia: parulidas Graeci
appellant. Haec initio leniter sale contrito perfricare
oportet; aut inter se mixtis sale fossili combusto,
cupresso, nepeta; deinde eluere os cremore lenticulae, inter haec hiare, donec pituita satis profluat.

2    In maiore vero inflammatione iisdem medicamentis
utendum est, quae ad ulcera oris supra (*cap.* XI)
posita sunt: et mollis linamenti paulum involvendum
ex iis aliqua compositione, quas antheras vocari dixi
(*cap.* XI, 2), demittendumque id inter dentem et
gingivam. Quod si † duriore id [1] prohibebit extrinsecus admovendus erit spongia vapor calidus,

---

[1] *The reading of one MS.* "durior erit et" *in place of*
"duriore" *is translated. Alternatively Targa suggests* tumor,
*Marx* dolor in ore *for* duriore.

generally gargle as described above. If the milder medicaments do little good, the caustic materials which induce crusts upon the ulcers should be applied, such as split alum or copper ore or blacking. Even hunger is beneficial and the greatest possible abstinence is to be ordered. The food ought to be bland; for cleansing the ulcers, however, sometimes cheese with honey is appropriately given.

**12.** Ulcerations of the tongue need no other treatment than that noted in the first part of the previous chapter. But those which arise at the side of the tongue last the longest; and it should be looked to, whether some tooth opposite the ulcer is too pointed, which often keeps an ulceration in that position from healing, in which case the tooth must be smoothed down.

**13.** There often occur on the gums adjacent to the teeth certain painful swellings: the Greeks call them parulides.[a] These at first should be gently rubbed over with powdered salt; or with a mixture of powdered rock-salt, cyprus oil and catmint; then the mouth is washed out with lentil gruel, and the mouth is held open at intervals until there has been a sufficient flow of phlegm.

When there is still more severe inflammation, the same medicaments are to be used as noted above for ulcerations of the mouth: and between the tooth and gum should be inserted a little roll of soft lint soaked in one of the compositions which I said are called antherae.[b] If the hardness of the gum prevents this, then hot steam by means of a sponge

[a] Parulis (παρουλίς, Galen, XIV. 785), a gumboil; not mentioned elsewhere by Celsus.
[b] p. 254, note b.

CELSUS

inponendumque ceratum. Si suppuratio se ostendet,
diutius eo vapore utendum erit, et continendum ore
calidum mulsum, in quo ficus decocta sit; idque
subcrudum incidendum, ne, si diutius ibi pus
3 remanserit, os laedat. Quod si maior is tumor est,
commodius totum exciditur, sic ut ex utraque parte
dens liberetur. Pure exempto si levis plaga est, satis
est ore calidam aquam continere, extrinsecus fovere
eodem vapore; si maior est, lenticulae cremore uti
iisdemque medicamentis, quibus cetera ulcera oris
curantur. Alia quoque ulcera in gingivis plerumque
oriuntur, quibus eadem quae in reliquo ore succurrunt;
maxime tamen mandere ligustrum oportet, sucumque
4 eum ore continere. Fit etiam interdum, ut gingivae
ulcere, sive parulis fuit sive non fuit, diutius pus
feratur; quod aut dente corrupto, aut fracto vel[1]
. . . aliterque vitiato osse; maximeque id per fissum
evenire consuevit. Ubi incidit, locus aperiendus,
dens eximendus; testa ossis, si qua excessit, re-
cipienda est; si quid vitiosi est, radendum. Post
quae quid fieri debeat, supra (*cap.* XI) in aliorum
ulcerum curatione conprehensum est. Si vero a
dentibus gingivae recedunt, eaedem antherae succurrunt. Utile est etiam pira aut mala non permatura
mandere, et ore eum umorem continere. Idemque
praestare non acre acetum in ore retentum potest.

[1] *Marx supplies* laeso oritur *after* vel, *and this is translated.*
*V. d. Linden deletes* quod.

is to be applied outside, followed by a cerate. If suppuration shows itself, the steaming is continued longer, and hot honey wine in which a fig has been boiled down is held in the mouth; and before the abscess is quite mature it should be cut into, for fear that the bone may suffer if the pus should be retained longer. But if there is greater swelling, it is better to cut all away so as to free the tooth on both sides. When the pus is let out, if the incision is small it will suffice to hold hot water in the mouth and to foment externally with its steam; if it is larger, lentil gruel should be used, and the same medicaments as for the treatment of ulcerations of the mouth in general. There are also other ulcerations, mostly arising in the gums, for which the same remedies are beneficial; in particular, however, privet should be chewed and the juice held in the mouth. It happens now and then, whether following a gumboil or not, that a discharge of pus persists from an ulcer on the gum; this is due to either a decayed tooth or to bone that is broken or injured and diseased in some other way, and it most commonly occurs through a fissure in the bone. When this is the case, the place must be laid open, the tooth extracted; any projecting scale of bone is to be removed; and any carious bone scraped away. What ought to be done after this has been included in the treatment of other ulcerations. If the gums have retracted from the teeth, the same antherae are of service. It is also useful to chew pears and apples which are not too ripe, and to hold their juice in the mouth. Vinegar that is not too sharp can also be held in the mouth with similar advantage.

**14.** Uvae vehemens inflammatio terrere quoque debet. Itaque in hac et abstinentia necessaria est, et sanguis recte mittitur; et si id aliqua res prohibet, alvus utiliter ducitur; caputque super haec velandum et sublimius habendum est: tum aqua gargarizandum, in qua simul rubus et lenticula decocta sit. Inlinenda autem ipsa uva vel omphacio vel galla vel alumine scissili, sic ut cuilibet eorum mel adiciatur; chelidoniae quoque suco per coclear inlita uva maximeque . . . prodest.[1] Est etiam medicamentum huc aptum, quod Andronium appellatur. Constat ex his: alumine scissili, squama aeris rubri, atramento sutorio, galla, murra, misy; quae per se contrita mixtaque rursus paulatim adiecto vino austero teruntur, donec his mellis crassitudo sit. 2 Ubi horum aliquo inlita uva est, fere multa pituita decurrit; cumque ea quievit, ex vino calido gargarizandum est. Quod si minor ea inflammatio est, laser terere, eique adicere frigidam aquam satis est, eamque aquam cocleario exceptam ipsi uvae subicere. Ac mediocriter eam tumentem aqua quoque frigida eodem modo subiecta reprimit. Ex eadem autem aqua gargarizandum quoque est, quae vel cum lasere vel sine eo hac ratione uvae subiecta est.

**15.** Si quando autem ulcera oris cancer invasit, primum considerandum est, num malus corporis habitus sit, eique occurrendum; deinde ipsa ulcera

---

[1] *The text is doubtful. Some editors and MSS. omit the words* chelidoniae . . . prodest. *If they are retained, something must be supplied after* maximeque. *Marx suggests* cum melle.

**14.** Inflammation of the uvula should also cause anxiety when severe. In this case, as before, abstinence is necessary, and it is right to let blood; and if anything prevents this, it is useful to clyster the bowel; and also the head must be kept covered and raised; and the patient must gargle with a decoction of blackberries and lentils. But the uvula itself is to be smeared either with omphacium or oak-galls or split alum to any one of which honey has been added; it is also good to smear the uvula with chelidonium juice by means of a spoon, and especially ⟨with honey⟩. For this purpose also the composition called Andronium is suitable; it consists of: split alum, red copper scales, blacking, oak-galls, myrrh and antimony sulphide; these are pounded separately and again pounded when mixed together, a dry wine being gradually added till the ingredients have the consistency of honey. After the uvula has been smeared with one of these compounds there is, as a rule, a free flow of phlegm; when this has subsided, hot wine should be gargled. But if there is less severe inflammation, it is sufficient to pound up assafoetida and add cold water to it, and to put the fluid into a spoon and apply it under the uvula itself. When there is only moderate swelling, even cold water held in the same way under the uvula subdues it. Also the same cold water is to be used as a gargle which, with or without the addition of assafoetida, has been applied in this manner to the uvula.

**15.** If at any time gangrene has attacked ulcers of the mouth, the first thing to consider is whether the general health is bad, and if so to obviate it; next the actual ulcers are to be treated. But if the

curanda. Quod si in summa parte id vitium est,
satis proficit anthera umido ulceri arida inspersa;
sicciori cum exigua parte mellis inlita: si paulo
altius, chartae conbustae partes duae, auripigmenti
pars una: si penitus malum descendit, chartae
conbustae partes tres, auripigmenti pars quarta,
aut pares portiones salis fricti et iridis frictae, aut
item pares portiones chalcitidis. calcis, auripigmenti.
2 Necessarium autem est linamentum in rosa tinguere,
et super adurentia medicamenta inponere, ne
vicinum et sanum locum laedant. Quidam etiam
in acris aceti heminam frictum salem coiciunt, donec
tabescere desinat; deinde id acetum coquunt, donec
exsiccetur; eumque salem contritum inspergunt.
Quotiens autem medicamentum inicitur, et ante
et post os diluendum est vel cremore lenticulae
vel aqua, in qua aut ervum aut oleae verbenaeve
decoctae sint, sic ut cuilibet eorum paulum mellis
3 misceatur. Acetum quoque ex scilla retentum
ore satis adversus haec ulcera proficit, item ex aceto cocto
sali, sicut supra (2) demonstratum est, rursus mixtum
acetum. Sed et diu continere utrumlibet, et id
bis aut ter die facere, prout vehemens malum est,
necessarium est. Quod si puer est, cui id incidit,
specillum lana involutum in medicamentum demittendum est, et super ulcus tenendum, ne per
inprudentiam adurentia devoret. Si in gingivis est,
moventurque aliqui dentes, refigi eos oportet:
4 nam curationes vehementer inpediunt. Si nihil
medicamenta proficient, ulcera erunt adurenda.
Quod tamen in labris ideo non est necessarium,

disease is superficial, it is sufficient to use a powdered anthera to dust on the ulcer if moist; if the ulcer is rather dry, to smear it on mixed with a little honey : for somewhat deeper ulcerations, apply burnt papyrus two parts, and orpiment one part; if the mischief penetrates very deeply, burnt papyrus three parts, orpiment one part, or equal parts of rock salt and roasted iris, or copper ore, quick-lime and orpiment, likewise equal parts. But in order that neighbouring spots may not be injured, it is necessary to apply lint dipped in rose oil over these caustic medicaments. Some also put the roasted salt into 250 c.cm. of strong vinegar until it ceases to dissolve; then the vinegar is boiled to dryness, and the salt pounded up and dusted on. But whenever this medicament is applied, the mouth should be washed out both before and after, either with lentil gruel, or with a decoction of vetches or of olives or of vervains, to any one of which a little honey is added.

Also vinegar of squills held sufficiently long in the mouth is beneficial for such ulceration, so too the salt after evaporation as described above dissolved again in vinegar. But whilst the affection continues to be severe it is necessary both to hold one or other of the remedies in the mouth for some time and to use them two or three times a day. If it is a child who is attacked, a probe wrapped round with wool is dipped in the medicament and held to the ulcer, lest by accident he should swallow the caustic. If it is the gums which are involved, and some teeth are loose, they should be extracted, for they greatly hinder treatment. If these medicaments do no good, the ulcers are to be cauterized. But this procedure is not necessary for any ulcer on

quoniam excidere commodius est. Et id quidem,
aeque adustum atque excisum, sine ea curatione,
quae corpori manu adhibetur, inpleri non potest.
Gingivarum vero ossa, quae hebetia sunt, in perpetuum ustione nudantur: neque enim postea caro
increscit. Inponenda tamen adustis lenticula est,
donec sanitatem, qualis esse potest, recipiant.

**16.** Haec in capite fere medicamentis egent.
Sub ipsis vero auribus oriri parotides solent, modo
in secunda valetudine ibi inflammatione orta, modo
post longas febres illuc inpetu morbi converso. Id
abscessus genus est: itaque nullam novam curationem
desiderat, animadversionem tantummodo hanc habet
necessariam: [quia,] si sine morbo id intumuit,
primum reprimentium faciendum experimentum
est; si adversa valetudine, illud inimicum est
maturarique et quam primum aperiri commodius est.

**17.** Ad umbilicos vero prominentes, ne manu
ferroque utendum sit, ante temptandum est, ut
abstineatur, alvus his ducatur, inponatur super
umbilicum id, quod ex his constat: cicutae et fuliginis,
singulorum P. ✳ I; cerussae elotae P. ✳ VI; plumbi
eloti P. ✳ VIII; ovis duobus, quibus etiam solani
sucus adicitur. Hoc etiam diutius inpositum esse
oportet: sed interim conquiescere hominem, cibo
modico uti, sic ut vitentur omnia inflantia.

---

*a* *Lenticula* may be a lentil poultice to cleanse the wound,
or dried and powdered lentils applied as an exedent. Some
commentators think a cutting chisel or gouge is referred to,
with a lentil shaped button on the point (*scalper lenticularis,*
cf. VIII. 3. 4; 4. 14) which was to be used to scrape the bone.
*b* The parotid swellings that occurred "during health"
were perhaps mumps (cf. Hippocrates I. 146, *Epidemics* I. 1):
"After prolonged fevers," dryness and foulness of the mouth
might produce an infection which spread up the ducts to the

the lips since excision is more convenient. Indeed such an ulcer, except by adopting surgical measures, whether cauterizing or excising, cannot be replenished with new flesh. But the bones of the gums, which are inert, continue bare after the cauterization; for no flesh grows up afterwards. A lentil dressing,[a] however, is to be applied to the parts cauterized until it is rendered as healthy as possible.

**16.** Such are the disorders in the head which generally require medicaments. But just below the ears parotid swellings[b] are inclined to occur, sometimes during health when inflammation occurs there, sometimes after prolonged fevers when the force of the disease has been turned in that direction. It is of the nature of an abscession; and so no novel treatment is called for, only what follows must be attended to : if there is swelling without previous disease, repressants are to be tried first; if there has been illness, repressives are objectionable, and it is more convenient that the abscess should mature and be opened as soon as may be.

**17.** For prominent navels, in order that surgical measures need not be used,[c] abstinence should first be tried, a clyster to induce a motion, and the following applications to the umbilicus : hemlock and soot 4 grms. each; washed white lead 24 grms.; washed lead 32 grms.; 2 eggs; to these nightshade juice also is added. This ought to be kept on for a long time, the patient meanwhile lying up, and taking food in such moderation that all flatulence is avoided.

parotid glands, while the " abscess " resulted from some general septic infection, especially an abdominal one.
  c VII. 14.

**18.** Proxima sunt ea, quae ad partes obscenas pertinent, quarum apud Graecos vocabula et tolerabilius se habent et accepta iam usu sunt, cum in omni fere medicorum volumine atque sermone iactentur: apud nos foediora verba ne consuetudine quidem aliqua verecundius loquentium commendata sunt, ut difficilior haec explanatio sit simul et pudorem et artis praecepta servantibus. Neque tamen ea res a scribendo me deterrere debuit: primum, ut omnia quae salutaria accepi, conprehenderem; dein, quia in volgus eorum curatio etiam praecipue cognoscenda est, quae invitissimus quisque alteri ostendit.

2 Igitur si ex inflammatione coles intumuit, reducique summa cutis aut rursus induci non potest, multa calida aqua fovendus locus est. Ubi vero glans contecta est, oriculario quoque clystere inter eam cutemque aqua calida inserenda est. Si mollita sic et extenuata cutis ducenti paruit, expeditior reliqua curatio est. Si tumor vicit, inponenda est vel lenticula vel marrubium vel oleae folia ex vino cocta, sic ut cuilibet eorum, dum teritur, mellis paululum adiciatur; sursumque coles ad ventrem deligandus B est. Quod in omni curatione eius necessarium est; isque homo continere se et abstinere a cibo debet, et potione aquae tantum a siti vindicari. Postero die rursum adhibendum iisdem rationibus aquae fomentum est, et cum vi quoque experiendum, an cutis

---

*a* Cf. VII. 25. 2, where the condition is called phimosis (φιμός, dicebox); the first known use of the special term for this condition.

**18.** Next come subjects relating to the privy
parts, for which the terms employed by the Greeks
are the more tolerable, and are now accepted for
use, since they are met with in almost every medical
book and discourse. Not even the common use has
commended our coarser words for those who would
speak with modesty. Hence it is more difficult to
set forth these matters and at the same time to
observe both propriety and the precepts of the art.
Nevertheless, this ought not to deter me from
writing, firstly in order that I may include everything
which I have heard of as salutary, secondly because
their treatment ought above all things to be generally
understood, since every one is most unwilling to show
such a complaint to another person.

So then when the penis swells up owing to inflammation, and the foreskin cannot be drawn back, or
conversely drawn forwards, the place should be
fomented freely with hot water. But when the
glans is covered up,[a] hot water should be injected,
between it and the foreskin, by means of an ear
syringe. If the foreskin is thus softened and rendered thinner, and yields when drawn upon, the
rest of the treatment is more speedy. If the swelling
goes on, either lentil meal or horehound or olive
leaves, boiled in wine, is to be laid on, to each of
which, whilst being pounded up, a little honey is to
be added; and the penis is to be bandaged upwards
to the belly. That is required in the treatment of
all its disorders; and the patient ought to keep
quiet and abstain from food, and drink water just
so much as is justified by thirst. On the next day
fomentations with water must again be applied in the
same way, and even force should be tried as to

269

sequatur; eaque si non parebit, leviter summa
scalpello concidenda erit. Nam cum sanies pro-
fluxerit, extenuabitur is locus, et facilius cutis
C ducetur. Sive autem hoc modo victa erit, sive
numquam repugnaverit, ulcera vel in cutis ulteriore
parte vel in glande ultrave eam in cole reperientur;
quae necesse est aut pura siccave sint aut umida
et purulenta. Si sicca sunt, primum aqua calida
fovenda sunt; deinde inponendum Lycium ex
vino aut amurca cocta cum eodem aut cum rosa
buturum. Si levis is umor inest, vino eluenda sunt,
tum buturo et rosae mellis paulum, et resinae terebenthinae pars quarta adicienda est; eoque utendum.
D At si pus ex iis profluit, ante omnia elui mulso calido
debent; tum inponi piperis P. ✳ I; murrae P. ✳ ═;
croci, misyos cocti, singulorum P. ✳ II; quae ex
vino austero cocuntur, donec mellis crassitudinem
habeant. Eadem autem conpositio tonsillis, uvae
madenti, oris nariumque ulceribus accommodata
est. Aliud ad eadem: piperis P. ✳ ═; murrae
P. ✳ ═; croci P. ✳ ═ ═; misy cocti P. ✳ I;
aeris combusti P. ✳ II; quae primum ex vino austero
conteruntur, deinde ubi inaruerunt, iterum teruntur
ex passi tribus cyathis et incocuntur, donec visci
E crassitudinem habeant. Aerugo quoque cum cocto
melle eaque quae ad oris ulcera supra (11, 1. 2)
conprensa sunt [curant] aut Erasistrati conpositio

---

*a* VI. **11.** 1, 2; also prescriptions in chaps. 8 to **15**.

whether the foreskin will yield; if it does not give
way, the foreskin is to be notched at its margin
with a scalpel. For when sanies has flowed out
this part will become thinner, and the foreskin the
more easily drawn upon. But whether the foreskin
is made to yield by this procedure, or whether it
has at no time proved resistant, ulcerations will be
found, either in the ulterior part of the foreskin, or
in the glans, or behind this in the penis, and these
ulcerations must of necessity be either clean or dry
or moist and purulent. If they are dry, they must
in the first place be fomented with hot water; then
apply either buckthorn in wine, or olive lees in the
same, or butter with rose oil. If there is a thin
humour, the ulcerations should be bathed with wine,
and then to butter and rose oil a little honey and a
fourth part of turpentine resin is to be added and
this dressing put on. But when pus runs from the
ulcers, first they are to be bathed with hot honey
wine; then there is put on : pepper 4 grms.; myrrh
0·66 grm.; saffron and boiled antimony sulphide
8 grms. each; these are heated in dry wine to the
consistency of honey. Moreover, the same composition is suitable for the tonsils, a dripping uvula, and
ulcerations of the mouth and nostrils. Another
for the same purpose consists of pepper and myrrh
0·66 grm. each; saffron 1·33 grm.; cooked antimony
sulphide 4 grms.; roasted copper 8 grms.; these are
first pounded together in dry wine, then, when they
are dry, are again pounded up in 125 c.cm. of raisin
wine and heated to the consistency of birdlime.
Verdigris too mixed with boiled honey, also those
compositions noted above for ulcerations of the
mouth,[a] or the compositions of Erasistratus or of

# CELSUS

aut Cratonis recte super purulenta naturalia inponitur.
Foliorum quoque oleae P. ✶ . . . ¹ ex novem cyathis
vini cocuntur; his adicitur aluminis scissilis P. ✶ IIII;
Lyci P. ✶ VIII; mellis sex cyathi: ac si plus puris
est, id medicamentum ex melle; si minus, ex vino
diluitur. Illud perpetuum est, post curationem,
dum inflammatio manet, quale supra (C) positum est,
cataplasma super dare, et cotidie ulcera eadem
F ratione curare. Quod si pus et multum et cum malo
odore coepit profluere, elui cremore lenticulae debet,
sic ut ei mellis paulum adiciatur. Aut oleae vel
lentisci folia vel marrubium decoquendum est,
eoque umore eodem modo cum melle utendum;
inponendaque eadem aut etiam omphacium cum
melle aut id, quod ex aerugine et melle ad aures fit;
aut conpositio Andronis aut anthera, sic ut ei paulum
G mellis adiciatur. Quidam omnia ulcera, de quibus
adhuc dictum est, Lycio ex vino curant. Si vero
ulcus latius atque altius serpit, eodem modo elui
debet, inponi vero aut aerugo aut omphacium cum
melle aut Andronis compositio aut marrubii, murrae
aut croci, aluminis scissilis cocti, rosae foliorum
aridorum, gallae, singulorum P. ✶ I; mini Sinopici
P. ✶ II. Quae per se singula primum teruntur,
deinde iuncta iterum melle adiecto, donec liquidi
cerati crassitudinem habeant; tum in aeneo vaso
H leniter cocuntur, ne superfluant. Cum iam guttae
indurescunt, vas ab igni removetur; idque medicamentum, prout opus est, aut ex melle aut ex

¹ *MSS.* folia *which Targa keeps, omitting the sign of quantity,
which is absent from one MS. Marx emends to* foliorum *and
marks the sign of quantity as incomplete.*

---

ᵃ VI. 7. 2 B, C.

Craton [a] are suitable for applying to suppurating genitals. Also . . . olive leaves [b] are boiled in 375 c.cm. of wine, to which is added split alum 16 grms., lycium 32 grms.; and 250 c.cm. of honey; and if there is more pus, this medicament is made up with honey; if less, with wine. After treatment, the general procedure, so long as the inflammation persists, is to apply a poultice such as was mentioned above, and to dress the ulcers daily in the same way. If a free discharge of foul pus begins, the ulcers should be bathed with lentil gruel to which a little honey has been added. Or a decoction is made of olive or of mastich leaves, or of horehound, and the liquid used with honey in the same way; and the same remedies are to be laid on or even omphacium with honey, or that prescription used for the ears containing verdigris and honey,[c] or Andron's composition,[d] or an anthera,[e] as long as a little honey is added to it. Some treat all ulcerations of the kind here spoken of with lycium and wine. If the ulceration spreads more widely and deeply, it should be bathed in the same way, and then there should be applied either verdigris or omphacium with honey or Andron's composition or that containing horehound, myrrh or saffron, split alum boiled, dried rose leaves and oak-galls, 4 grms. each; Sinopic minium 8 grms. These are pounded up first separately, then together again, with honey added, until of the consistency of a liquid cerate; then gently heated in a bronze pot but not allowed to boil over. When drops from it begin to solidify, the pot is taken off the fire; and this composition when it is to be

[b] The quantity is doubtful, see critical note.
[c] VI. 7. 5.    [d] V. 20. 4.    [e] VI. 11. 2.

vino liquatur. Idem autem per se etiam ad fistulas
utile est. Solet etiam interdum ad nervos ulcus
descendere, profluitque pituita multa, sanies tenuis
malique odoris non cocta [1] aut aquae similis, in qua
caro recens lota est; doloresque is locus et punc-
I tiones habet. Id genus quamvis inter purulenta
est, tamen lenibus medicamentis curandum est,
quale est emplastrum tetrapharmacum ex rosa
liquatum, sic ut turis quoque paulum ei misceatur;
aut id, quod ex buturo, rosa, resina, melle fit, supra
(C) vero a me positum est; praecipueque id ulcus
multa calida aqua fovendum est, velandumque neque
frigori committendum. Interdum autem per ipsa
ulcera coles sub cute exestur sic ut glans excidat;
K sub quo casu cutis ipsa circumcidenda est. Perpetu-
umque est, quotiens glans aut ex cole aliquid vel
excidit vel absciditur, hanc non esse servandam,
ne considat ulcerique adglutinetur, ac neque reduci
possit postea, et fortasse fistulam quoque urinae
claudat. Tubercula etiam, quae phumata Graeci
vocant, circa glandem, oriuntur, quae vel medicamentis vel ferro aduruntur; et cum crustae exciderunt,
squama aeris inspergitur, ne quid ibi rursus increscat.
3   Haec citra cancrum sunt; qui cum in reliquis
partibus tum in his quoque vel praecipue ulcera
infestat. Incipit a nigritie. Quae si cutem occupavit,
protinus specillum subiciendum, eaque incidenda
est; deinde orae vulsella prendendae; tum quicquid

---

[1] *The text is corrupt.   Marx suggests* colorata *for* non cocta,
*and this is translated.*

---

[a] V. **19**. 4.        [b] Par. 2 C.
[c] For these and their treatment see V. **18**. 16 ff. and **28**. 9.
[d] See Appendix, p. 589.

used is dissolved in honey or wine. But the same by itself is also good for fistulae. The ulceration at times even penetrates to fibrous tissues; there is a running discharge, then sanies, thin and foul, coloured or like water in which fresh meat has been soaked; and the place is painful and has a pricking sensation. This kind, although purulent, is none the less to be treated by bland applications, such as the tetrapharmacum plaster [a] dissolved in rose oil with the addition of a little frankincense; or the composition made of butter, rose oil, resin and honey noted by me above.[b] In particular this ulcer should be fomented freely with hot water, and should be kept covered, not exposed to cold. Sometimes through such an ulceration the penis is so eaten away underneath the foreskin that the glans falls off; in which case the foreskin itself must be cut away all round. It is the rule, whenever the glans or any part of the penis has fallen off, or has been cut away, that the foreskin should not be preserved, lest it come into contact, and adhere to the ulceration, so that afterwards it cannot be drawn back, and further perhaps may choke the urethra. Again, little tumours, which the Greeks call phymata,[c] spring up around the glans; they are burnt away by caustic or the cautery; when the crusts fall off, copper scales are dusted that no more may grow there.

The foregoing ulcerations stop short of canker,[d] which in other parts, but here the more especially, attacks ulcerations. It begins in a black patch. If it invades the foreskin, at once a probe should be passed underneath, upon which the foreskin is to be incised and the margins seized with forceps; then

corruptum est excidendum, sic ut ex integro quoque
paulum dematur; idque adurendum. Quotiens
quid ustum est, hic quoque sequitur, ut inponenda
lenticula sit; deinde ubi crustae exciderunt, ulcera
B sicut alia curentur. Ac si cancer ipsum colem
occupavit, inspergenda aliqua sunt ex adurentibus,
maximeque id, quod ex calce, chalcitide, auripig-
mento componitur. Si medicamenta vincuntur,
hic quoque scalpello quicquid corruptum est, sic ut
aliquid etiam integri trahat, praecidi debet. Illud
quoque aeque perpetuum est, exciso cancro vulnus
esse adurendum. Sed sive ex medicamentis sive
ex ferro crustae occalluerunt, magnum periculum
est, ne his decidentibus ex cole profusio sanguinis
C insequatur. Ergo longa quiete et inmobili paene
corpore opus est, donec ex ipso crustae [1] leniter
resolvantur. Ac si vel volens aliquis vel inprudens,
dum ingreditur inmature, crustas diduxit, et fluvit
sanguis frigida aqua adhibenda est. Si haec parum
valet, decurrendum est ad medicamenta, quae
sanguinem supprimunt. Si ne haec quidem succurrunt, aduri diligenter et timide debet, neque ullo
postea motu dandus eidem periculo locus est.
4  Nonnumquam etiam id genus ibi cancri, quod
phagedaena a Graecis nominatur, oriri solet. In
quo minime differendum sed protinus iisdem medicamentis et, si parum valent, ferro adurendum. Quaedam etiam nigrities est, quae non sentitur, sed

---

[1] Crustae *so Targa for the* pure eae *or* cruste pure *of the*
MSS.

---

[a] V. 28. 3 B.

what is corrupted is cut away, a little of the sound
tissue being also removed; this is followed by cauterization.    Whenever there is any cauterization, it
follows too that here lentil meal is to be applied; next
when the crusts have separated the ulcers are treated
like others.    But if the canker invades the penis itself,
some one of the caustics is dusted on, and especially
that composed of quick-lime, copper ore and orpiment.    If medicaments fail, in this case also whatever
is corrupted should be cut away with a scalpel, so
far that some sound tissue is also removed.    It is
likewise the rule here that after the canker has been
cut out, the wound is to be cauterized.    But if
hard scabs form, whether after caustics or the
cautery, there is a great danger that haemorrhage
from the penis will follow upon their separation.
Therefore there is need for prolonged rest with the
body almost immobile until the scabs gently separate
from the penis.    But if the patient, either purposely
or accidentally, from moving about too soon, has
detached the scabs and haemorrhage has occurred,
cold water should be applied.    If this has little
effect, recourse must be had to medicaments which
suppress haemorrhage.    If these do not succeed
either, the spot should be carefully and cautiously
cauterized, and no opportunity afterwards given for
the same risk by any sort of movement.
    Occasionally on this part there arises that kind of
canker which the Greeks call phagedaena.[a]    In
such a case there must be no delay whatever : the
treatment is immediate cauterization, whether with
medicaments as above, or, if these have little effect,
with the cautery.    There is also a sort of blackness,
which is insensitive, but spreads and, if we leave it

277

serpit ac, si sustinuimus, usque ad vesicam tendit,
neque succurri postea potest.   Si id in summa glande
circa fistulam urinae est, prius in eam tenue specillum
demittendum est, ne claudatur; deinde id ferro
adurendum.   Si vero alte penetravit, quicquid
occupatum est, praecidendum est.   Cetera eadem,
quae in aliis cancris, facienda sunt.

5    Occallescit etiam in cole interdum aliquid, idque
omne paene sensu caret; quod ipsum quoque excidi
debet.   Carbunculus autem ibi natus primum aqua
per oricularium clysterem eluendus est; deinde
ipse quoque medicamentis urendus, maximeque
chalcitide cum melle aut aerugine cum cocto melle,
aut ovillo stercore fricto et contrito cum eodem melle.
Ubi is excidit, liquidis medicamentis utendum est,
quae ad oris ulcera conponuntur.

6    In testiculis vero si qua inflammatio sine ictu orta
est, sanguis a talo mittendus est; a cibo abstinendum;
inponenda ex faba farina eo ex mulso cocta cum
cumino contrito et ex melle cocto; aut contritum
cuminum cum cerato ex rosa facto; aut lini semen
frictum, contritum et in mulso coctum; aut tritici
farina ex mulso cocta cum cupresso; aut lilii radix
contrita.   At si idem induruerunt, inponi debet lini
vel faeni Graeci semen ex mulso coctum; aut ex
cyprino ceratum; aut simila ex vino contrita, cui
paulum croci sit adiectum.   Si vetustior iam
durities est, maxime proficit cucumeris agrestis radix
B in mulso cocta, deinde contrita.   Si ex ictu tument,

---

  *a* V. **28. 1.**  Cf. Scribonius Largus, 25, *carbunculos quos
ἄνθρακας dicunt.*   For Carbunculus oculi, VI. **6. 10.**
  *b* V. **8.**
  *c* Vol. I. p. 162 notes.   (II. **10. 12.**)

alone, extends even to the bladder, after which nothing
can avail.   If it is situated at the lip of the glans
around the urethra, a fine probe should be inserted
into the urethra first that it may not be closed up;
then the black patch burnt with the cautery.   If it
has gone deep, whatever is involved is to be cut away.
The rest of the treatment is the same as for other
kinds of canker.

Again, now and then a callosity forms in the penis;
and it is almost entirely without feeling; this also
should be excised.   But if a carbuncle *a* occurs here,
it is first to be irrigated with water through an ear
syringe; next the growth is to be cauterized with
medicaments, especially copper ore with honey or
verdigris with boiled honey, or fried sheep's dung *b*
pounded up similarly with honey.   When the carbuncle falls off, use the fluid medicaments prepared
for ulcers of the mouth.

But if any inflammation occurs in the testicles,
not due to injury, blood is to be let from the ankle; *c*
there must be abstinence from food; and bean meal
boiled in honey wine must be applied, along with
cumin rubbed up in boiled honey; or pounded cumin
with the rose oil cerate; or parched linseed, pounded
up and boiled in honey wine; or wheat flour in
honey wine boiled with cyprus shoots; or pounded
lily root.   If the testicles have become indurated,
apply linseed or fenugreek seed boiled in honey
wine; or the cyprus oil cerate; or fine wheat flour
pounded up in wine to which a little saffron has been
added.   If the induration is already of long standing,
the most efficacious thing is wild cucumber root
boiled in honey wine, then pounded up.   If the
testicles swell as the result of an injury, it is necessary

sanguinem mitti necessarium est, magisque si etiam
livent. Inponendum vero utrumlibet ex iis, quae
cum cumino conponuntur supraque (A) posita sunt;
aut ea conpositio, quae habet: nitri cocti P. ✳ I;
resinae pineae, cumini, singulorum P. ✳ II; uvae
taminiae sine seminibus P.✳ IIII; mellis quantum
satis sit ad ea cogenda. Quod si ex ictu testiculus
ali desit, fere pus quoque increscit, neque aliter
succurri potest quam si inciso scroto et pus emissum
et ipse testiculus excisus est.

7 Anus quoque multa taediique plena mala recipit,
neque inter se multum abhorrentes curationes habet.
Ac primum in eo saepe, et quidem pluribus locis, cutis
scinditur: ragadia Graeci vocant. Id si recens est,
quiescere homo debet, et in aqua calida desidere.
Columbina quoque ova coquenda sunt, et, ubi
induruerunt, purganda; deinde alterum deponefacere
in aqua bene calida debet, alterum calidum loco
subicere, sic ut invicem utroque aliquis utatur. Tum
tetrapharmacum aut rhypodes ad hoc rosa diluendum
est, aut oesypum recens miscendum cum cerato
liquido ex rosa facto aut eidem cerato plumbum
B elotum: aut adiciendum aut resinae terebenthinae
murrae paulum, aut spumae argenti vetus oleum,
et quolibet ex his id perunguendum. Si, quicquid
laesum est, extra est neque intus reconditum, eodem
medicamento tinctum linamentum superdandum est
et, quicquid ante adhibuimus, cerato contegendum.
In hoc autem casu neque acribus cibis utendum
est neque asperis neque alvum conprimentibus,
ne aridum quidem quicquam satis utile est nisi

---

*a* For these, cf. Galen XIII. 516 and 715. The surgical
treatment of anal fissure is described in Book VII. **30.** 1 ff.

to let blood, especially if they are livid as well. Then
one of the compositions containing cumin mentioned
above should be put on; or the composition which
contains : fused soda 4 grms.; pine resin and cumin,
8 grms. each; black bryony berries without the
seeds 16 grms.; along with sufficient honey to combine them. If, as the result of an injury, the testicle
lacks nutrition, generally pus develops; then the
only thing to be done is to cut into the scrotum,
and let out the pus, and to excise the testicle
itself.

The anus also is subject to many most tedious
maladies, which do not require much variation in
their treatment. In the first place, the skin of the anus
is often fissured at several places; the Greeks call
these ragadia.[a] If this is recent, the patient should
keep quiet and sit in hot water. Further, pigeon's
eggs are to be boiled until hard, shelled, and then
one should be covered completely in very hot water,
the other is applied hot to the place, the eggs being
used thus turn and turn about. Then the tetrapharmacum [b] or the rhypodes [c] is to be diluted for use
with rose oil; or fresh wool-grease is mixed with the
liquid cerate made up with rose oil; or washed lead
with the same cerate; or a little myrrh is added
to turpentine resin; or old oil to litharge; with
any one of which the anus is smeared. If the lesion
is external, not hidden inside, lint may be soaked
in the same medicament and applied; whatever is
put on is to be covered by a cerate. In such a case
also neither acrid nor coarse food is to be taken nor
such as constipates; dry food is not satisfactory

[b] V. 19. 9.        [c] V. 19. 15.

admodum paulum : liquida, lenia, pinguia, glutinosa
meliora sunt.   Vino leni uti nihil prohibet.

8    Condyloma autem est tuberculum, quod ex
quadam inflammatione nasci solet.   Id ubi ortum
est, quod ad quietem, cibos potionesque pertinet,
eadem servari debent, quae proxime (7 A) scripta
sunt : iisdem etiam ovis recte tuberculum id fovetur.
Sed desidere ante homo in aqua debet, in qua verbenae
decoctae sunt ex reprimentibus.   Tum recte inponitur et lenticula cum exigua parte mellis et
sertula Campana ex vino cocta ; et rubi folia contrita cum cerato ex rosa facto ; et cum eodem cerato
contritum vel Cotonium malum, vel malicori ex
vino cocti pars interior ; et chalcitis cocta atque
contrita, deinde oesypo ac rosa excepta ; et ex ea
B conpositione, quae habet : turis P. ✳ I ; aluminis
scissilis P. ✳ II ; cerussae P. ✳ III ; spumae argenti
P. ✳ V ; quibus, dum teruntur, invicem rosa et
vinum instillatur.   Vinculum autem ei loco linteolum
aut panniculus quadratus est, qui ad duo capita duas
ansas, ad latera duo totidem fascias habet ; cumque
subiectus est, ansis ad ventrem datis, posteriore
parte in eas adductae fasciae coiciuntur, atque ubi
artatae sunt, dexterior sinistra, sinisterior dextra
procedit, circumdataeque circa alvum inter se novis-
C sime deligantur.   Sed si vetus condyloma iam
induruit, neque sub his curationibus desidit, aduri
medicamento potest, quod ex his constat : aeruginis

---

*a* Cf. V. **28**. 2 B.

unless in very small amount; liquid, mild, fatty and glutinous nutriment is better. There is nothing to prevent the use of mild wine.

A condyloma *a* is a small tumour due to inflammation of some kind. When it appears the same prescriptions apply regarding rest, food and drink as have just been set out. Also the tumour itself may be properly treated by fomenting similarly with eggs. But the patient should first sit in a repressant decoction of vervains. Then we may properly apply lentil meal with a little honey, also mellilot boiled in wine, bramble leaves pounded up with the rose oil cerate or a quince, or the inner rind of a pomegranate boiled in wine, pounded up in the same cerate; or copper ore boiled and pounded, then taken up in wool-grease and rose oil; and the composition containing: frankincense 4 grms., split alum 8 grms., white lead 12 grms., litharge 20 grms., into which whilst it is being pounded up rose oil and wine are dropped by turns. But the binder for this part is a square of linen or woollen cloth, which has a loop at each of two adjacent angles and a tape at each of the two opposite ones. The square having been applied underneath with the two loops upon the abdominal wall, the tapes are brought round from behind and passed through the loop on its corresponding side. Each tape being drawn tight, that on the right side is carried round the back to the left, and the left tape back and round to the right side. Finally, the ends of the tapes are tied together in front of the abdomen. But if a long-standing condyloma is already indurated and does not yield to the foregoing measures, it can be burnt with a caustic consisting of: verdigris 4

P. ✳ I; murrae P. ✳ IIII; cummis P. ✳ VIII; turis P. ✳ XII; stibis, papaveris lacrimae, acaciae, singulorum P. ✳ XVI, quo medicamento quidam etiam ulcera, de quibus proxime (2 CD) dixi, renovant. Si hoc parum in condylomate proficit, adhiberi possunt etiam vehementer adurentia. Ubi consumptus est tumor, ad medicamenta lenia transeundum est.

9 Tertium autem vitium ora venarum tamquam ex capitulis quibusdam surgentia, quae saepe sanguinem fundunt: haemorroidas Graeci vocant; idque etiam in ore volvae feminarum incidere consuevit. Atque in quibusdam parum tuto supprimitur, qui sanguinis profluvio inbecilliores non fiunt: habent enim purgationem hanc, non morbum. Ideoque curati quidam, cum sanguis exitum non haberet, inclinata ad praecordia et ad viscera materia, subitis et gravissimis

B morbis correpti sunt.—Si cui vero id nocet, is desidere in aqua ex verbenis debet, inponere maxime malicorium cum aridis rosae foliis contritum, aut ex iis aliquid, quae sanguinem supprimunt. Solet autem oriri inflammatio maxime ubi maior [1] . . . dura alvus eum locum laesit. Tum in aqua dulci desidendum est, et fovendum ovis; inponendi vitelli cum rosae foliis ex passo subactis; idque si intus est, digito inlinendum; si extra, superinlitum panniculo imponendum est. Ea quoque medicamenta, quae recentibus scissuris posita (7 A B) sunt, huc idonea sunt. Cibis vero in hoc casu isdem quibus in prioribus

---

[1] *Marx would add after* maior: impetus ventris cutem primum perrupit, deinde, *and this is translated.*

---

[a] p. 271.
[b] Cf. VII. **30.** 2 for the surgical treatment of condylomata.
[c] Cf. VII. **30.** 3 for the surgical treatment of haemorrhoids.

grms.; myrrh 16 grms.; cumin 32 grms.; frankincense 48 grms.; antimony sulphide, poppy juice, and
acacia juice, 64 grms. each, and by this medicament
some also produce a fresh surface on the ulcers, which
I have described above.[a]  If this has little effect upon
the condyloma it is possible to apply strong caustics.
When the tumour has been eaten away, a change is
made to mild medicaments.[b]

There is also a third lesion, in which vein mouths
rise up as from little heads,[c] which at frequent intervals
pour out blood : the Greeks call them haemorrhoids.
In women they may even appear at the vulvar
orifice.  There are some in whom it is hardly safe
to suppress such a flux of blood, those who are
not the weaker for it; for to these it is a purga-
tion, not a disease.  Hence some, after being cured,
since the blood had no way out, and diseased matter
was diverted towards the praecordia and viscera,
have been carried off by sudden diseases of the
gravest kind.  But if the bleeding is doing harm to
anyone, he should sit in a decoction of vervains, and
the best thing to apply is pomegranate rind pounded
up with dried rose leaves, or anything else that stops
bleeding.  But inflammation especially tends to occur
when first a rather violent evacuation of the bowels
has ruptured the epidermis, and later a hard stool
has injured this spot.[d]  Then the patient should sit
in soft water and foment with eggs; yolk of egg
which has been stirred up with rose leaves and boiled
in raisin wine is to be applied; if the haemorrhoids are
internal, by the finger, if external, spread upon linen.
The medicaments[e] described above for recent fissures are suitable here also.  In this case the diet

---

[d] An inflamed pile is the result.          [e] VI. **18.** 7 A.

utendum est. Si ista parum iuvant, solent inposita
C medicamenta adurentia ea capitula absumere. Ac
si iam vetustiora sunt, sub auctore Dionysio inspergenda sandraca est, deinde inponendum id quod ex
his constat : squamae aeris, auripigmenti, singulorum
P. ✳ V ; saxi calcis P. ✳ VIII ; postero die acu
conpungendum. Adustis capitulis fit cicatrix, quae
sanguinem fundi prohibet. Sed quotiens is sup-
pressus est, ne quid periculi adferat, multa exercitatione digerenda materia est. Praetereaque viris
et feminis, quibus menstrua non proveniunt, interdum
ex brachio sanguis mittendus est.

10  At si anus ipse vel os vulvae procidit (nam id
quoque interdum fit), considerari debet, purumne
id sit, quod provolutum est, an umore muccoso
circumdatum. Si purum est, in aqua desidere homo
debet ; aut salsa aut cum verbenis vel malicorio
incocta. Si umidum, vino austero subluendum est
inlinendumque faece vini conbusta. Ubi utrolibet
modo curatum est, intus reponendum est, inponendaque plantago contrita vel folia salicis in aceto cocta.
tum linteolum, et super lana ; eaque deliganda sunt
cruribus inter se devinctis.

11  Fungo quoque simile ulcus in eadem sede nasci
solet : id, si hiemps est, egelida ; si aliud tempus,
frigida aqua fovendum est, dein squama aeris
inspergenda, supraque ceratum ex murteo factum,

286

should be the same as in the preceding one. But if the above treatment has little effect, it is usual to apply caustics to destroy these small heads. If they are already of long standing, then, on the authority of Dionysius, sandarach should be dusted on, and after that the composition should be applied containing copper scales and orpiment 20 grms., limestone 32 grms.; the next day the haemorrhoids are to be punctured with a needle. The small heads having been cauterized, a scab is produced which prevents blood from running out. But whenever haemorrhage is thus suppressed, the diseased matter is to be dispersed by free exercise that no danger may ensue. And besides, in men and in women who are not menstruating, blood should be let from the arm now and then.

If the anus itself, or, as sometimes happens, the mouth of the womb, prolapses, examination should be made to see whether what is protruding is clean, or is covered by a mucous humour. If it is clean, the patient should sit in water; either in salt water or in water boiled with vervains or pomegranate rind. If it is moist, it should be bathed with dry wine and smeared with roasted wine lees. After being treated in one of these ways, it is to be replaced, and pounded plantain or willow leaves boiled in vinegar applied, next lint, and wool over it: and these must be bandaged on, whilst the legs are kept tied together.

In the same place an ulceration like a fungus may arise, which must be bathed with lukewarm water in winter, at other seasons in cold water; then copper scales are dusted on, and over that is applied a cerate made with myrtle oil to which has been

cui paulum squamae, fuliginis, calcis sit adiectum.
Si hac ratione non tollitur, vel medicamentis vehemen
tioribus vel ferro adurendum est.

**19.** Digitorum autem vetera ulcera commodissime
curantur aut Lycio aut amurca cocta, cum utrilibet
vinum adiectum est. In iisdem recedere ab ungue
caruncula cum magno dolore consuevit: pterygion
Graeci appellant.—Oportet alumen Melinum rotundum in aqua liquare, donec mellis crassitudinem
habeat; tum quantum eius aridi fuit, tantundem
mellis infundere, et rudicula miscere, donec similis
croco color effiat, eoque inlinere. Quidam . . .[1] ad
eundem usum decoquere simul malunt, cum paria
2 pondera aluminis aridi et mellis miscuerunt. Si hac
ratione ea non exciderunt, excidenda sunt; deinde
digiti fovendi aqua ex verbenis, inponendumque super
medicamentum ita factum: chalcitis, malicorium,
squama aeris excipiuntur fico pingui leniter cocta ex
melle; aut chartae combustae, auripigmenti, sulpuris
ignem non experti par modus cerato miscetur ex
murteo facto; aut aeruginis rasae P. ✳ I, squamae
P. ✳ II mellis cyatho coguntur; aut pares portiones
miscentur saxi calcis, chalcitidis, auripigmenti.
Quicquid horum impositum est, tegendum linteolo
3 aqua madefacto est. Tertio die digitus resolvendus,

---

[1] *Marx suggests that* eadem *has dropped out.*

[a] A paronychia or whitlow. Hippocrates (*Epidemics* II.
27; Littré V. 139) calls it παρωνυχία. The Latin name
(not used by Celsus) was *reduvia*, and πτερύγιον, which he

added a little of copper scales, soot, and lime. If this treatment gives no relief, it is to be cauterized, either with more active medicaments or with the cautery.

19. Old-standing ulcerations of the fingers are most suitably treated by buckthorn juice, or by boiled olive lees, in either case with the addition of wine. In the same parts a small piece of flesh sometimes grows out from the nail, causing great pain; the Greeks call it pterygium.[a] Round alum from Melos should be dissolved in water to the consistency of honey; the same quantity of honey as there was of dry alum is then poured in, and the mixture is stirred with a rod until it is of a saffron colour, and then smeared on. Some prefer to boil up the same ingredients together for the same purpose after mixing equal quantities of dry alum and honey. If the whitlow is not removed by this treatment, it should be cut away; next the finger is bathed in a decoction of vervains, and over it is then put the following composition : copper ore, pomegranate rind, and copper scales, mixed with ripe figs, lightly boiled in honey ; or burnt papyrus, orpiment, and crude sulphur in equal parts may be mixed with a cerate containing myrtle oil; or scraped verdigris 4 grms., copper scales 8 grms., mixed together in 42 c.cm. of honey ; or equal parts of limestone, copper ore and orpiment are mixed together. Whichever of these is applied, it is covered over by linen wetted with water. On the third day the finger is dressed again, any dried part is

gives as the Greek, is seldom found in this sense in any extant writings, though *pterygium* is often found in Latin writers. For another meaning of *pterygium* see III. 328, note *b*.

# CELSUS

et si quid aridi est, iterum excidendum, similisque adibenda curatio est. Si non vincitur purgandum est scalpello tenuibusque ferramentis adurendum et sicut reliqua usta curandum est.

At ubi scabri ungues sunt, circum aperiri debent, corpus qua contingunt; tum super eos ex hac compositione aeque inponi: sandracae, sulpuris, singulorum P. ✱ II; nitri, auripigmenti, singulorum P. ✱ IIII; resinae liquidae P. ✱ VIII; tertioque id die resolvendum est. Sub quo medicamento vitiosi ungues cadunt, et in eorum locum meliores renascuntur.

removed, and similar treatment continued. When this does not succeed, the whitlow is cleaned by means of a scalpel, and the place burnt with a fine cautery, followed by the dressing usual after cauterization.

And when nails are scabrous, they must be loosened all round, where they are in contact with the flesh; next some of the following composition is put on them : sandarach and sulphur 8 grms. each; soda and orpiment 16 grms. each; liquid resin 32 grms. The finger is dressed again on the third day. Under this medicament, diseased nails fall off and in their stead better ones grow.

PRINTED IN GREAT BRITAIN BY
RICHARD CLAY AND COMPANY, LTD.,
BUNGAY, SUFFOLK.

# THE LOEB CLASSICAL LIBRARY

---

## VOLUMES ALREADY PUBLISHED

---

### *Latin Authors*

AMMIANUS MARCELLINUS. Translated by J. C. Rolfe. 3 Vols.

APULEIUS: THE GOLDEN ASS (METAMORPHOSES). W. Adlington (1566). Revised by S. Gaselee.

ST. AUGUSTINE: CITY OF GOD. 7 Vols. Vol. I. G. H. McCracken. Vol. VI. W. C. Greene.

ST. AUGUSTINE, CONFESSIONS OF. W. Watts (1631). 2 Vols.

ST. AUGUSTINE, SELECT LETTERS. J. H. Baxter.

AUSONIUS. H. G. Evelyn White. 2 Vols.

BEDE. J. E. King. 2 Vols.

BOETHIUS: TRACTS and DE CONSOLATIONE PHILOSOPHIAE. Rev. H. F. Stewart and E. K. Rand.

CAESAR: ALEXANDRIAN, AFRICAN and SPANISH WARS. A. G. Way.

CAESAR: CIVIL WARS. A. G. Peskett.

CAESAR: GALLIC WAR. H. J. Edwards.

CATO: DE RE RUSTICA; VARRO: DE RE RUSTICA. H. B. Ash and W. D. Hooper.

CATULLUS. F. W. Cornish; TIBULLUS. J. B. Postgate; PERVIGILIUM VENERIS. J. W. Mackail.

CELSUS: DE MEDICINA. W. G. Spencer. 3 Vols.

CICERO: BRUTUS, and ORATOR. G. L. Hendrickson and H. M. Hubbell.

[CICERO]: AD HERENNIUM. H. Caplan.

CICERO: DE ORATORE, etc. 2 Vols. Vol. I. DE ORATORE, Books I. and II. E. W. Sutton and H. Rackham. Vol. II. DE ORATORE, Book III. De Fato; Paradoxa Stoicorum; De Partitione Oratoria. H. Rackham.

CICERO: DE FINIBUS. H. Rackham.

CICERO: DE INVENTIONE, etc. H. M. Hubbell.

CICERO: DE NATURA DEORUM and ACADEMICA. H. Rackham.

CICERO: DE OFFICIIS. Walter Miller.

CICERO: DE REPUBLICA and DE LEGIBUS; SOMNIUM SCIPIONIS. Clinton W. Keyes.

CICERO: DE SENECTUTE, DE AMICITIA, DE DIVINATIONE. W. A. Falconer.
CICERO: IN CATILINAM, PRO FLACCO, PRO MURENA, PRO SULLA. Louis E. Lord.
CICERO: LETTERS to ATTICUS. E. O. Winstedt. 3 Vols.
CICERO: LETTERS TO HIS FRIENDS. W. Glynn Williams. 3 Vols.
CICERO: PHILIPPICS. W. C. A. Ker.
CICERO: PRO ARCHIA POST REDITUM, DE DOMO, DE HARUS-PICUM RESPONSIS, PRO PLANCIO. N. H. Watts.
CICERO: PRO CAECINA, PRO LEGE MANILIA, PRO CLUENTIO, PRO RABIRIO. H. Grose Hodge.
CICERO: PRO CAELIO, DE PROVINCIIS CONSULARIBUS, PRO BALBO. R. Gardner.
CICERO: PRO MILONE, IN PISONEM, PRO SCAURO, PRO FONTEIO, PRO RABIRIO POSTUMO, PRO MARCELLO, PRO LIGARIO, PRO REGE DEIOTARO. N. H. Watts.
CICERO: PRO QUINCTIO, PRO ROSCIO AMERINO, PRO ROSCIO COMOEDO, CONTRA RULLUM. J. H. Freese.
CICERO: PRO SESTIO, IN VATINIUM. R. Gardner.
CICERO: TUSCULAN DISPUTATIONS. J. E. King.
CICERO: VERRINE ORATIONS. L. H. G. Greenwood. 2 Vols.
CLAUDIAN. M. Platnauer. 2 Vols.
COLUMELLA: DE RE RUSTICA. DE ARBORIBUS. H. B. Ash, E. S. Forster and E. Heffner. 3 Vols.
CURTIUS, Q.: HISTORY OF ALEXANDER. J. C. Rolfe. 2 Vols.
FLORUS. E. S. Forster; and CORNELIUS NEPOS. J. C. Rolfe.
FRONTINUS: STRATAGEMS and AQUEDUCTS. C. E. Bennett and M. B. McElwain.
FRONTO: CORRESPONDENCE. C. R. Haines. 2 Vols.
GELLIUS, J. C. Rolfe. 3 Vols.
HORACE: ODES AND EPODES. C. E. Bennett.
HORACE: SATIRES, EPISTLES, ARS POETICA. H. R. Fairclough.
JEROME: SELECTED LETTERS. F. A. Wright.
JUVENAL and PERSIUS. G. G. Ramsay.
LIVY. B. O. Foster, F. G. Moore, Evan T. Sage, and A. C. Schlesinger and R. M. Geer (General Index). 14 Vols.
LUCAN. J. D. Duff.
LUCRETIUS. W. H. D. Rouse.
MARTIAL. W. C. A. Ker. 2 Vols.
MINOR LATIN POETS: from PUBLILIUS SYRUS TO RUTILIUS NAMATIANUS, including GRATTIUS, CALPURNIUS SICULUS, NEMESIANUS, AVIANUS, and others with " Aetna " and the " Phoenix." J. Wight Duff and Arnold M. Duff.
OVID: THE ART OF LOVE and OTHER POEMS. J. H. Mozley.

Ovid: Fasti. Sir James G. Frazer.
Ovid: Heroides and Amores. Grant Showerman.
Ovid: Metamorphoses. F. J. Miller. 2 Vols.
Ovid: Tristia and Ex Ponto. A. L. Wheeler.
Persius. Cf. Juvenal.
Petronius. M. Heseltine; Seneca; Apocolocyntosis. W. H. D. Rouse.
Plautus. Paul Nixon. 5 Vols.
Pliny: Letters. Melmoth's Translation revised by W. M. L. Hutchinson. 2 Vols.
Pliny: Natural History. H. Rackham and W. H. S. Jones. 10 Vols. Vols. I.–V. and IX. H. Rackham. Vols. VI. and VII. W. H. S. Jones.
Propertius. H. E. Butler.
Prudentius. H. J. Thomson. 2 Vols.
Quintilian. H. E. Butler. 4 Vols.
Remains of Old Latin. E. H. Warmington. 4 Vols. Vol. I. (Ennius and Caecilius.) Vol. II. (Livius, Naevius, Pacuvius, Accius.) Vol. III. (Lucilius and Laws of XII Tables.) (Archaic Inscriptions.)
Sallust. J. C. Rolfe.
Scriptores Historiae Augustae. D. Magie. 3 Vols.
Seneca: Apocolocyntosis. Cf. Petronius.
Seneca: Epistulae Morales. R. M. Gummere. 3 Vols.
Seneca: Moral Essays. J. W. Basore. 3 Vols.
Seneca: Tragedies. F. J. Miller. 2 Vols.
Sidonius: Poems and Letters. W. B. Anderson. 2 Vols.
Silius Italicus. J. D. Duff. 2 Vols.
Statius. J. H. Mozley. 2 Vols.
Suetonius. J. C. Rolfe. 2 Vols.
Tacitus: Dialogues. Sir Wm. Peterson. Agricola and Germania. Maurice Hutton.
Tacitus: Histories and Annals. C. H. Moore and J. Jackson. 4 Vols.
Terence. John Sargeaunt. 2 Vols.
Tertullian: Apologia and De Spectaculis. T. R. Glover. Minucius Felix. G. H. Rendall.
Valerius Flaccus. J. H. Mozley.
Varro: De Lingua Latina. R. G. Kent. 2 Vols.
Velleius Paterculus and Res Gestae Divi Augusti. F. W. Shipley.
Virgil. H. R. Fairclough. 2 Vols.
Vitruvius: De Architectura. F. Granger. 2 Vols.

3

# *Greek Authors*

ACHILLES TATIUS. S. Gaselee.

AELIAN: ON THE NATURE OF ANIMALS. A. F. Scholfield. 3 Vols.

AENEAS TACTICUS, ASCLEPIODOTUS and ONASANDER. The Illinois Greek Club.

AESCHINES. C. D. Adams.

AESCHYLUS. H. Weir Smyth. 2 Vols.

ALCIPHRON, AELIAN, PHILOSTRATUS: LETTERS. A. R. Benner and F. H. Fobes.

ANDOCIDES, ANTIPHON, Cf. MINOR ATTIC ORATORS.

APOLLODORUS. Sir James G. Frazer. 2 Vols.

APOLLONIUS RHODIUS. R. C. Seaton.

THE APOSTOLIC FATHERS. Kirsopp Lake. 2 Vols.

APPIAN: ROMAN HISTORY. Horace White. 4 Vols.

ARATUS. Cf. CALLIMACHUS.

ARISTOPHANES. Benjamin Bickley Rogers. 3 Vols. Verse trans.

ARISTOTLE: ART OF RHETORIC. J. H. Freese.

ARISTOTLE: ATHENIAN CONSTITUTION, EUDEMIAN ETHICS, VICES AND VIRTUES. H. Rackham.

ARISTOTLE: GENERATION OF ANIMALS. A. L. Peck.

ARISTOTLE: METAPHYSICS. H. Tredennick. 2 Vols.

ARISTOTLE: METEROLOGICA. H. D. P. Lee.

ARISTOTLE: MINOR WORKS. W. S. Hett. On Colours, On Things Heard, On Physiognomies, On Plants, On Marvellous Things Heard, Mechanical Problems, On Indivisible Lines, On Situations and Names of Winds, On Melissus, Xenophanes, and Gorgias.

ARISTOTLE: NICOMACHEAN ETHICS. H. Rackham.

ARISTOTLE: OECONOMICA and MAGNA MORALIA. G. C. Armstrong; (with Metaphysics, Vol. II.).

ARISTOTLE: ON THE HEAVENS. W. K. C. Guthrie.

ARISTOTLE: ON THE SOUL. PARVA NATURALIA. ON BREATH. W. S. Hett.

ARISTOTLE: CATEGORIES, ON INTERPRETATION, PRIOR ANALYTICS. H. P. Cooke and H. Tredennick.

ARISTOTLE: POSTERIOR ANALYTICS, TOPICS. H. Tredennick and E. S. Forster.

ARISTOTLE: ON SOPHISTICAL REFUTATIONS.
On Coming to be and Passing Away, On the Cosmos. E. S. Forster and D. J. Furley.

ARISTOTLE: PARTS OF ANIMALS. A. L. Peck; MOTION AND PROGRESSION OF ANIMALS. E. S. Forster.

ARISTOTLE: PHYSICS. Rev. P. Wicksteed and F. M. Cornford. 2 Vols.

ARISTOTLE: POETICS and LONGINUS. W. Hamilton Fyfe; DEMETRIUS ON STYLE. W. Rhys Roberts.

ARISTOTLE: POLITICS. H. Rackham.

ARISTOTLE: PROBLEMS. W. S. Hett. 2 Vols.

ARISTOTLE: RHETORICA AD ALEXANDRUM (with PROBLEMS. Vol. II.) H. Rackham.

ARRIAN: HISTORY OF ALEXANDER and INDICA. Rev. E. Iliffe Robson. 2 Vols.

ATHENAEUS: DEIPNOSOPHISTAE. C. B. GULICK. 7 Vols.

ST. BASIL: LETTERS. R. J. Deferrari. 4 Vols.

CALLIMACHUS: FRAGMENTS. C. A. Trypanis.

CALLIMACHUS, Hymns and Epigrams, and LYCOPHRON. A. W. Mair; ARATUS. G. R. MAIR.

CLEMENT of ALEXANDRIA. Rev. G. W. Butterworth.

COLLUTHUS. Cf. OPPIAN.

DAPHNIS AND CHLOE. Thornley's Translation revised by J. M. Edmonds; and PARTHENIUS. S. Gaselee.

DEMOSTHENES I.: OLYNTHIACS, PHILIPPICS and MINOR ORATIONS. I.–XVII. AND XX. J. H. Vince.

DEMOSTHENES II.: DE CORONA and DE FALSA LEGATIONE. C. A. Vince and J. H. Vince.

DEMOSTHENES III.: MEIDIAS, ANDROTION, ARISTOCRATES, TIMOCRATES and ARISTOGEITON, I. AND II. J. H. Vince.

DEMOSTHENES IV.–VI.: PRIVATE ORATIONS and IN NEAERAM. A. T. Murray.

DEMOSTHENES VII.: FUNERAL SPEECH, EROTIC ESSAY, EXORDIA and LETTERS. N. W. and N. J. DeWitt.

DIO CASSIUS: ROMAN HISTORY. E. Cary. 9 Vols.

DIO CHRYSOSTOM. J. W. Cohoon and H. Lamar Crosby. 5 Vols.

DIODORUS SICULUS. 12 Vols. Vols. I.–VI. C. H. Oldfather. Vol. VII. C. L. Sherman. Vols. IX. and X. R. M. Geer. Vol. XI. F. Walton.

DIOGENES LAERITIUS. R. D. Hicks. 2 Vols.

DIONYSIUS OF HALICARNASSUS: ROMAN ANTIQUITIES. Spelman's translation revised by E. Cary. 7 Vols.

EPICTETUS. W. A. Oldfather. 2 Vols.

EURIPIDES. A. S. Way. 4 Vols. Verse trans.

EUSEBIUS: ECCLESIASTICAL HISTORY. Kirsopp Lake and J. E. L. Oulton. 2 Vols.

GALEN: ON THE NATURAL FACULTIES. A. J. Brock.

THE GREEK ANTHOLOGY. W. R. Paton. 5 Vols.

GREEK ELEGY AND IAMBUS with the ANACREONTEA. J. M. Edmonds. 2 Vols.

THE GREEK BUCOLIC POETS (THEOCRITUS, BION, MOSCHUS). J. M. Edmonds.

GREEK MATHEMATICAL WORKS. Ivor Thomas. 2 Vols.

HERODES. Cf. THEOPHRASTUS: CHARACTERS.

HERODOTUS. A. D. Godley. 4 Vols.

HESIOD AND THE HOMERIC HYMNS. H. G. Evelyn White.

HIPPOCRATES and the FRAGMENTS OF HERACLEITUS. W. H. S. Jones and E. T. Withington. 4 Vols.

HOMER: ILIAD. A. T. Murray. 2 Vols.

HOMER: ODYSSEY. A. T. Murray. 2 Vols.

ISAEUS. E. W. Forster.

ISOCRATES. George Norlin and LaRue Van Hook. 3 Vols.

ST. JOHN DAMASCENE: BARLAAM AND IOASAPH. Rev. G. R. Woodward and Harold Mattingly.

JOSEPHUS. H. St. J. Thackeray and Ralph Marcus. 9 Vols. Vols. I.–VII.

JULIAN. Wilmer Cave Wright. 3 Vols.

LUCIAN. 8 Vols. Vols. I.–V. A. M. Harmon. Vol. VI. K. Kilburn.

LYCOPHRON. Cf. CALLIMACHUS.

LYRA GRAECA. J. M. Edmonds. 3 Vols.

LYSIAS. W. R. M. Lamb.

MANETHO. W. G. Waddell: PTOLEMY: TETRABIBLOS. F. E. Robbins.

MARCUS AURELIUS. C. R. Haines.

MENANDER. F. G. Allinson.

MINOR ATTIC ORATORS (ANTIPHON, ANDOCIDES, LYCURGUS, DEMADES, DINARCHUS, HYPEREIDES). K. J. Maidment and J. O. Burtt. 2 Vols.

NONNOS: DIONYSIACA. W. H. D. Rouse. 3 Vols.

OPPIAN, COLLUTHUS, TRYPHIODORUS. A. W. Mair.

PAPYRI. NON-LITERARY SELECTIONS. A. S. Hunt and C. C. Edgar. 2 Vols. LITERARY SELECTIONS (Poetry). D. L. Page.

PARTHENIUS. Cf. DAPHNIS and CHLOE.

PAUSANIAS: DESCRIPTION OF GREECE. W. H. S. Jones. 4 Vols. and Companion Vol. arranged by R. E. Wycherley.

PHILO. 10 Vols. Vols. I.–V.; F. H. Colson and Rev. G. H. Whitaker. Vols. VI.–IX.; F. H. Colson.

PHILO: two supplementary Vols. (*Translation only.*) Ralph Marcus.

PHILOSTRATUS: THE LIFE OF APOLLONIUS OF TYANA. F. C. Conybeare. 2 Vols.

PHILOSTRATUS: IMAGINES; CALLISTRATUS: DESCRIPTIONS. A. Fairbanks.

PHILOSTRATUS and EUNAPIUS: LIVES OF THE SOPHISTS. Wilmer Cave Wright.

PINDAR. Sir J. E. Sandys.

PLATO: CHARMIDES, ALCIBIADES, HIPPARCHUS, THE LOVERS, THEAGES, MINOS and EPINOMIS. W. R. M. Lamb.

PLATO: CRATYLUS, PARMENIDES, GREATER HIPPIAS, LESSER HIPPIAS. H. N. Fowler.

PLATO: EUTHYPHRO, APOLOGY, CRITO, PHAEDO, PHAEDRUS. H. N. Fowler.

PLATO: LACHES, PROTAGORAS, MENO, EUTHYDEMUS. W. R. M. Lamb.

PLATO: LAWS. Rev. R. G. Bury. 2 Vols.

PLATO: LYSIS, SYMPOSIUM, GORGIAS. W. R. M. Lamb.

PLATO: REPUBLIC. Paul Shorey. 2 Vols.

PLATO: STATESMAN, PHILEBUS. H. N. Fowler; ION. W. R. M. Lamb.

PLATO: THEAETETUS and SOPHIST. H. N. Fowler.

PLATO: TIMAEUS, CRITIAS, CLITOPHO, MENEXENUS, EPISTULAE. Rev. R. G. Bury.

PLUTARCH: MORALIA. 15 Vols. Vols. I.–V. F. C. Babbitt. Vol. VI. W. C. Helmbold. Vol. VII. P. H. De Lacy and B. Einarson. Vol. IX. E. L. Minar, Jr., F. H. Sandbach, W. C. Helmbold. Vol. X. H. N. Fowler. Vol. XII. H. Cherniss and W. C. Helmbold.

PLUTARCH: THE PARALLEL LIVES. B. Perrin. 11 Vols.

POLYBIUS. W. R. Paton. 6 Vols.

PROCOPIUS: HISTORY OF THE WARS. H. B. Dewing. 7 Vols.

PTOLEMY: TETRABIBLOS. Cf. MANETHO.

QUINTUS SMYRNAEUS. A. S. Way. Verse trans.

SEXTUS EMPIRICUS. Rev. R. G. Bury. 4 Vols.

SOPHOCLES. F. Storr. 2 Vols. Verse trans.

STRABO: GEOGRAPHY. Horace L. Jones. 8 Vols.

THEOPHRASTUS: CHARACTERS. J. M. Edmonds. HERODES, etc. A. D. Knox.

THEOPHRASTUS: ENQUIRY INTO PLANTS. Sir Arthur Hort, Bart. 2 Vols.

THUCYDIDES. C. F. Smith. 4 Vols.

TRYPHIODORUS. Cf. OPPIAN.

XENOPHON: CYROPAEDIA. Walter Miller. 2 Vols.

XENOPHON: HELLENICA, ANABASIS, APOLOGY, and SYMPOSIUM. C. L. Brownson and O. J. Todd. 3 Vols.

XENOPHON: MEMORABILIA and OECONOMICUS. E. C. Marchant.

XENOPHON: SCRIPTA MINORA. E. C. Marchant.

# IN PREPARATION

## *Greek Authors*

ARISTOTLE: HISTORY OF ANIMALS. A. L. Peck.
PLOTINUS: A. H. Armstrong.

## *Latin Authors*

BABRIUS AND PHAEDRUS. Ben E. Perry.

## *DESCRIPTIVE PROSPECTUS ON APPLICATION*

London                                    WILLIAM HEINEMANN LTD
Cambridge, Mass.                  HARVARD UNIVERSITY PRESS

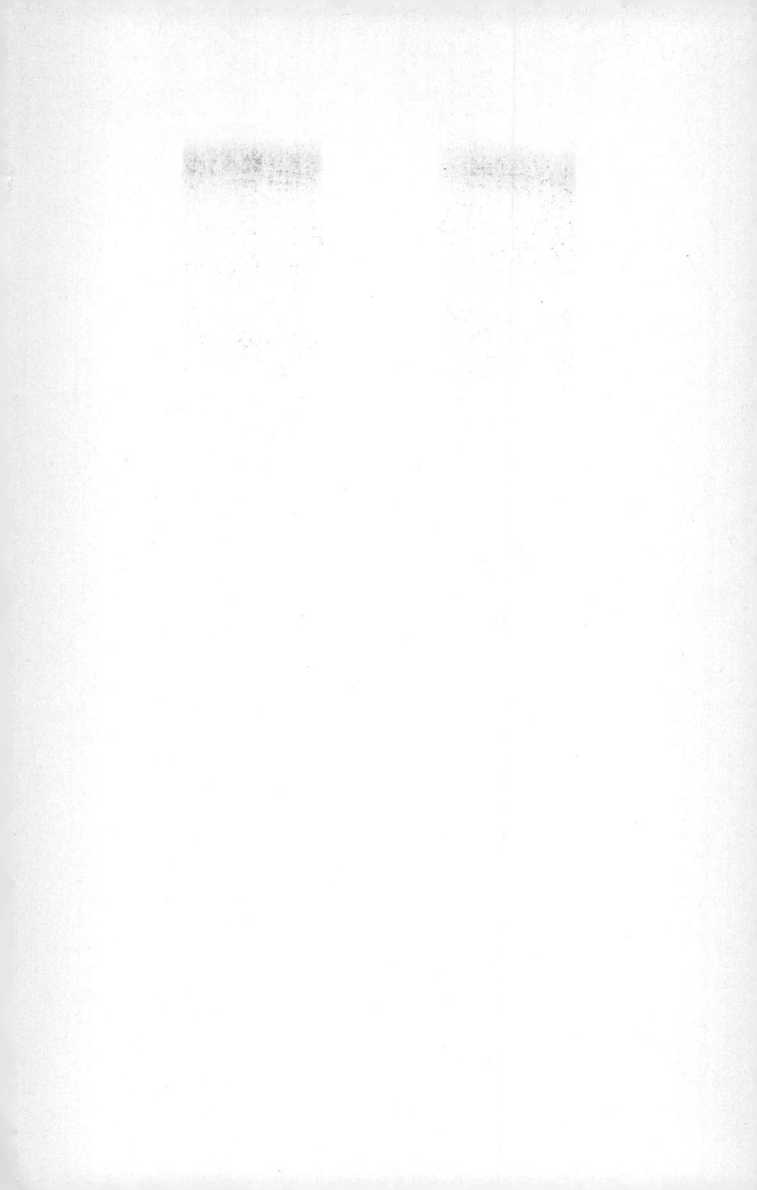